KEY STAGE 3

Mastering Mathematics

Second Edition

3

BOX HILL SCHOOL

Name	Form	Out	In
Charlotte Smith			

THIS BOOK IS THE PROPERTY OF
BOX HILL SCHOOL AND IF IT IS LOST
OR DAMAGED, YOU WILL BE CHARGED

Boost

HODDER
EDUCATION
AN HACHETTE UK COM

Developed in partnership with our teacher team

We'd like to say a huge thank you to the following teachers for their advice and contributions:

Asma Begam

Ann Dean

Mrs Jillian Dolder

Johanna Louise Downing-Green

Melanie Ann Griffiths

Susan Heaton

Belinda Howell

Sarah Latge

Daniel Maher

Zahid Mahmood

Jonathon Pritchard

David A. Rennie

Rim Saada

Mrs Jill M Thomson

Photo credits

p.73 *l* © GLandStudio/stock.adobe.com; *m* © khuruzero/stock.adobe.com; p. 112 *t* © NASA/Johns Hopkins University Applied Physics Laboratory/Carnegie Institution of Washington. Edited version of Image: Mercury in color - Prockter07.jpg by Papa Lima Whiskey. Public domain); *m* © NASA/JPL-Caltech (Public Domain); *b* © NASA/Apollo 17 crew (Public Domain); p. 113 *t-b* © ESA & MPS for OSIRIS Team MPS/UPD/LAM/IAA/RSSD/INTA/UPM/DASP/IDA, CC BY-SA 3.0 IGO; © NASA/JPL/Space Science Institute (Public Domain); © NASA/JPL/Space Science Institute (Public Domain); © NASA/JPL/Space Science Institute (Public Domain); © NASA; p. 114 *l-r* © Luke Robinson; p.122 © Luke Robinson

Acknowledgments

Every effort has been made to trace all copyright holders, but if any have been inadvertently overlooked, the Publishers will be pleased to make the necessary arrangements at the first opportunity.

Although every effort has been made to ensure that website addresses are correct at time of going to press, Hodder Education cannot be held responsible for the content of any website mentioned in this book. It is sometimes possible to find a relocated web page by typing in the address of the home page for a website in the URL window of your browser.

Hachette UK's policy is to use papers that are natural, renewable and recyclable products and made from wood grown in well-managed forests and other controlled sources. The logging and manufacturing processes are expected to conform to the environmental regulations of the country of origin.

Orders: please contact Hachette UK Distribution, Hely Hutchinson Centre, Milton Road, Didcot, Oxfordshire, OX11 7HH. Telephone: +44 (0)1235 827827. Email education@hachette.co.uk Lines are open from 9 a.m. to 5 p.m., Monday to Friday. You can also order through our website: www.hoddereducation.co.uk

ISBN: 978 1 3983 0841 1

© Hodder & Stoughton Limited 2021

First published in 2021 by

Hodder Education,

An Hachette UK Company

Carmelite House

50 Victoria Embankment

London EC4Y 0DZ

www.hoddereducation.co.uk

Impression number   10 9 8 7 6 5 4 3 2 1

Year   2025 2024 2023 2022 2021

Cover photo © Marek Uliasz – stock.adobe.com

Illustrations by Aptara, Inc.

Typeset in India by Aptara, Inc.

Printed in Slovenia

A catalogue record for this title is available from the British Library.

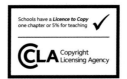

Contents

How to use this book

How to get the most from this book

Hodder Education's Key Stage 3 Maths resources cover all you need to know for years 7–9 and are comprised of:

- three textbooks covering the entire Key Stage 3 National Curriculum
- three intervention and three extension practice books, designed to complement the textbooks for those that need more support or more challenging maths
- Boost online content.

Our year 9 material (it can be used for other years) is split into 15 chapters, and each chapter comprises two, three or four units. In total there are 46 units in the book.

Each **chapter** includes:

- *Coming up* – a list of learning objectives that will be tackled in the chapter
- a *Starter* problem – either an activity or a puzzle – to engage the students with a new topic and designed to be used before the first lesson, or at the start of the first lesson in that topic

- Activities, investigations and whole-class discussion points
- a Review exercise at the end of the chapter; this encompasses all of the units covered in the chapter.

Each of the **individual units** within the chapter includes:

- a *Skill checker* – simple diagnostic questions to test basic understanding in preparation for the unit
- clear and detailed explanation of the topic
- plenty of worked examples with solutions
- a Mastery-friendly approach throughout, including concrete-pictorial-abstract (CPA), manipulatives and bar-modelling
- a focus on fluency, with a carefully structured approach that takes into account cognitive load theory
- helpful hints and guidance on misconceptions and pitfalls to watch out for
- *Now try these* exercise questions:
  - ▶ Split up into three bands of difficulty: Band 1 questions are for those students who are working towards age-related expectations, Band 2 for those at age-related expectations, and Band 3 for those working beyond age-related expectations. Most students will engage with Band 2 questions, and either Band 1 or Band 3 depending on which is most appropriate.
  - ▶ Defined as either Fluency (AO1), Reasoning (AO2) or Problem solving (AO3) and indicated as such.
  - ▶ All exercise questions are carefully calibrated to enable the whole class to understand each question and answer before moving on.
  - ▶ Non-calculator questions are indicated.
- a list of key words (highlighted in the text). These are fully explained in a glossary at the back of the book.

A full set of review questions (*Progress Review*) is included at the end of each group of chapters – that is, a sequence of two or three chapters that cover the same subject area (number, algebra, geometry, ratio/proportion, statistics, probability). These are designed to cover each half term's work. There are six of these in this book.

All answers are provided online at www.hoddereducation. co.uk/KS3MasteringMathematics and are freely accessible.

CHAPTER 1

Powers and indices

▶ Coming up...

◆ Index notation and the laws of indices

◆ Using standard form

◆ Writing integers as a product of prime factors

◆ Finding the least common multiple and highest common factor of two numbers

→ The tower of Hanoi

This puzzle is called 'The tower of Hanoi'.

You have 3 poles and 4 coloured discs of different sizes set on one of the poles.

The aim is to move the discs onto one of the other poles.

There are two rules for moving the discs.

Rule 1: You can only move one disc at a time

Rule 2: You must never put a larger disc on top of a smaller disc

① Make your own Tower of Hanoi.

▶ Cut out 4 circles of card of different diameters to use as your discs.

▶ Make 3 large square bases for your towers.

▶ Put the circles on one of your towers in order of size.

② What is the smallest number of moves needed to move all your discs to another tower?

③ Investigate further for different number of discs.

Find a rule for the smallest number of moves, m, needed to move d discs from one tower to another.

1.1 Index notation

✔ Skill checker

Make a copy of this cross-number and then solve the clues.

Across

1 $7^3 - 5^3$

4 $3^2 + 4^2$

5 2×3^3

6 $4^2 \times \sqrt{36}$

10 $2 \times \sqrt{100}$

11 $\dfrac{5^2 \times 4^3}{\sqrt{4}}$

Down

1 5^2

2 $10^3 - 5^3$

3 $\sqrt{256}$

4 $6^2 - \sqrt{100}$

7 3×6^3

8 $\dfrac{\sqrt{10\,000}}{2}$

9 $\dfrac{6^3}{2^3}$

10 5×2^2

Using indices

Remember that 5×5 is written as 5^2 ◄── Say 5 squared.

You say that 5 is the **base** and 2 is the **index** or **power**.

In the same way, repeated multiplications can be written using **index notation** like this:

$\underbrace{5 \times 5 \times 5}_{3 \text{ fives}} = 5^3$ ◄── Say 5 cubed.

$\underbrace{5 \times 5 \times 5 \times 5}_{4 \text{ fives}} = 5^4$ ◄── Say 5 to the power of 4.

Note

You have a power button on your calculator; it may look like $x^\square$ or x^y.
Make sure you know how to use it: press 5 $x^\square$ 4 $=$ and check you get an answer of 625.

You can have any number as the base.

For example, $\underbrace{7 \times 7 \times 7 \times 7 \times 7 \times 7 \times 7 \times 7}_{8 \text{ sevens}} = 7^8$

Check you can use your calculator to work out 7^8. You should get $5\,764\,801$.

In general, $\underbrace{a \times a \times a \times \ldots \times a \times a}_{n \text{ times}} = a^n$

The next examples show you how to multiply and divide numbers written using index notation.

Worked example

Write $3^5 \times 3^4$ as a single power of 3.

Solution

$3^5 \times 3^4$

$= (3 \times 3 \times 3 \times 3 \times 3) \times (3 \times 3 \times 3 \times 3)$ ◄

> There are 5 threes multiplied together multiplied by 4 threes multiplied together which makes 9 threes multiplied together.

$= 3^9$ ◄

> The powers have been added $5 + 4 = 9$.

Worked example

Write $3^6 \div 3^4$ as a single power of 3.

Solution

$3^6 \div 3^4 = \dfrac{3^6}{3^4}$ ◄

> It is easier to write this as a fraction.

$= \dfrac{3 \times 3 \times \cancel{3} \times \cancel{3} \times \cancel{3} \times \cancel{3}}{\cancel{3} \times \cancel{3} \times \cancel{3} \times \cancel{3}}$ ◄

> If you multiply by 3 and then divide by 3 it cancels out, so 4 of the 3s cancel from the top and bottom.

$= 3 \times 3$

$= 3^2$ ◄

> The powers have been subtracted $6 - 4 = 2$.

In the examples the base was 3, but the same would be true for any base.

Here are the rules for multiplying and dividing powers.

$$a^m \times a^n = a^{m+n} \qquad a^m \div a^n = a^{m-n}$$

> Take care! The bases must be the same – you can't combine powers if the bases are different. There is no way to simplify $3^7 \times 5^4$ any further.

For example, $9^3 \times 9^8 = 9^{3+8} = 9^{11}$

and $\dfrac{4^{12}}{4^7}$ or $4^{12} \div 4^7$ is $4^{12-7} = 4^5$

Sometimes powers involve brackets like in this next example.

Worked example

Write $(3^2)^4$ as a single power of 3.

Solution

$(3^2)^4$ means $\underbrace{(3^2) \times (3^2) \times (3^2) \times (3^2)}_{4 \text{ times}}$

So $(3^2) \times (3^2) \times (3^2) \times (3^2) = (3 \times 3) \times (3 \times 3) \times (3 \times 3) \times (3 \times 3)$ ◄

> There are 2 threes multiplied together 4 times.

$= 3^8$ ◄

> The powers have been multiplied; $2 \times 4 = 8$.

$(3^2)^4$ is sometimes called a power of a power. Again, the example would have worked for any base, not just 3.

Here is the rule for a power of a power.

$$(a^m)^n = a^{m \times n}$$

For example, $(11^4)^5 = 11^{4 \times 5} = 11^{20}$

Activity

a Work out these powers of 2:

  i 2^0 ii 2^1 iii 2^2

  iv 2^3 v 2^4 vi 2^5

b Using only your answers to part **a**, complete these sums.
The first one has been done for you.

> You can only use each number once!

> You are writing each number as a sum of powers of 2.

  i $21 = \boxed{16} + \boxed{4} + \boxed{1}$

  ii $7 = \square + \square + \square$

  iii $10 = \square + \square$

  iv $31 = \square + \square + \square + \square + \square$

  v $51 = \square + \square + \square + \square$

c The table shows how you can write the numbers 1 to 8 as sums of powers of 2.

- 1 means that the power of 2 is needed.
- 0 means that the power of 2 is NOT needed.
- You don't need to write in any zeros **before** the first 1.

Number	Powers of 2					
	32	16	8	4	2	1
1						1
2					1	0
3					1	1
4				1	0	0
5				1	0	1
6				1	1	0
7				1	1	1
8			1	0	0	0

  $5 = 4 + 1$

  $7 = 4 + 2 + 1$

Carry on the table for the numbers up to 32.

Can all numbers be written using powers of 2?

d The table in part **c** is used to write numbers in **binary**.

In binary, 7 is written as 111 and 8 is 1000.

Convert these binary numbers back to ordinary numbers.

  i   100000   ii   101010

  iii   1101011   iv   10000000

Each binary digit is called a 'bit'. The number 10000000 uses 8 bits, and 8 bits is called a byte. A kilobyte is 1024 bytes and a megabyte is roughly 1 million bytes. Binary numbers are used in computers to store information. Binary is a very powerful tool as data can be represented as strings of 0s and 1s which are represented as 'on/off' signals.

e Find out more about binary numbers and how they are used in computing.

Can every number be represented as a binary number?

How do you think text is converted to binary?

Powers of 1 and 0

 Activity

① Complete these.

    a Use your calculator to work out

        i $3^7 \div 3^6$ **ii** $4^8 \div 4^7$ **iii** $9^{11} \div 9^{10}$

    b Use the laws of indices to write these as a single power.

        i $3^7 \div 3^6 = 3^{\square}$ **ii** $4^8 \div 4^7 = 4^{\square}$ **iii** $9^{11} \div 9^{10} = 9^{\square}$

    c What do you notice?

        Write down the value of 56^1.

② Complete these.

    a Use your calculator to work out

        i $2^9 \div 2^9$ **ii** $5^8 \div 5^8$ **iii** $19^3 \div 19^3$

    b Use the laws of indices to write these as a single power.

        i $2^9 \div 2^9 = 2^{\square}$ **ii** $5^8 \div 5^8 = 5^{\square}$ **iii** $19^3 \div 19^3 = 19^{\square}$

    c What do you notice?

        Write down the value of 56°.

In the activity you found that

- any number to the power 1 is itself
- any number divided by itself is 1.

Using indices these are written as

$$a^1 = a \qquad\qquad a^0 = 1$$

Negative powers

Look at this pattern.

$$2^3 = 2 \times 2 \times 2 = 8 \Big\}\div 2$$
$$2^2 = 2 \times 2 = 4 \Big\}\div 2$$
$$2^1 = 2 \Big\}\div 2$$
$$2^0 = 1 \Big\}\div 2$$
$$2^{-1} = \frac{1}{2^1} = \frac{1}{2} \Big\}\div 2$$
$$2^{-2} = \frac{1}{2^2} = \frac{1}{4} \Big\}\div 2$$
$$2^{-3} = \frac{1}{2^3} = \frac{1}{8}$$

You can carry on the pattern so $2^{-8} = \dfrac{1}{2^8}$ and $2^{-n} = \dfrac{1}{2^n}$

You could have used any base so you can say

$$a^{-n} = \frac{1}{a^n}$$ ←   A negative power means '1 over'.

Worked example

Write 10^{-3} as a decimal.

Solution

$$10^{-3} = \frac{1}{10 \times 10 \times 10}$$

$$= \frac{1}{1000} \quad \longleftarrow \boxed{\text{Find } 1 \div 1000.}$$

$$= 0.001$$

Roots

Remember that you can take roots to 'undo' squaring and cubing.

For example, $3^2 = 9$ so $\sqrt{9} = 3$ $\longleftarrow$ Say the square root of 9 is 3.

and $5^3 = 125$ so $\sqrt[3]{125} = 5$ $\longleftarrow$ Say the cube root of 125 is 5.

In the same way you can take roots to 'undo' higher powers.

For example, $4^6 = 4096$

so $\sqrt[6]{4096} = 4$ $\longleftarrow$ Say the sixth root of 4096 is 4.

> You have a root button on your calculator; it may look like ⬛ or ⬛. You may have to use the **SHIFT** key or **2nd** key to reach it. Make sure you know how to use the root button: press **6** ⬛ **4096** **=** and check you get an answer of 4.

> **Watch out!**
> 9 has two square roots +3 and −3 as $(-3) \times (-3) = 9$ and $3 \times 3 = 9$
> However, the symbol $\sqrt{}$ means the positive square root only, so $\sqrt{9} = 3$.

Worked example

Calculate

a $5^4 + 4^5$

b $\sqrt[5]{343} - \sqrt[4]{64}$

Solution

a $5^4 + 4^5 = 625 + 1024$

$\qquad = 1649$

b $\sqrt[5]{243} - \sqrt[6]{64} = 3 - 2$

$\qquad\qquad = 1$

> Watch out! You can't combine sums and differences into a single power because the base number is different, so you just need to use your calculator to work these out.

Key Stage 3 Mastering Mathematics: Book 3

1.1 Now try these

Band 1 questions

1 Write each expression as a power of 2.

  a $2 \times 2 \times 2 \times 2$

  b $2 \times 2 \times 2 \times 2 \times 2 \times 2 \times 2$

  c $2 \times 2 \times 2 \times 2 \times 2 \times 2 \times 2 \times 2 \times 2 \times 2 \times 2 \times 2$

  d $2 \times 2 \times 2 \times 2 \times 2 \times 2$

2 Write each expression as a single power.

  a $7 \times 7 \times 7$

  b $5 \times 5 \times 5 \times 5 \times 5$

  c $14 \times 14 \times 14 \times 14 \times 14 \times 14 \times 14$

  d $12 \times 12 \times 12 \times 12 \times 12 \times 12$

  e $8 \times 8 \times 8 \times 8 \times 8 \times 8 \times 8$

  f $33 \times 33 \times 33 \times 33 \times 33 \times 33 \times 33 \times 33 \times 33$

3 **a**   Calculate the difference between 3^2 and 2^3.

  b   Find the value of $3^3 + 4^2 + 2^4$.

4 5^4 can be written in several ways.

Here are some.

   $5 \times 5 \times 5 \times 5$ $5^2 \times 5^2$ $5^3 \times 5^1$

Write 4^5 in as many different ways as you can.

5 Copy and complete these.

  a $4^2 = \Box$

  b $\Box^3 = 125$

  c $2^{\Box} = 32$

Band 2 questions

6 Write the correct symbol $<$, $>$ or $=$ between each pair of numbers.

  a $2^5 \ \Box \ 6^2$

  b $2^7 \ \Box \ 5^3$

  c $4^3 \ \Box \ 3^4$

  d $2^9 \ \Box \ 8^3$

  e $10^3 \ \Box \ 2^{10}$

  f $12^5 \ \Box \ 3^8$

7 The expressions on these 12 cards can be matched into six pairs.

All the missing numbers are the same.

| $4^{\Box}$ | $3 \times \Box$ | 9 | 32 | $\Box^3$ | 6 | 10 | $\Box \times 5$ | 16 | $3^{\Box}$ | 8 | $\Box^5$ |

  a   Match the cards into pairs.

  b   What is the missing number?

8 Write each of these as a single power.

  a $4^5 \times 4^3$

  b $6^{12} \times 6^4$

  c $5^9 \times 5^3$

9 Write each of these as a single power.

  a $3^5 \div 3^3$

  b $7^{14} \div 7^8$

  c $8^9 \div 8^5$

  d $\dfrac{2^7}{2^3}$

  e $\dfrac{10^8}{10^3}$

  f $\dfrac{20^6}{20}$

10 Write each of these as a single power.

  a $(6^2)^3$

  b $(2^4)^5$

  c $(13^6)^3$

11 **a** Write down the value of $49 \div 49$.

b Write 49 as a power of 7.

c Write $7^2 \div 7^2$

    i as a power of 7   **ii** as a number.

d What is the value of 7^0?

e What are the values of

    i 2^0 **ii** 3^0 **iii** 17^0?

f State a general value for the power zero.

12 Write each of these calculations as a single power.

a $\left(13^7\right)^8$ **b** $7^9 \div 7^2$ **c** $4^5 \times 4^9$

d $3^6 \div 3^4$ **e** $\left(12^4\right)^6$ **f** $11^3 \times 11^4 \times 11^5$

13 Work out the value of these. Give each of your answers as a decimal.

a 2^{-1} **b** 10^{-1} **c** 5^{-1} **d** 4^{-1} **e** 100^{-1} **f** 8^{-1}

14 Jemima says that $3^4 \times 2^2$ is equal to 6^6.

Show that Jemima is wrong.

What mistake has she made?

Band 3 questions

15 Work out the value of these. Give each of your answers as a decimal.

a 2^{-2} **b** 10^{-2} **c** 5^{-2} **d** 2^{-3} **e** 10^{-3} **f** 5^{-3}

16 Work out the value of these.

a $\sqrt[5]{243}$ **b** $\sqrt[7]{128}$ **c** $\sqrt[4]{625}$

17 Write these as a single power of 5.

a $5^3 \times 5^{-2}$ **b** $5^3 \div 5^{-2}$ **c** $\left(5^{-2}\right)^3$

d $5^{-4} \times 5^8$ **e** $5^{-1} \times 5$ **f** $5^{-2} \div 5^{-2}$

18 Find the missing digits.

a $7^{\square} = 7^5 \div 7^2$ **b** $7^3 = 7^3 \times 7^{\square}$ **c** $\left(7^{\square}\right)^4 = 7^8$ **d** $7^6 \div 7^2 = 7^{\square} \times 7^3$

19 Write each of these as a single power.

a $\dfrac{3^5 \times 3^4}{3^6}$ **b** $\left(2^4 \times 2^2\right)^3$ **c** $\dfrac{\left(2^2\right)^3}{\left(2^4\right)^2}$

d $\dfrac{6^{-7}}{6^{-3}}$ **e** $\left(5^{-3} \times 5^4\right)^5$ **f** $\dfrac{9^3 \times 9^2}{9^{-2} \times 9^{-1}}$

20 **a** Priya says that $\left(5^3\right)^2$ is the same as $\left(5^2\right)^3$.

    Show that Priya is right.

b Show that $\left(a^m\right)^n$ is the same as $\left(a^n\right)^m$.

c Is it **always true, sometimes true or never true** that $a^m \div a^n$ the same as $a^n \div a^m$? Explain your answer fully.

1.2 Standard form

✔ Skill checker

① Work out these powers of 10.

a 10^1
b 10^2
c 10^3
d 10^4
e 10^5
f 10^6

② a Write down 1 million as
  i an ordinary number
  ii a power of 10.
 b Write down 1 billion as
  i an ordinary number
  ii a power of 10.
 c A googol is 10^{100}.
   Alfie writes a googol down as an ordinary number.
   How many zeros should follow the 1?

③ a Copy and complete this pattern.

$2.7 \times 10 = \boxed{}$

$2.7 \times 10^2 = 2.7 \times 100 \quad = \boxed{}$

$2.7 \times 10^3 = 2.7 \times 1000 = \boxed{}$

$2.7 \times 10^4 = 2.7 \times \boxed{} = \boxed{}$

$2.7 \times 10^5 = 2.7 \times \boxed{} = \boxed{}$

$2.7 \times \boxed{} = 2.7 \times \boxed{} = 2\,700\,000$

 b Work out the value of 2.7×10^9

   Which of these is the correct way to say this number?

2.7 billion	27 hundred million
27 thousand million	2 thousand 7 hundred million

Using standard form for large numbers

You often see headlines in newspapers that involve large numbers. For example, there are more than 400 billion Lego bricks in the world or there are 8.9 million school children in the UK.

In newspapers, large numbers are usually written using the words 'billion' and 'million' rather than being written out in full like this:

400 000 000 000 Lego bricks or 8 900 000 school children

In maths and science, large numbers are usually written using powers of 10

For example, 4×10^{11} Lego bricks or 8.9×10^6 school children

Standard form is a way of writing down large numbers without writing down all the zeros.

A number is in standard form when it is written as

a number between 1 and 10 multiplied by a power of 10

In symbols this is written as

$A \times 10^n$

- A can be any number from 1 up to 10 (but not 10). ← $1 \leq A < 10$
- n must be an integer (whole number).

The Pacific Ocean has a surface area of $168\,000\,000\,km^2$.

Write this number in standard form.

Solution

$168\,000\,000$ in standard form is $1.68 \times 10^?$ ← *A* is always between 1 and 10.

Use a place value diagram to help you work out what the power of 10 should be.

H M	T M	M	H Th	T Th	Th	H	T	O	.	t	h
		.						1	.	6	8
1	6	8	0	0	0	0	0	0	.		

$168\,000\,000 = 1.68 \times 10\,000\,000$

$ = 1.68 \times 10^8$ ← You have to multiply 1.68 by ten 8 times to get $168\,000\,000$.

So the Pacific Ocean has a surface area of $1.68 \times 10^8\,km^2$

You don't need to draw a place value diagram each time. The digits move 8 places so that the decimal point is now between the 1 and the 6, so you multiply by 10^8.

$168\,000\,000. = 1.68 \times 10^8$ ← Count the arrows. They tell you the power of 10.

Using standard form for small numbers

Activity

① Complete this pattern.

$\div 10$ ⟨ $10^2 = 100$ ⟩ $\div 10$
$\div 10$ ⟨ $10^1 = 10$ ⟩ $\div 10$
$\div 10$ ⟨ $10^0 = \underline{\quad}$ ⟩ $\div 10$
$10^{-1} = 0.1$

$10^{-2} = \underline{\quad}$

$10^{-3} = \underline{\quad}$

$10^{-4} = \underline{\quad}$

② **a** Work these out.

   i 2×10^{-1} 2×10^{-2} 2×10^{-3}

   ii 84×10^{-1} 84×10^{-2} 84×10^{-3}

   iii 7.9×10^{-1} 7.9×10^{-2} 7.9×10^{-3}

b Complete each statement.

Multiplying by 10^{-1} is the same as dividing by $\underline{\quad}$ once

Multiplying by 10^{-2} is the same as dividing by 10 $\underline{\quad}$

Multiplying by 10^{-3} is the same as dividing by 10 $\underline{\quad}$

Worked example

A flea weighs around 0.000 087 kg.

Write this number in standard form.

Solution

> A is always between 1 and 10.

0.000 087 in standard form is 8.7×10^{-5}

Use a place value diagram to help you work out what the power of 10 should be.

O	.	t	h	th	t th	t th	m	
8	.	7						
0	.	0	0	0	0	8	7	

$0.000\,087 = 8.7 \div 10 \div 10 \div 10 \div 10 \div 10$

$\qquad\quad = 8.7 \times 10^{-5}$

So the flea weighs 8.7×10^{-5} kg

> Remember: dividing by 10 is the same as multiplying by 10^{-1}.
>
> You have to divide 8.7 by ten five times to get 0.000 087.
>
> Dividing by 10 five times is the same as multiplying by 10^{-5}.
>
> You don't need to draw a place value diagram each time.
>
> You have moved the digits 5 places to get the decimal point between the 8 and the 7, so you multiply by 10^{-5}
>
> $$0.000\,087 = 8.7 \times 10^{-5}$$

Converting numbers from standard form

You also need to be able to convert from standard form back to ordinary numbers.

Remember when the power of 10:

- is positive, then the number is BIG
- is negative, then the number is SMALL.

Worked example

Convert these numbers from standard form to ordinary numbers.

a 5.67×10^4

b 3.08×10^{-6}

Solution

a 5.67×10^4 means you multiply 5.67 by 10 four times.

The digits move 4 places.

56 700.

So $5.67 \times 10^4 = 56\,700$ ← A positive power means the number is big!

b 3.08×10^{-6} means you divide 3.08 by 10 six times.

The digits move 6 places.

0.00000308

So $3.08 \times 10^{-6} = 0.000\,003\,08$ ← A negative power means the number is small!

1.2 Now try these

Fluency

1 Write each of these numbers as a power of 10.

    a 1 000 000   **b** 100 000 000   **c** 10

    d 0.01   **e** 0.001   **f** one hundred thousand

    g one thousand million   **h** one ten thousandth

2 Write each of these as an ordinary number.

    a 10^5 **b** 10^{10} **c** 10^{-1} **d** 10^{-2} **e** 10^{-3}

3 Work out these multiplications. Part **a** has been answered for you.

    a $2.6 \times 10^3 = 2.6 \times 1000 = 2600$ **b** 4×10^2

    c 4.8×10^5 **d** 1.3×10^4

    e 2.4×10^7 **f** 9.3×10^6

Problem solving

4 Copy and complete these. Fill in the missing numbers.

    a $\boxed{} \times 10^2 = 500$ **b** $\boxed{} \times 10^3 = 3000$ **c** $6 \times 10^{\boxed{}} = 6\,000\,000$

    d $\boxed{} \times 10^2 = 350$ **e** $4.2 \times 10^{\boxed{}} = 42\,000$ **f** $\boxed{} \times 10^5 = 450\,000$

Band 2 questions

Fluency

5 These numbers are in standard form. Write them as ordinary numbers.

    a 2×10^3 **b** 7×10^6 **c** 4.2×10^5 **d** 7.1×10^7 **e** 8.6×10^9

6 Write these numbers in standard form.

    a 200   **b** 5000   **c** 7 000 000   **d** 3600   **e** 7 200 000

7 Work out these multiplications.

    a 3×10^{-1} **b** 4×10^{-2} **c** 5×10^{-3}

8 Copy and complete these.

Fill in the missing numbers.

    a $4 \times 10^{\boxed{}} = 0.4$ **b** $\boxed{} \times 10^{-3} = 0.006$ **c** $3 \times 10^{\boxed{}} = 0.03$

Problem solving

9 Write these as ordinary numbers.

    a The length of a human chromosome is 5×10^{-6} m.

    b The CN tower in Toronto is 5.53×10^2 m tall.

    c The mass of an electron is 9.11×10^{-31} kg.

10 Write these numbers in standard form.

    a The distance between the Earth and the Moon is 239 000 miles.

    b A £5 note is 0.000 22 m thick.

    c Quartz fibre has a diameter of 0.000 001 m.

Band 3 questions

Reasoning

11 **a** Write the correct inequality symbol < or > between each of these pairs of numbers.

      i $3 \times 10^4 \boxed{} 3 \times 10^5$ **ii** $4.6 \times 10^6 \boxed{} 5.8 \times 10^6$

      iii $7 \times 10^9 \boxed{} 5.3 \times 10^9$ **iv** $6 \times 10^5 \boxed{} 1$ million

    b Explain how you can compare the sizes of numbers written in standard form.

Key Stage 3 Mastering Mathematics: Book 3

12 Write these numbers in order, starting with the smallest.

4.56×10^5 3.4×10^4 563 000 7.4×10^6 820 000

13 Correct each of these pieces of homework below.

For each question say who has got it right and explain where the other has gone wrong.

Samuel
Write 3800 in standard form
3.8×10^2
Write 0.000 006 78 in standard form
6.78×10^{-6}
Write 5×10^7 as an ordinary number
50 000 000
Write 9.6×10^{-5} as an ordinary number
9 600 000
Put in order of size, small to big:
2.6×10^4, 2.9×10^2, 2.7×10^{-3}
2.6×10^4, 2.9×10^2, 2.7×10^{-3}
Double 6.7×10^5
1 340 000

Ben
Write 3800 in standard form
3.8×10^3
Write 0.000 006 78 in standard form
6.78×10^{-8}
Write 5×10^7 as an ordinary number
50 000 000
Write 9.6×10^{-5} as an ordinary number
0.000 96
Put in order of size, small to big:
2.6×10^4, 2.9×10^2, 2.7×10^{-3}
2.6×10^4, 2.7×10^{-3}, 2.6×10^4
Double 6.7×10^5
1.34×10^6

14 **a** **i**   Explain how to work out 2000×300 in your head.

ii   Now write your answer in standard form.

b **i**   Write the answer to $(2 \times 10^3) \times (3 \times 10^2)$ in standard form.

Look carefully at your answer.

ii   How is the number worked out?

iii   How is the power of 10 worked out?

c   Work out

i $(4 \times 10^2) \times (2 \times 10^3)$ **ii** $(1.2 \times 10^4) \times (3 \times 10^2)$

d   Explain how to multiply numbers when they are written in standard form.

e   Use your method to work out $(3 \times 10^{-2}) \times (4 \times 10^{-3})$.

Make sure you write your answer in standard form.

15 The problems below can be solved by either multiplying or by dividing.

Choose the correct operation for each one and then answer the question.

a   A mouse weighs 1.5×10^{-2} kg.

An owl eats 1000 mice in a year.

What weight of mice is this?

b   The speed of sound is 3.3×10^2 metres per second.

How far does sound travel in an hour?

c   A grain of salt weighs 2×10^{-5} grams.

How many grains of salt are there in a 750 gram packet?

d   A packet of 500 sheets of paper is 55 mm thick.

How thick is each sheet of paper?

e   The average number of clover leaves in a square metre of lawn is 1.5×10^3.

Estimate the number of clover leaves in a park with 5×10^4 m² of lawns.

16 The galaxy that the Earth is in is called the Milky Way.

The Milky Way is about 120 000 light years across.

The Earth is around 27 000 light years from the centre of the Milky Way.

A light year is the distance that light can travel in a year and it is 9.46×10^{15} metres.

a Imagine a spaceship that can travel at half the speed of light.

It sets off from the Earth towards the centre of the Milky Way. How long would it take?

b How many generations of astronauts do you think it would take?

c Assuming an original crew of 20 people, how many people do you think would arrive at the centre of the Milky Way?

17 Which of these numbers are not in standard form? Why/why not?

Where possible re-write the number so it is in standard form.

a 0.3×10^4 **b** 7×10^{-3} **c** 10.1×10^{-4}

d $4 \times 10^{0.5}$ **e** 10^9 **f** 9.9×10^{100}

1.3 Prime factorisation

✔ Skill checker

① Look at the numbers in this box.

9	7	51	36	20
16	37	2	27	24
11	21	100	1	42
8	64	6	12	5

Write down all the numbers from the box that are

a square

b cubes

c factors of 36

d prime

e multiples of 6

f factors of 100 and prime.

② Write down the first ten prime numbers.

> **Remember**
>
> **Prime numbers** are numbers that have exactly 2 factors: 1 and the number itself.

Writing numbers as a product of prime factors

Remember that the **factors** of a number divide into it exactly.

For example, the factors of 12 are 1, 2, 3, 4, 6 and 12

A **prime factor** is a factor of a number that is also prime.

The prime factors of 12 are 2 and 3.

> **Remember**
>
> 1 is not a prime number.

Activity

Show that every number between 2 and 20 is either prime or can be made by multiplying prime numbers together.

Number	Answer
2	2 (prime)
3	3 (prime)
4	2 × 2
5	5 (prime)
6	2 × 3
7	

In the activity you found that every number up to 20 is either prime or can be made by multiplying together prime numbers. In fact, every whole number above 1 is either prime or can be made by multiplying together prime numbers.

This is known as the Fundamental Theorem of Arithmetic.

For example, $60 = 2 \times 2 \times 3 \times 5$

$= 2^2 \times 3 \times 5$

> This is called a **product** of prime factors.
> Remember: product means multiply.

The next example shows you how to use a factor tree to help you write a number as a product of prime factors.

Worked example

Write 1540 as a product of prime factors.

Solution

Using a factor tree:

> Find any product that gives 1540, e.g. 770 × 2.

> 2 is prime so put a ring around it.

> Find any product that gives 770, e.g. 77 × 10.

> Put a ring around any primes and stop when all the numbers at the end of the branches are ringed.

Note

Every whole number greater than 1 has one unique way to rewrite it as a product of prime factors. A different product of prime factors will give a different number!

So $1540 = 7 \times 11 \times 2 \times 5 \times 2$

$= 2^2 \times 5 \times 7 \times 11$

> Multiply all the numbers in the circles together.

> You can multiply in any order. 2 × 2 can be written as 2^2.

> If you use a different factor tree is the final answer always the same?

Finding the HCF and LCM of two numbers

The highest common factor (HCF) of two numbers is the largest factor that they share.

You can find the HCF of two numbers by listing their factors, as in this example for 20 and 30.

> Factors of 20: 1 2 4 5 10 20
> Factors of 30: 1 2 3 5 6 10 15 30

The highest number in both lists is 10 so this is the HCF of 20 and 30.

> The HCF is often quite a small number.

The lowest common multiple (LCM) of two numbers is the lowest multiple that they share.

You can find the LCM of two numbers by listing their multiples, as in this example, again using 20 and 30.

> Multiples of 20: 20 40 60 80 100
> Multiples of 30: 30 60 90 120 150

The lowest number in both lists is 60 so this is the LCM of 20 and 30.

The next example shows you how to use a Venn diagram to help you find the HCF and LCM of two numbers.

Worked example

a Show that 270 written as a product of prime factors is $2 \times 3^3 \times 5$.
b Write 315 as a product of prime factors.
c Find the HCF and LCM of 270 and 315.

Remember

- Writing a number as a product of its prime factors means writing all of the prime factors as a multiplication.
- Use index notation to write a product of prime factors neatly.

Solution

a $2 \times 3^3 \times 5 = 2 \times 27 \times 5$
$= 10 \times 27 = 270$

b
315
5   63 $315 \div 5 = 63$
7   9 $63 \div 7 = 9$
3   3 $9 = 3 \times 3$

Multiply together all the prime (circled) numbers in the factor tree:
$315 = 5 \times 7 \times 3 \times 3$
$= 3^2 \times 5 \times 7$

c $270 = 2 \times 3 \times 3 \times 3 \times 5$ and $315 = 3 \times 3 \times 5 \times 7$

Placing these factors in a Venn diagram gives

270   315

2   3
3   3   7
5

> 3, 3 and 5 are common factors so they go in the intersection. The intersection is the middle/crossover of the two circles.

Note

Venn diagrams are covered in full in chapter 15 (unit 15.2).

The HCF is found by multiplying the numbers in the intersection:

$3 \times 3 \times 5 = 45$

So the HCF of 270 and 315 is 45.

> These are the common factors of both numbers so when you multiply them together you'll get the highest common factor.

The LCM is found by multiplying all of the numbers in the Venn diagram:

> Check: $1890 = 6 \times 315$ which means 1890 is a multiple of 315 and $1890 = 270 \times 7$ which means 1890 is also a multiple of 270. Can you see why this method works?

1.3 Now try these

Band 1 questions

1 Work out these.

    a $3 \times 5 \times 7$ **b** $3 \times 7 \times 11$ **c** $2 \times 3 \times 5$ **d** $2 \times 3 \times 11$ **e** 2^3

    f 2^4 **g** $3^2 \times 5$ **h** $2^2 \times 3$ **i** $2^2 \times 5^2$

2 **a** What are the first ten multiples of 5?

    b What are the first ten multiples of 6?

    c What is the lowest common multiple (LCM) of 5 and 6?

3 **a** List the first eight multiples of 30.

    b List the first eight multiples of 24.

    c What is the lowest common multiple (LCM) of 30 and 24?

4 Find the lowest common multiple (LCM) of each pair of numbers.

    a 3 and 5   **b** 4 and 6   **c** 9 and 12

5 **a** What are the factors of 12?

    b What are the factors of 16?

    c What is the highest common factor (HCF) of 12 and 16?

6 Find the HCF of each pair of numbers.

    a 15 and 20   **b** 18 and 24

Band 2 questions

7 **a** Copy and complete this diagram to find the prime factors of 18.

    b Write 18 as the product of prime factors.

    c Rewrite your answer using indices.

8 **a** Complete this list of the factors of 60.

    1, 2, 3, ..., 60

    b Write a list of the prime factors of 60.

    c Write 60 as a product of prime factors.

9 Draw factor trees to write these numbers as products of the prime factors.

    a 12   **b** 8   **c** 15   **d** 20   **e** 30

10 Write each of these numbers as a product of its prime factors.

    Write your answers using indices.

    a 50   **b** 140   **c** 84   **d** 36   **e** 200

11 Find the **i** LCM and **ii** HCF of these pairs of numbers by first finding their prime factors and then using a Venn diagram.

    a 64 and 72   **b** 20 and 35   **c** 16 and 28

12 **a** Find the HCF of 90 and 360.

    b Find the LCM of 90 and 360.

    c What do you notice about your answers to parts **a** and **b**?

    Find another pair of numbers with this pattern.

13 **a** Find a number with prime factors of only 13, 17 and 19.

    b Find a number between 100 and 200 with prime factors that are all even.

    c Find a pair of numbers that have prime factors of only 2, 3 and 5.

    One of your pair should be a two-digit number and one should be a three-digit number.

Fluency

Fluency

Reasoning

⑭ **a** Show the prime factors of 24 and 90 on a Venn diagram.

b Use the Venn diagram to find the HCF and LCM of 24 and 90.

⑮ Pete makes rosewood jewellery.

Pieces of wood are joined together to make bracelets, necklaces and anklets.

All the pieces of wood are the same length.

Look at the poster.

What is the greatest possible length for one of the pieces of wood?

Pete's jewellery	
Bracelets	18 cm
Short Necklaces	48 cm
Long Necklaces	54 cm
Anklets	24 cm
GUARANTEED TO BRING YOU LUCK	

⑯ Find the LCM and HCF of 90, 75 and 60.

⑰ These dials are set at 0:

After the left dial has been turned through one complete turn they look like this:

a Draw a diagram to show what they will look like after two complete turns of the left dial.

b How many complete turns of the left dial are needed before the first two dials are both set to 0?

c How many complete turns of the left dial are needed before all three dials are again set to 0?

⑱

BUSES AVAILABLE FROM THIS STOP			
	1b	**3a**	**4**
Departing every	5 mins	8 mins	10 mins
First departure	9.00 am	9.00 am	9.00 am

All three buses leave together at 9.00 a.m.

When is the next time that all three buses leave together?

Key words

Here is a list of the key words you met in this chapter.

Cube	Cube root	Factor	Highest common factor (HCF)
Indices	Lowest common multiple (LCM)	Multiple	Power Prime
Product	Square	Square root	Standard form
Venn diagram			

Use the glossary at the back of this book to check any you are unsure about.

Review exercise: powers and indices

Band 1 questions

Fluency

1 Multiply out these.

   a $2^2 \times 3^2$ **b** 3×5^2 **c** 2×7^2 **d** $2^3 \times 3^3$

Reasoning

2 Write 64 as a power of

   a   2   **b**   4   **c**   8   **d**   64

Problem solving

3 Write the number in each statement as a power of 10.

   a   There are 100 steps to the top of the tower.

   b   The winner won by just 0.1 of a second.

   c   The car costs £10 000.

Fluency

4 In the number 4.12×10^6, the first digit has a value of 4 million or 4 000 000.

The numbers in the table are written in standard form.

Copy the tables and fill in the value of the first digit for each number.

a

Number	Value of first digit
6.1×10^4	
3.52×10^4	
2.9×10^7	
1.352×10^7	
4.5×10^9	
1.236×10^9	

b

Number	Value of first digit
2×10^{-2}	
1.46×10^{-2}	
3×10^{-4}	
6.2×10^{-4}	
5×10^{-6}	
3.21×10^{-6}	

5 Find the LCM and HCF of these pairs of numbers by first finding their prime factors.

   a   8 and 14   **b**   30 and 35   **c**   18 and 24

Band 2 questions

Fluency

6 Find the values of these.

   a $(2^2)^3$ **b** $2^2 \times 2^3$ **c** $2^2 + 2^3$ **d** $2^3 \times 2^3$

   e $2^3 \times 2^3$ **f** $2^5 \div 2^3$ **g** $2^{99} \div 2^{96}$ **h** $\dfrac{2^5}{(2 \times 2 \times 2 \times 2 \times 2)}$

7 Find the LCM and HCF of these pairs of numbers by first finding their prime factors.

   a   80 and 100   **b**   210 and 240

Problem solving

8 Work out the missing digits in these. There may be more than one answer.

   a $\boxed{}^2 = 25$ **b** $\boxed{}\,\boxed{}^2 = \boxed{}\,\boxed{}5$

   c $\boxed{}^3 = \boxed{}\,\boxed{}6$ **d** $\boxed{}^6 = \boxed{}^3$

Fluency

9 Write these numbers in standard form.

   a   2000   **b**   32 000   **c**   1450   **d**   36 000 000

10 Write these numbers in standard form.

   a   0.067   **b**   0.003 41   **c**   0.000 006   **d**   0.23

11 Write these as ordinary numbers.

   a 2×10^3 **b** 1.4×10^2 **c** 4.56×10^4 **d** 5.6×10^5

   e 3.576×10^{12} **f** 2.7×10^{-3} **g** 8.32×10^{-7} **h** 4.9×10^{-10}

12 Write these numbers in standard form.

 a China has an estimated population of 1 393 000 000.

 b It takes 0.000 000 003 3 seconds for light to travel a distance of 1 metre.

 c The world's longest river, the Nile, is 6695 km long.

 d An amoeba is 0.0005 metres across.

 e The Star Wars films had a worldwide box office gross of £10 320 000 000.

13 Write each expression as a single power of 3 or 5.

 a $3^4 \times 3^2$ **b** $3^5 \div 3^2$ **c** $(3^2)^4$ **d** $5^2 \div 5^2$ **e** $5^2 \div 5^4$ **f** $5^2 \div 5^3$

Band 3 questions

14 Lucy has got all of her homework wrong.

The numbers are correct, but they should be written in standard form.

Correct Lucy's homework.

 a 100×10^5 ✗ **b** 0.3×10^9 ✗

 c 0.5×10^{-3} ✗ **d** 200×10^{-6} ✗

15 Write these sets of numbers in order of size, starting with the smallest.

 a 2.3×10^4 32 000 5.47×10^3 1.36×10^3 40 thousand

 b 4×10^{-5} 3.7×10^{-4} 1.8×10^{-4} 0.000 65   0.000 03

16 Nomsa thinks she has found a counter-example to the rule that any number has only one set of prime factors. She says,

'My number is 24 871. I can factorise it in two ways. It can be 209 × 119 or it can be 187 × 133. I have found an exception to the rule!'

Is Nomsa correct?

17 The prime factors of a cube number can be grouped in threes like this:

$216 = (2 \times 2 \times 2) \times (3 \times 3 \times 3)$ is the cube of (2×3).

 a $15 = 3 \times 5$. Write down the cube of 15.

 b What is the cube root of $3^3 \times 7^3$?

$64 = 2 \times 2 \times 2 \times 2 \times 2 \times 2 = 2^6$ is a square number and a cube number.

 c Show that its factors can be grouped in pairs and in threes.

 d Find two more numbers that are both square numbers and cube numbers.

18 In a motor race, the faster car completes the circuit in 5 minutes and the slower car takes 7 minutes.

 a How long is it before the faster car overtakes the slower car at the same time as they pass through the starting position?

 b How many laps has each car completed?

 c Does the faster car overtake the slower car anywhere else on the circuit?

 d If so, where does this happen and after how long?

19 a You are given that $\dfrac{2^3 \times 2^{2n}}{2^5} = (2^2)^3$.

Write each side as a single power of 2.

Work out the value of n.

 b You are given that $3^m \times 3^{m+1} = (3^m)^3 \times 3^4$.

Work out the value of m.

CHAPTER 2

Fractions

▶ **Coming up…**

- ◆ Understanding equivalent fractions
- ◆ Adding, subtracting, multiplying and dividing fractions
- ◆ Understanding mixed numbers
- ◆ Converting between mixed numbers and improper fractions

→ Fraction arithmagons

The number in each square is the SUM of the numbers in the circles adjacent to it.

Make a copy of each arithmagon and fill in the missing numbers.

①

②

③

④

⑤

⑥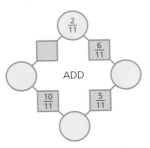

2.1 Fractions review

✓ Skill checker

① Work out what fraction of this square is

 a stripes

 b orange

 c white

② Jamal has drawn this pie chart to show how he spends his pocket money.

Find what fraction of his money he spends on

a   entertainment

b   sweets and snacks

c   clothes and travel

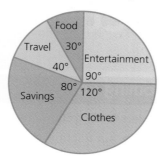

Fractions to decimals

Remember you can change a fraction into a decimal by dividing the numerator (top) by the denominator (bottom).

For example, $\frac{3}{8} = 3 \div 8 = 0.375$.

Equivalent fractions

You can find **equivalent fractions** by multiplying or dividing **both the top and bottom** of a fraction by the same number.

So

$$\overset{\times 2}{\frac{3}{8}} = \underset{\times 2}{\frac{6}{16}}$$

and

$$\overset{\div 4}{\frac{12}{32}} = \underset{\div 4}{\frac{3}{8}}$$

> This is called simplifying or cancelling. You can't simplify $\frac{3}{8}$ any further, so you say $\frac{3}{8}$ is in its **lowest terms** or **simplest form**.

> **Note**
>
> Use your calculator to check that $6 \div 16 = 0.375$ and $12 \div 32 = 0.375$.

Equivalent fractions simplify to give the same fraction in its lowest terms.

For example

$$\overset{\div 5}{\frac{10}{15}} = \underset{\div 5}{\frac{2}{3}} \qquad \overset{\div 8}{\frac{16}{24}} = \underset{\div 8}{\frac{2}{3}}$$

$\frac{10}{15}$ and $\frac{16}{24}$ are equivalent as they both simplify to give $\frac{2}{3}$

You can use equivalent fractions to rewrite a decimal as a fraction.

For example, 0.375 means 375 thousandths which is $\frac{375}{1000}$

Simplifying gives $\frac{375}{1000} = \frac{75}{200} = \frac{15}{40} = \frac{3}{8}$

Key Stage 3 Mastering Mathematics: Book 3

⬟ Discussion activity

① What is a fraction? Look at what these people think.
   Who is right? Explain your answer fully.

② Fractions, decimals and integers together are called **real numbers**.
   How many real numbers are there?

③ Numbers that can be written as a fraction are called **rational numbers**.
   Which of these numbers are **rational**?

   $$\pi \qquad 7 \qquad -\frac{1}{2} \qquad 1.25$$

   Show how to write each number as a fraction.
   How many rational numbers are there?

④ Ben says there are more positive integers than square numbers.
   Is Ben correct?

> **Amir:** It is a type of number

> **Callum:** It is a part of a whole

> **Harvey:** It is a number – all numbers are fractions

> **Jess:** It is a decimal – every decimal is a fraction

> **Lilia:** It is a proportion

Adding and subtracting fractions

Worked example

Work out

a $\dfrac{3}{4} + \dfrac{1}{5}$

b $\dfrac{13}{18} - \dfrac{2}{3}$

> **Remember**
> You can only add or subtract fractions when they have the same denominator (bottom).

Solution

a
$$\overset{\times 5}{\frac{3}{4} = \frac{15}{20}} \qquad \overset{\times 4}{\frac{1}{5} = \frac{4}{20}}$$
$$\underset{\times 5}{} \qquad \underset{\times 4}{}$$

$$\frac{3}{4} + \frac{1}{5} = \frac{15}{20} + \frac{4}{20}$$

$$= \frac{19}{20}$$

> 20 is the **lowest common denominator**. It is the smallest number that is a multiple of both 4 and 5.

b
$$\overset{}{\frac{2}{3} = \frac{12}{18}} \qquad \overset{\times 6}{\frac{2}{3} = \frac{12}{18}}$$
$$\underset{\times 6}{}$$

> 18 is a multiple of 3 so you don't need to rewrite both fractions to get the lowest common denominator. If you didn't spot this then you could rewrite both fractions with a **common denominator** of 3 x 18 = 54 and then simplify your answer.

$$\frac{13}{18} - \frac{2}{3} = \frac{13}{18} - \frac{12}{18}$$

$$= \frac{1}{18}$$

Multiplying fractions

This number line shows that $6 \times \frac{2}{3} = 4$.

6 lots of $\frac{2}{3}$

Remember it doesn't matter which order you multiply so $\frac{2}{3} \times 6 = 4$.

The number line also shows that $\frac{2}{3}$ of 6 = 4.

To shade $\frac{2}{3}$ of 6 you need to shade up to 4.

$6 \times \frac{2}{3}$, $\frac{2}{3} \times 6$ and $\frac{2}{3}$ of 6 are all different ways of writing the same thing.

You can also work out $\frac{2}{3}$ of 6 by finding $\frac{1}{3}$ of 6 and then doubling your answer.

$\frac{1}{3}$ of 6 = 2

Remember: finding $\frac{1}{3}$ is the same as dividing by 3.

So $\frac{2}{3} \times 6 = 4$.

You can also multiply fractions together.

For example, $\frac{1}{4} \times \frac{3}{5}$ means $\frac{1}{4}$ of $\frac{3}{5}$

In maths, 'of' means multiply.

The number line shows that $\frac{1}{4}$ of $\frac{3}{5} = \frac{3}{20}$

So $\frac{1}{4} \times \frac{3}{5} = \frac{3}{20}$

Remember
To multiply fractions you multiply the numerators (tops) and then the denominators (bottoms).

Worked example

Find **a** $\frac{3}{7}$ of £84   **b** $\frac{3}{5} \times \frac{7}{9} \times \frac{10}{21}$

Solution

a $\frac{1}{7}$ of £84 = £84 ÷ 7 = 12

So $\frac{3}{7}$ of £84 = 3 × £12 = £36

This is the same as $\frac{3}{7}$ x 84 and 84 x $\frac{3}{7}$.

b **Method 1: Multiply then cancel**

$$\frac{3}{5} \times \frac{7}{9} \times \frac{10}{21} = \frac{3 \times 7 \times 10}{5 \times 9 \times 21}$$

$$= \frac{210}{945}$$

You can simplify this fraction.

$$\frac{210}{945} = \frac{42}{189} = \frac{14}{63} = \frac{2}{9}$$

$$\overset{\div 5}{\overset{\frown}{\underset{\div 5}{\underset{\smile}{\frac{210}{945}}}}} = \overset{\div 3}{\overset{\frown}{\underset{\div 3}{\underset{\smile}{\frac{42}{189}}}}} = \overset{\div 7}{\overset{\frown}{\underset{\div 7}{\underset{\smile}{\frac{14}{63}}}}} = \frac{2}{9}$$

Method 2: Cancel then multiply

$$\frac{3}{5} \times \frac{7}{9} \times \frac{10}{21} = \frac{\cancel{3}^1}{\cancel{5}^1} \times \frac{\cancel{7}^1}{\cancel{9}^3} \times \frac{\cancel{10}^2}{\cancel{21}^3}$$

> Can you see how to cancel this in one step? Which method do you think is easier?

$$= \frac{1}{1} \times \frac{1}{3} \times \frac{2}{3}$$

$$= \frac{1 \times 1 \times 2}{1 \times 3 \times 3}$$

> Multiplying by 3 and dividing by 9 is the same as dividing by 3.
> Multiplying by 7 and then dividing by 21 is the same as dividing by 3.
> Multiplying by 10 and then dividing by 5 is the same as multiplying by 2.

$$= \frac{2}{9}$$

Dividing fractions

Remember: $1 \div \frac{1}{5}$ means 'how many fifths go into 1?'

So $1 \div \frac{1}{5} = 5$

> Dividing by $\frac{1}{5}$ is the same as multiplying by 5: $1 \div \frac{1}{5} = 5$.

and so $6 \div \frac{1}{5} = 30$.

> 6 is six times bigger than 1, so the answer is 6 times bigger!

$6 \div \frac{3}{5} = 10$

> $\frac{3}{5}$ is three times bigger than $\frac{1}{5}$, so the answer is one third the size.

When you divide by $\frac{3}{5}$ you multiply by 5 (to divide by $\frac{1}{5}$) and then divide by 3.

So dividing by $\frac{3}{5}$ is the same as multiplying by $\frac{5}{3}$.

> $6 \times \frac{5}{3} = \frac{6 \times 5}{3} = \frac{30}{3} = 10$

$\frac{5}{3}$ is called the **reciprocal** of $\frac{3}{5}$.

Note

The reciprocal of a number is '1 ÷ the number' or '1 over the number'. When you have a fraction you just turn it upside down.

Worked example

Work out

a $8 \div \dfrac{2}{3}$ **b** $\dfrac{2}{5} \div \dfrac{6}{7}$

Solution

a $8 \div \dfrac{2}{3} = 8 \times \dfrac{3}{2}$ ← Turn the 2nd fraction 'upside down' and multiply.

$= \dfrac{8 \times 3}{2}$

$= \dfrac{24}{2}$

$= 12$

The diagram shows that $\dfrac{2}{3}$ 'goes into' 8 twelve times.

b $\dfrac{2}{5} \div \dfrac{6}{7} = \dfrac{2}{5} \times \dfrac{7}{6}$ ← Turn the 2nd fraction 'upside down' and multiply.

$= \dfrac{14}{30}$ ← You can simplify this: divide 'top' and 'bottom' by 2:

$= \dfrac{7}{15}$

2.1 Now try these

Band 1 questions

1 Simplify these fractions.

  a $\dfrac{80}{90}$ **b** $\dfrac{5}{10}$ **c** $\dfrac{25}{100}$ **d** $\dfrac{8}{12}$ **e** $\dfrac{15}{20}$ **f** $\dfrac{7}{21}$

2 Write these fractions as decimals.

  The first one has been done for you.

  a $\dfrac{2}{5} = \dfrac{4}{10} = 0.4$ **b** $\dfrac{1}{5}$ **c** $\dfrac{1}{2}$ **d** $\dfrac{1}{4}$ **e** $\dfrac{3}{4}$ **f** $\dfrac{7}{8}$

3 Work out the following.

Use the grid to help you.

  a $\dfrac{9}{12} - \dfrac{2}{12}$ **b** $\dfrac{1}{4} + \dfrac{1}{2}$ **c** $\dfrac{1}{6} + \dfrac{2}{3}$ **d** $\dfrac{1}{3} + \dfrac{1}{2}$ **e** $\dfrac{2}{3} - \dfrac{1}{2}$ **f** $\dfrac{11}{12} - \dfrac{1}{2}$

Fluency

Fluency

4 Work out these.

a $\frac{1}{5}$ of 20   **b** $\frac{1}{3} \times 12$ **c** $60 \times \frac{1}{10}$ **d** $\frac{1}{6} \times 30$ **e** $\frac{1}{7}$ of 63   **f** $72 \times \frac{1}{12}$

Reasoning

5 This bar diagram illustrates

$4 \div \frac{1}{2} = 8$

State the division represented by each of the following bar diagrams.

a

b

c

d

Band 2 questions

Fluency

6 Work out these.

a $4 \div \frac{1}{2}$ **b** $3 \div \frac{1}{10}$ **c** $2 \div \frac{1}{6}$ **d** $3 \div \frac{1}{7}$ **e** $4 \div \frac{1}{5}$ **f** $10 \div \frac{1}{9}$

Reasoning

7 Write down the reciprocal of each of these.

a 8   **b** $\frac{1}{9}$ **c** $\frac{4}{7}$

Problem solving

8 Write the fractions in order of size, starting with the smallest.

$\frac{2}{5}$ $\frac{3}{10}$ $\frac{1}{2}$ $\frac{7}{25}$

Fluency

9 Work out these.

Give each answer as a fraction in its lowest terms.

a $\frac{3}{7} + \frac{4}{9}$ **b** $\frac{5}{6} - \frac{2}{3}$ **c** $\frac{7}{9} - \frac{5}{18}$ **d** $\frac{1}{6} + \frac{1}{4}$ **e** $\frac{3}{8} + \frac{5}{12}$ **f** $\frac{2}{3} - \frac{2}{7}$

10 Work out these.

Give each answer as a fraction in its lowest terms.

a $\frac{1}{2} \times \frac{1}{5}$ **b** $\frac{1}{3} \times \frac{2}{7}$ **c** $\frac{2}{3} \times \frac{3}{8}$ **d** $\frac{5}{6} \times \frac{3}{4}$ **e** $\frac{3}{11} \times \frac{5}{6}$ **f** $\frac{4}{9} \times \frac{7}{12}$

11 Use a bar diagram to help you work out these.

a $4 \div \frac{1}{3}$ **b** $6 \div \frac{2}{3}$ **c** $\frac{1}{2} \div \frac{1}{4}$ **d** $\frac{1}{6} \div 3$ **e** $\frac{1}{4} \div 5$ **f** $\frac{2}{5} \div 5$

12 Write each of these decimals as a fraction in its lowest terms.

a 0.4   **b** 0.95   **c** 0.875

13 Jo, Sophie and Meena share £60 between them.

Jo gets $\frac{1}{2}$ and Sophie gets $\frac{1}{3}$.

a What fraction does Meena get?

b How much money does Meena get?

Band 3 questions

14 Work out these.

Give each answer as a fraction in its lowest terms.

a $\frac{1}{5} \div \frac{1}{3}$ **b** $\frac{1}{7} \div \frac{1}{2}$ **c** $\frac{1}{6} \div \frac{2}{3}$ **d** $\frac{2}{5} \div 4$ **e** $\frac{4}{9} \div 3$ **f** $\frac{7}{12} \div \frac{2}{3}$

15 There are 240 pupils in year 9 at Hodder High.

The students are surveyed to find out how they get to school.

160 students walk to school.

45 students catch the bus.

$\frac{1}{12}$ of the students cycle.

The rest of the pupils travel to school by car.

Find what fraction of year 9 pupils:

a walk to school

b catch the bus

c travel by car.

Give each of your answers as a fraction in its lowest terms.

16 Work out these.

Give each answer as a fraction in its lowest terms.

a $4 \times \frac{2}{5} - 5 \times \frac{1}{6}$ **b** $\left(\frac{3}{5} - \frac{1}{4} \right)^2$ **c** $\frac{8}{9} - \frac{2}{3} \times \frac{5}{6}$

17 John is a fisherman.

One day he lands 600 kg of fish.

$\frac{2}{3}$ of this is flat fish.

$\frac{4}{5}$ of the rest is codling.

The remainder is a variety of other species.

What weight of John's fish were neither flatfish nor codling?

18 Pippa has read $\frac{5}{7}$ of her book.

She has 100 pages left to read.

How many pages has she read so far?

2.2 Mixed numbers

✔ Skill checker

Complete each of these puzzles.

▶ The number in each circle is the sum of the numbers in the rectangles.
▶ The number in the triangle is the product of the numbers in the rectangles.

> **Remember**
>
> **Product** means multiply.

a

b

c

d
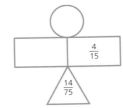

Converting between mixed numbers and top-heavy fractions

Fractions can be used to represent numbers which are greater than 1.

This number line shows $\frac{5}{2}$.

> There are 2 halves in one whole.

So there are 4 halves in 2 wholes. 5 halves make 2 and a half.

This number line shows $\frac{5}{3}$.

> There are 3 thirds in one whole.
> 5 thirds make 1 and 2 thirds.

Fractions like $\frac{5}{2}$ and $\frac{5}{3}$ are called **top heavy** or **improper fractions**.

They can also be written as **mixed numbers**.

For example, $\frac{5}{2} = 2\frac{1}{2}$ and $\frac{5}{3} = 1\frac{2}{3}$

> A mix of a whole number and a fraction

Every improper fraction can be written as a mixed number.

Worked example

a Express $\frac{19}{5}$ as a mixed number.

b Express $2\frac{7}{8}$ as an improper fraction.

Solution

a You change $\frac{19}{5}$ by working out $19 \div 5$.

$19 \div 5 = 3$ remainder 4.

So $\frac{19}{5} = 3\frac{4}{5}$. $\longleftarrow$

> You can also split the improper fraction into two fractions: $\frac{19}{5} = \frac{15}{5} + \frac{4}{5} = 3 + \frac{4}{5} = 3\frac{4}{5}$.

b There are 16 eighths in 2 so $2 = \frac{16}{8}$

So $2\frac{7}{8} = \frac{16}{8} + \frac{7}{8}$

$\qquad = \frac{23}{8}$.

You can add and subtract mixed numbers by dealing with the whole numbers first or converting them to improper fractions.

Worked example

Work out:

a $2\frac{1}{3} + 1\frac{4}{5}$

b $2\frac{1}{3} - 1\frac{4}{5}$

Solution

Method 1 Working with the whole numbers and the fractions separately

First write the fraction parts with a common denominator

$\overset{\times 5}{\frown}$ $\qquad\qquad$ $\overset{\times 3}{\frown}$

$\frac{1}{3} = \frac{5}{15}$ $\qquad\qquad$ $\frac{4}{5} = \frac{12}{15}$

$\underset{\times 5}{\smile}$ $\qquad\qquad$ $\underset{\times 3}{\smile}$

a $2\frac{1}{3} + 1\frac{4}{5} = 2\frac{5}{15} + 1\frac{12}{15}$

$\qquad = 2 + 1 + \frac{5}{15} + \frac{12}{15}$

$\qquad = 3 + \frac{17}{15}$ $\longleftarrow$

> Write $\frac{17}{15}$ as a mixed number.

$\qquad = 3 + 1 + \frac{2}{15}$

$\qquad = 4\frac{2}{15}$

b
$$2\frac{1}{3} - 1\frac{4}{5} = 2\frac{5}{15} - 1\frac{12}{15}$$
$$= 2 - 1 + \frac{5}{15} - \frac{12}{15}$$
$$= 1 - \frac{7}{15}$$
$$= \frac{8}{15}$$

Method 2: Converting to improper fractions

Start by writing $2\frac{1}{3}$ and $1\frac{4}{5}$ as top-heavy fractions.

$$2\frac{1}{3} = \frac{6}{3} + \frac{1}{3} = \frac{7}{3} \text{ and } 1\frac{4}{5} = \frac{5}{5} + \frac{4}{5} = \frac{9}{5}$$

a
$$2\frac{1}{3} + 1\frac{4}{5} = \frac{7}{3} + \frac{9}{5}$$
$$= \frac{35}{15} + \frac{27}{15}$$
$$= \frac{62}{15}$$
$$= \frac{60}{15} + \frac{2}{15}$$
$$= 4\frac{2}{15}$$

 Rewrite the top-heavy fractions to equivalent fractions with the same denominator.

$$\times 5 \qquad \frac{7}{3} = \frac{35}{15} \qquad \times 5$$

$$\times 3 \qquad \frac{9}{5} = \frac{27}{15} \qquad \times 3$$

$62 \div 15 = 4$ remainder 2

b
$$2\frac{1}{3} - 1\frac{4}{5} = \frac{7}{3} - \frac{9}{5}$$
$$= \frac{35}{15} - \frac{27}{15}$$
$$= \frac{8}{15}$$

 Which method do you prefer?

2.2 Now try these

Band 1 questions

① The diagram shows the mixed number $1\frac{5}{6}$.

    a How many sixths are there in the diagram?

    b Write $1\frac{5}{6}$ as a top-heavy fraction.

Fluency

2 **a** Colour a copy of this diagram to show the mixed number $1\frac{3}{4}$.

b Write $1\frac{3}{4}$ as a top-heavy fraction.

3 Colour a copy of these diagrams to show these fractions.

  a $\dfrac{11}{8}$ **b** $\dfrac{16}{6}$

4 Find the missing number in each statement.

  a $1 = \dfrac{\square}{3}$ **b** $1 = \dfrac{\square}{4}$ **c** $1 = \dfrac{\square}{5}$ **d** $2 = \dfrac{\square}{3}$ **e** $2 = \dfrac{\square}{4}$

  f $2 = \dfrac{\square}{5}$ **g** $3 = \dfrac{\square}{3}$ **h** $3 = \dfrac{\square}{4}$ **i** $3 = \dfrac{\square}{5}$

5 Copy and complete these to change the mixed numbers to top-heavy fractions.

  a $1\dfrac{1}{2} = \dfrac{\square}{2} + \dfrac{1}{2} = \dfrac{\square}{2}$ **b** $1\dfrac{1}{4} = \dfrac{\square}{4} + \dfrac{1}{4} = \dfrac{\square}{4}$

  c $1\dfrac{2}{3} = \dfrac{\square}{3} + \dfrac{2}{3} = \dfrac{\square}{3}$ **d** $1\dfrac{5}{6} = \dfrac{\square}{6} + \dfrac{5}{6} = \dfrac{\square}{6}$

Band 2 questions

6 Write these improper fractions as mixed numbers.

  a $\dfrac{8}{5} = 1\dfrac{\square}{5}$ **b** $\dfrac{7}{2} = \square\dfrac{1}{2}$ **c** $\dfrac{11}{9} = \square\dfrac{2}{\square}$ **d** $\dfrac{13}{8} = \square\dfrac{\square}{8}$ **e** $\dfrac{11}{3} = 3\dfrac{\square}{\square}$ **f** $\dfrac{17}{6} = \square\dfrac{5}{\square}$

7 Write these mixed numbers as improper fractions.

  a $2\dfrac{3}{4} = \dfrac{\square}{4}$ **b** $6\dfrac{1}{2} = \dfrac{\square}{2}$ **c** $2\dfrac{3}{5} = \dfrac{\square}{5}$ **d** $2\dfrac{4}{7} = \dfrac{18}{\square}$ **e** $3\dfrac{1}{9} = \dfrac{\square}{9}$ **f** $3\dfrac{1}{8} = \dfrac{\square}{\square}$

8 Write these as mixed numbers.

  a 80 minutes in hours   **b** 2325 grams in kilograms   **c** 24 days in weeks

  d 420 centimetres in metres   **e** 500 seconds in minutes

9 Work out these.

Give your answers as mixed numbers.

  a $\dfrac{2}{5} + \dfrac{4}{5}$ **b** $\dfrac{4}{5} + \dfrac{7}{10}$ **c** $\dfrac{1}{2} + \dfrac{2}{3}$ **d** $\dfrac{13}{4} + \dfrac{15}{7}$ **e** $\dfrac{15}{8} + \dfrac{5}{3}$ **f** $\dfrac{17}{6} + \dfrac{7}{4}$

10 Work out these.

Give your answers as mixed numbers where appropriate.

  a $\dfrac{7}{4} - \dfrac{7}{8}$ **b** $\dfrac{5}{3} - \dfrac{5}{6}$ **c** $\dfrac{13}{8} - \dfrac{9}{16}$ **d** $\dfrac{5}{2} - \dfrac{5}{3}$ **e** $\dfrac{10}{3} - \dfrac{15}{8}$ **f** $\dfrac{13}{4} - \dfrac{19}{10}$

Fluency

Problem solving

Fluency

Problem solving

Fluency

Fluency

11 Work out these.

Give your answers as mixed numbers where appropriate.

a $1\frac{1}{2} + 1\frac{7}{10}$ b $6\frac{2}{3} - 2\frac{7}{9}$ c $2\frac{1}{3} - \frac{7}{8}$ d $1\frac{1}{2} - \frac{9}{10}$ e $5\frac{1}{4} + 2\frac{7}{8}$ f $2\frac{1}{3} + 1\frac{7}{9}$

Problem solving

12 Tom needs $3\frac{1}{2}$ cups of dried fruit for a cake recipe.

He only has $\frac{3}{4}$ cup of sultanas and $1\frac{1}{3}$ cups of raisins.

He has plenty of currants.

How many cups of currants does he need to use?

Band 3 questions

Reasoning

13 Put these fractions into size order, smallest first.

$\frac{13}{6}$ $2\frac{1}{5}$ $1\frac{3}{4}$ $\frac{9}{5}$ $2\frac{1}{3}$

Fluency

14 Work out these.

Give your answers as mixed numbers.

a $1\frac{3}{4} + 3\frac{1}{2} - \frac{1}{4}$ b $5\frac{1}{3} - 1\frac{1}{5} + \frac{13}{15}$ c $3\frac{5}{6} + 4\frac{7}{8} - 1\frac{2}{3}$

d $4\frac{4}{5} - 1\frac{8}{9} - 1\frac{1}{9}$ e $3\frac{2}{3} + 1\frac{4}{5} + 2\frac{1}{2}$ f $2\frac{5}{8} + 3\frac{6}{7} - 4\frac{1}{2}$

Problem solving

15 A children's play area needs to be fenced off from the local park.

The rectangle shows the dimensions of the play area.

Calculate the amount of fencing needed.

Give your answer as a mixed number.

$12\frac{3}{5}$ m

$5\frac{5}{6}$ m

16 A cross country race circuit is 2500 metres.

a On Monday Ailsa runs 7000 metres.

How many circuits is this? (Give your answer as a mixed number.)

b On Tuesday Ailsa runs 9000 metres. How many circuits is this?

c Add your answers to parts **a** and **b**.

d How many metres does Ailsa run on Monday and Tuesday together? Convert your answer to a number of circuits.

2.3 Multiplying and dividing mixed numbers

✔ Skill checker

Here is Josh's maths homework.

1	$\frac{45}{7} = 6\frac{3}{7}$		6	$3\frac{9}{10} = \frac{39}{10}$
2	$2\frac{3}{4} = \frac{9}{4}$		7	$\frac{44}{15} = 3\frac{1}{15}$
3	$\frac{5}{7} - \frac{2}{3} = \frac{3}{4}$		8	$\frac{2}{3} \div \frac{1}{2} = \frac{3}{2} \times \frac{1}{2} = \frac{3}{4}$
4	$\frac{\cancel{6}^2}{7} \times \frac{2}{\cancel{3}^3} = \frac{4}{21}$		9	$\frac{33}{8} - \frac{9}{4} = 1\frac{7}{8}$
5	$\frac{25}{9} = 2\frac{7}{9}$		10	$3\frac{5}{11} = \frac{37}{11}$

Which questions has he got wrong?
What should the correct answers be?

Calculations with mixed numbers

To multiply or divide mixed numbers, you need to start by rewriting each fraction as an improper fraction.

Worked example

Work out:

a $2\frac{2}{5} \times 1\frac{1}{9}$ **b** $2\frac{2}{5} \div 1\frac{1}{9}$

Solution

$2\frac{2}{5} = \frac{10}{5} + \frac{2}{5} = \frac{12}{5}$ and $1\frac{1}{9} = \frac{9}{9} + \frac{1}{9} = \frac{10}{9}$ ← Write $2\frac{2}{5}$ and $1\frac{1}{9}$ as top-heavy fractions.

a Method 1: Cancel and then multiply

So $2\frac{2}{5} \times 1\frac{1}{9} = \frac{12}{5} \times \frac{10}{9}$

$= \frac{\cancel{12}^4}{\cancel{5}^1} \times \frac{\cancel{10}^2}{\cancel{9}^3}$ ← Cancel the common factors.

$= \frac{4}{1} \times \frac{2}{3} = \frac{8}{3}$

$= 2\frac{2}{3}$

Method 2: Multiply and then cancel

So $2\frac{2}{5} \times 1\frac{1}{9} = \frac{12}{5} \times \frac{10}{9}$

$= \frac{120}{45}$ ← Divide top and bottom by 15.

$= \frac{8}{3}$

$= 2\frac{2}{3}$

b $2\frac{2}{5} \div 1\frac{1}{9} = \frac{12}{5} \div \frac{10}{9}$ ← Flip the 2nd fraction and then multiply. $\frac{9}{10}$ is the reciprocal of $\frac{10}{9}$.

$= \frac{\cancel{12}^{6}}{5} \times \frac{9}{\cancel{10}^{5}}$ ← 2 is a factor of 12 and 10, so you can cancel.

$= \frac{6}{5} \times \frac{9}{5}$

$= \frac{54}{25}$

$= 2\frac{4}{25}$

2.3 Now try these

Band 1 questions

1 Find the reciprocal of each of these fractions.

 a $\frac{5}{2}$ **b** $\frac{7}{3}$ **c** $\frac{9}{4}$

2 Work out these.

 a **i** $\frac{1}{2} \times 6$ **ii** $\frac{3}{2} \times 6$ **iii** $6 \times \frac{3}{2}$

 b **i** $\frac{1}{5}$ of 10   **ii** $\frac{6}{5}$ of 10   **iii** $\frac{6}{5} \times 10$

 c **i** $24 \times \frac{1}{8}$ **ii** $24 \times \frac{11}{8}$ **iii** $\frac{11}{8} \times 24$

What do you notice about your answers?

3 Work out these.

 a **i** $1 \div \frac{1}{2}$ **ii** $5 \div \frac{1}{2}$ **iii** $5 \div \frac{3}{2}$

 b **i** $1 \div \frac{1}{3}$ **ii** $4 \div \frac{1}{3}$ **iii** $4 \div \frac{5}{3}$

 c **i** $1 \div \frac{1}{4}$ **ii** $2 \div \frac{1}{4}$ **iii** $2 \div \frac{5}{4}$

Fluency

Reasoning

Fluency

4 **i** Write each of these fractions as a top-heavy fraction.

    ii Write down the reciprocal of each fraction.

    a $2\frac{1}{2}$ **b** $1\frac{3}{4}$ **c** $2\frac{1}{4}$ **d** $4\frac{2}{3}$ **e** $3\frac{2}{5}$ **f** $2\frac{7}{8}$

5 Four people share $2\frac{1}{2}$ pizzas equally.

    What fraction of a whole pizza do they get each?

Band 2 questions

6 Work out these.

    Give your answers as mixed numbers where appropriate.

    a $2\frac{1}{5} \times \frac{1}{3}$ **b** $1\frac{1}{4} \times \frac{4}{7}$ **c** $1\frac{4}{5} \times 1\frac{2}{3}$ **d** $2\frac{1}{7} \times 1\frac{3}{8}$ **e** $3\frac{7}{10} \times 2\frac{1}{2}$ **f** $1\frac{7}{8} \times 3\frac{4}{5}$

7 Work out these.

    a $1\frac{3}{4} \div 2$ **b** $2\frac{3}{8} \div 4$ **c** $4\frac{2}{3} \div 5$

8 Work out these.

    a **i** $1\frac{1}{4} \div 1\frac{1}{2}$ **ii** $1\frac{1}{2} \div 1\frac{1}{4}$ **b** **i** $2\frac{3}{5} \div 1\frac{1}{3}$ **ii** $1\frac{1}{3} \div 2\frac{3}{5}$

    c **i** $4\frac{3}{4} \div 2\frac{1}{6}$ **ii** $2\frac{1}{6} \div 4\frac{3}{4}$

    What do you notice about your answers?

9 Calculate the area of each of these shapes.

    a   **b**

10 George paints $\frac{2}{5}$ of his garage in $1\frac{1}{2}$ hours.

    How long would he take to paint:

    a $\frac{1}{5}$ **b** $\frac{3}{5}$ **c** all of the garage?

Band 3 questions

11 Work out these.

    Give your answers as mixed numbers where appropriate.

    a $2\frac{1}{4} \times 3\frac{2}{5} \times \frac{2}{17}$ **b** $2\frac{3}{5} \times 2\frac{2}{3} \times 1\frac{2}{13}$ **c** $1\frac{3}{4} + 2\frac{1}{5} \times 3\frac{2}{3}$

    d $8\frac{1}{2} - 4\frac{1}{3} \times 1\frac{7}{8}$ **e** $2\frac{1}{4} \times 1\frac{1}{5} + 2\frac{3}{10}$ **f** $2\frac{2}{3} \times 1\frac{3}{4} \times 2\frac{1}{2}$

    g $1\frac{7}{8} \div 3\frac{1}{2} + 2\frac{1}{2}$ **h** $2\frac{3}{4} - 1\frac{5}{6} \div 2\frac{1}{3}$ **i** $3\frac{3}{4} \div 2\frac{2}{3} \div 1\frac{1}{2}$

Problem solving

12 Seb goes cycling on Friday, Saturday and Sunday.

He cycles $32\frac{3}{4}$ km altogether.

On Friday he cycles $5\frac{4}{5}$ km.

On Saturday he cycles three times as far as he did on Friday.

How far did Seb cycle on Sunday?

13 Kelly is a long-distance runner.

She runs at a steady pace of $7\frac{1}{2}$ miles each hour.

How far does she run in:

a $2\frac{1}{2}$ hours

b   3 hours 20 minutes?

Reasoning

14 Dan says that the reciprocal of 2 is $\frac{1}{2}$ and the reciprocal of $\frac{1}{3}$ is 3.

So the reciprocal of $2\frac{1}{3}$ is $3\frac{1}{2}$.

Is Dan correct? Explain your answer fully.

Problem solving

15 The area of a rectangle is $10\frac{4}{5}$ m.

The width of the rectangle is $6\frac{1}{4}$ m.

Calculate the perimeter of the rectangle.

Key words

Here is a list of the key words you met in this chapter.

Denominator	Equivalent	Fraction	Improper fraction
Lowest terms	Mixed number	Numerator	Reciprocal

Use the glossary at the back of this book to check any you are unsure about.

Band 1 questions

1 Look at this table.

$\frac{2}{4}$	$\frac{8}{12}$	$\frac{9}{27}$	$\frac{5}{10}$
$\frac{2}{6}$	$\frac{15}{20}$	$\frac{6}{8}$	$\frac{3}{12}$
$\frac{6}{10}$	$\frac{9}{12}$	$\frac{12}{16}$	$\frac{3}{9}$
$\frac{7}{14}$	$\frac{11}{33}$	$\frac{4}{16}$	$\frac{14}{28}$

a Write down all the fractions that are equivalent to:

     i $\frac{1}{2}$ **ii** $\frac{1}{3}$ **iii** $\frac{3}{4}$

b Write all the other fractions in the table in their simplest form.

2 Say whether these statements are true or false.

If false, change it to make a true statement.

a 20 minutes is $\frac{1}{3}$ of an hour.
             b 10 grams are $\frac{1}{10}$ of a kilogram.

c 20 pence are $\frac{1}{5}$ of £1.
                 d 3 millimetres are $\frac{3}{10}$ of a centimetre.

e 5 weeks are $\frac{1}{10}$ of a year.

3 Change these mixed numbers to top-heavy fractions.

     a $1\frac{4}{5}$ **b** $1\frac{2}{7}$ **c** $1\frac{4}{9}$

4 Jenny is trying to limit her screen time to 3 hours a day.

One day she uses her screen time like this.

Computer games	$\frac{1}{2}$ hour
Watching videos on the internet	$\frac{3}{4}$ hour
TV	$\frac{1}{2}$ hour
Social media	$\frac{5}{6}$ hour

a How much screen time has she spent?

b How much screen time does she have left? Give your answer in minutes.

Problem solving

5 Write each of these sets of fractions in order of size, starting with the smallest.

a $\dfrac{3}{4}$ $\dfrac{5}{6}$ $\dfrac{3}{7}$ $\dfrac{7}{10}$ $\dfrac{4}{5}$ $\dfrac{9}{10}$ b $\dfrac{9}{21}$ $\dfrac{40}{50}$ $\dfrac{1}{3}$ $\dfrac{2}{4}$ $\dfrac{15}{18}$ c $\dfrac{4}{8}$ $\dfrac{6}{10}$ $\dfrac{50}{60}$ $\dfrac{13}{39}$ $\dfrac{16}{20}$

6 Alfie, Ben and Chloe share £72 between them.

Alfie gets £32, Ben gets £18 and Chloe gets the rest.

What fraction does each get?

Write the fractions in their simplest form.

Fluency

7 Work out these.

Give your answers as mixed numbers where appropriate.

a $\dfrac{39}{10} + \dfrac{13}{8}$ b $\dfrac{9}{2} - \dfrac{16}{9}$ c $\dfrac{1}{2} + \dfrac{2}{3}$

8 Work out these. Give your answers as mixed numbers where appropriate.

a $5 \times 1\dfrac{1}{2}$ b $6 \times 2\dfrac{2}{3}$ c $5\dfrac{1}{4} \times 1\dfrac{1}{3}$

Problem solving

9 Jake can buy two different tins of sweets. He likes toffees best.

a In Tin A, he finds that $\dfrac{1}{5}$ are soft toffees and $\dfrac{1}{4}$ are hard toffees.

   What fraction of Tin A are toffees?

b In Tin B, $\dfrac{3}{10}$ are truffles and $\dfrac{1}{4}$ are plain chocolate, the rest are toffees.

   What fraction of Tin B are toffees?

c Tin A costs £5 and holds approximately 20 sweets, Tin B costs £3 and holds approximately 15 sweets.
   Which tin is the best buy?

Fluency

10 Work these out. Give your answers as mixed numbers where appropriate.

a $1\dfrac{9}{10} + 2\dfrac{5}{6}$ b $8 - 5\dfrac{1}{3}$ c $6\dfrac{6}{7} + 3\dfrac{7}{10}$

d $5\dfrac{2}{7} - 2\dfrac{6}{11}$ e $2\dfrac{1}{3} - 1\dfrac{4}{5}$ f $2\dfrac{1}{4} - 1\dfrac{5}{6}$

g $3\dfrac{2}{5} - 2\dfrac{7}{8}$ h $4\dfrac{1}{2} - 1\dfrac{9}{10}$ i $3\dfrac{5}{8} + 2\dfrac{3}{4}$

Band 3 questions

Reasoning

11 Give your answers to these questions as mixed numbers.

a A glass contains 200 ml. How many glasses amount to 750 ml?

b Jennie earns £9 per hour. How many hours would she need to work to make £100?

c Abdul takes 4 minutes to read one page. How many pages does he read in 15 minutes?

d A bag of sugar weighs 250 grams. How many bags are needed to get 1300 grams?

12 The area of a rectangle is $\frac{3}{10}$ m².

The width of the rectangle is $\frac{3}{4}$ m.

Work out the perimeter of the rectangle.

13 The formula for speed is

speed = distance ÷ time taken

Work out the speed of an object that travels

a $\frac{4}{5}$ of a kilometre in $\frac{3}{4}$ of an hour

b $\frac{3}{10}$ of a kilometre in $\frac{4}{5}$ of an hour

c $\frac{5}{8}$ of a kilometre in $\frac{1}{3}$ of an hour

d 6 kilometres in $\frac{1}{10}$ of an hour.

14 **a** Casey says that the square of $2\frac{3}{4}$ is $4\frac{9}{16}$.

Is Casey correct? Explain your answer fully.

b Work out these.

i $\left(1\frac{2}{3}\right)^2$

ii $\left(2\frac{1}{4}\right)^2 - \left(1\frac{1}{2}\right)^2$

iii $\left(2\frac{1}{4} - 1\frac{1}{2}\right)^2$

c Show that $\sqrt{\frac{9}{16}} = \frac{3}{4}$.

d Work out these.

i $\sqrt{\frac{1}{25}}$

ii $\sqrt{\frac{81}{100}} - \sqrt{\frac{16}{25}}$

iii $\sqrt{1\frac{11}{25}}$

15 A square has an area of $1\frac{9}{16}$ m².

Work out the perimeter of the square.

CHAPTER 3

Accuracy

▶ Coming up...

- ◆ Rounding using significant figures
- ◆ Approximating the answer to calculations
- ◆ Finding the limits of accuracy

→ Estimators

Play this estimation game with a partner.

The winner is the person who gave the best estimate in the most rounds.

Round 1: How long?

Estimate the length of this line.

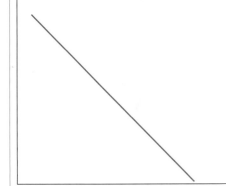

Round 2: Just a minute!

You'll need one stopwatch each – or take it in turns.

Start a stopwatch and shut your eyes.

Open your eyes and stop the clock when you think 1 minute has passed.

The person closest to a minute wins.

Round 3: Spider senses!

You have 10 seconds to estimate the number of 🕷 in this rectangle.

Count the spiders to see who was closest.

Round 4: How big?

Estimate the area of this triangle.

Measure the area to see who is closest.

Who won?

What strategies did you use?

3.1 Significant figures

① Round the numbers on these calculator displays to the nearest integer (whole number).

a 345.67299

b 127.94535

c 4367.8437

② Round the numbers on these calculator displays to 1 decimal place.

a 6.48279

b 19.873245

c 7.014255

③ Round the numbers on these calculator displays to 2 decimal places.

a 1.8745597

b 0.476589324

c 0.87587587

④ Write the numbers on these calculator displays to 3 decimal places.

a 37.964375

b 8.6749523

c 90.090909

d 0.6666666

Rounding using significant figures

Look at this number.

319 062

The digit that tells you the most about the size of the number is the 3 – it tells you the number is around 300 000.

You say that 3 is the 1st significant figure. ◄──── [1st s.f. or 1st sig. fig.]

The next most significant digit is the '1' – that is the 2nd significant figure.

- The 1st significant figure of a number is the **first non-zero digit** in that number (moving from left to right).
- The 2nd significant figure is the digit (**including zero**) immediately to the right of the 1st significant figure and so on.

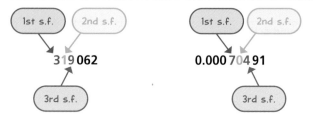

Significant figures are used in rounding. You are usually asked to round to 1, 2 or 3 significant figures.

Here is how you round to 3 significant figures.

- Underline the first 3 significant figures.
- Look at the next significant figure.
  - If it is 4 or less, leave the 3rd significant figure as it is.
  - If it is 5 or more, round the 3rd significant figure UP.
- Replace any other digits BEFORE the decimal point with a 0.

When you round you must still keep the size of the number. So in numbers greater than 10 it is important to fill in the zeros to the right of the significant figures so you can still see how big the unrounded number was.

319 062 = 300 000 to 1 s.f. ✓

319 062 = 3 to 1 s.f. ✗

In numbers less than 1, you need to keep the place-holding zeros but you don't need to replace the other digits with 0.

$0.000\,70\,91 = 0.000\,70$ to 2 s.f. ✓ ←

$0.000\,70\,91 = 0.70$ to 2 s.f. ✗

> When you round to 2 or more significant figures, then you must give 2 significant figures even if one of them is 0.

$0.000\,70\,91 = 0.0007$ to 2 s.f. ✗ ←

> It's wrong because it only has 1 significant figure!

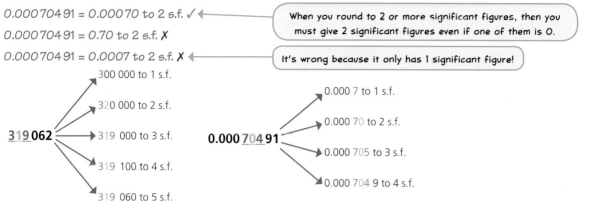

319 062
- 300 000 to 1 s.f.
- 320 000 to 2 s.f.
- 319 000 to 3 s.f.
- 319 100 to 4 s.f.
- 319 060 to 5 s.f.

0.000 704 91
- 0.000 7 to 1 s.f.
- 0.000 70 to 2 s.f.
- 0.000 705 to 3 s.f.
- 0.000 704 9 to 4 s.f.

🔍 Discussion activity

① How should you round negative numbers?

Jamal and Chiara are rounding −15 to one significant figure.

Jamal says, '−15 should round up to −10, as the 5 means you round up'.

Chiara says, '15 rounds to 20, so −15 should round to −20 to mirror that.'

Who do you think is right? Why?

② Always rounding '0.5' up can cause a problem.

Estimate the answer to $4.5 + 6.5 + 7.5 + 9.5$.

Jamal says, 'The answer is roughly $5 + 7 + 8 + 10$ which is 30.'

Chiara says, 'I am going to use banker's rounding to get '$4 + 6 + 8 + 10$ which gives 28.'

What is the actual answer to $4.5 + 6.5 + 7.5 + 9.5$?

What do you think the rule is for 'banker's rounding'?

Why did Chiara round some of the numbers down and others up?

What are the advantages and disadvantages of rounding in this way?

③ Investigate other methods for rounding.

3.1 Now try these

Band 1 questions

❶ Write these numbers correct to 1 significant figure.
  - a 43.34
  - b 372.12
  - c 8934
  - d 21 456
  - e 1.765

❷ a Copy these numbers and underline the first 2 significant figures in each of them.
  - i 45.3
  - ii 12 706
  - iii 587 210
  - iv 408
  - v 301 999

  b Use your answers to part **a** to write each number correct to 2 significant figures.

❸ a Copy these numbers and underline the first 3 significant figures in each of them.
  - i 2745.3
  - ii 127 453
  - iii 50 087 210
  - iv 3002
  - v 7009

  b Write each of the numbers correct to 3 significant figures.

❹ The first significant figure is underlined in red in each of these numbers.

   <u>4</u>136   <u>1</u>2.8   0.<u>5</u>23   0.000 0<u>6</u>3 2   <u>4</u> 200 000

   Is the first significant figure always the first figure? Explain your answer.

Fluency

Reasoning

Reasoning

⑤ Round these numbers to:

   i   the nearest 10   **ii**   2 significant figures.

   a   254   **b**   1785   **c**   21.35   **d**   103.67   **e**   458 361

   Are your answers the same? Why/why not?

⑥ Write these numbers correct to:

   i   1 decimal place   **ii**   2 significant figures.

   a   34.43   **b**   12.372   **c**   1.567   **d**   0.432   **e**   0.2561

   Are your answers the same? Why/why not?

Fluency

⑦ Write the number 324 860 correct to

   a   1 s.f.   **b**   2 s.f.   **c**   3 s.f.   **d**   4 s.f.   **e**   5 s.f.

⑧ Write the numbers on these calculator displays to 3 significant figures.

   a   [65.9083461]   **b**   [108.275621]   **c**   [0.94860321]

⑨ Write these numbers correct to the number of significant figures shown in brackets.

   a   0.003 45 **(1)**   **b**   0.000 456 8 **(2)**   **c**   0.100 04 **(3)**   **d**   0.000 000 899 **(1)**

   e   0.070 99 **(2)**   **f**   0.700 515 **(3)**

⑩ Use your calculator to do these calculations.

   Give your answers correct to 3 significant figures.

   a $56 \times 112 \div 37$ **b** $5.6 \times 11.2 \div 3.7$ **c** $0.56 \times 1.12 \div 37$

Reasoning

⑪   **a**   Kate says that 3.98 rounded to 2 significant figures is 4.

       Explain why Kate is incorrect.

    b   Round each of these numbers to the number of significant figures shown in brackets.

       i   19.9 **(2)**   **ii**   797 123 **(2)**   **iii**   0.8595 **(3)**   **iv**   0.003 598 **(3)**

⑫ Each of the statements **a** to **e** contains a mistake.

   Rewrite the statements correctly and explain the mistakes.

   a $354 = 35$ correct to 2 significant figures.

   b   The digit 4 is the second significant figure in the number 20 453.

   c $2135 = 2130$ correct to 3 significant figures.

   d $0.4196 = 0.42$ correct to 3 significant figures.

   e   0.23 is exactly the same as 0.230.

Problem solving

⑬ Here are five answers from calculator displays.

    [3.4457982]   [3.4561207]   [3.5471035]   [3.5568156]   [3.467233]

   i   Match each of them to three of the answers below.

   ii   Then write each of the calculator answers to 3 significant figures.

   a   3.45 to 2 d.p.   **b**   3.6 to 1 d.p.   **c**   3.456 to 3 d.p.

   d   3.5 to 1 d.p.   **e**   3.557 to 3 d.p.   **f**   3.47 to 2 d.p.

   g   3.46 to 2 d.p.   **h**   3.547 to 3 d.p.   **i**   3.4 to 1 d.p.

   j   3.446 to 3 d.p.   **k**   3.56 to 2 d.p.   **l**   3.467 to 3 d.p.

   m   3.55 to 2 d.p.

> **Remember**
>
> d.p. means decimal places

Reasoning

⑭ Write the number 0.999 999 correct to

   a   1 s.f.   **b**   2 s.f.   **c**   3 s.f.   **d**   4 s.f.   **e**   5 s.f.

3.2 Approximating

✓ Skill checker

Aki asks you to check his homework for him.

Which questions has he got right?

Find and correct any mistakes that he has made.

1. $4 + 2 \times 5 = 30$

2. $2 \times 5^2 = 100$

3. $\dfrac{10 - 4}{8} \times 12 = 9$

4. $3^2 - 2^2 + 1^2 = 1$

5. $\sqrt{3^2 + 4^2} = 7$

6. $(2 + 5)(8 - 2 \times 3) = 14$

7. $\dfrac{1 - 2 + 3 - 4 + 5}{1 + 2 - 3 + 4 - 5} = 3$

8. $\dfrac{\sqrt{144}}{\sqrt[3]{27}} = 4$

9. $1 + \dfrac{3 \times 4 + 3}{1 + 2^2} = 3$

10. $\dfrac{10 - 4 + 3^2}{5} = 3$

Using rounding

You can use rounding to 1 significant figure to get an estimate to a calculation without having to work out the exact answer. It is also a useful way to check that an answer is about right.

Worked example

Eliza and Albie work out the answer to

$$\dfrac{64.9 \times (43.3 + 7.7)}{30.4 - 19.1}$$

Eliza says that the answer is 298 to 3 significant figures.

Albie says that the answer is 91.7 to 3 significant figures.

Estimate the answer to the calculation.

Who is definitely wrong? Is the other person definitely right?

Solution

$$\dfrac{64.9 \times (43.3 + 7.7)}{30.4 - 19.1} \approx \dfrac{60 \times (40 + 10)}{30 - 20}$$

≈ means approximately equal to

$$\dfrac{60 \times (40 + 10)}{30 - 20} = \dfrac{60 \times 50}{10}$$
$$= 6 \times 50$$
$$= 300$$

So $\dfrac{64.9 \times (43.3 + 7.7)}{30.4 - 19.1} \approx 300$

Albie is definitely wrong.

Eliza's answer is about right, but the only way to tell for sure is to work out the calculation exactly.

Approximating is about:

- rounding numbers for a calculation so that you can do it in your head
- making a rough calculation to anticipate what sort of answer to expect
- recognising when an error has been made
- giving a number to the level of accuracy that suits the context.

3.2 Now try these

Band 1 questions

1 Is each of these true or false? Explain your answer.

a 76.3 is about 76.

b 457.8 is about 48.

c 141.2 is about 141.

d 9607 is about 9600.

e 47 132 is about 4713.

f 191 is about 200.

2 A greengrocer has 203 kg of potatoes. Estimate how many 5 kg bags she can fill.

3 Haydn and three friends go out for a meal. They share the cost of the meal equally.

Haydn has £20. Use estimation to check that he has enough money.

Write down the calculations you used.

4 Seasons Pizzeria	
4 pizzas	£38
2 garlic bread	£12.50
2 side salads	£7
4 colas	£5.60

4 Here is a problem and some calculations.

> There are 1230 pupils in the school.
> There are 47 tutor groups. Approximately how many pupils are in each tutor group?

$$1230 \times 47 \qquad 1230 \div 47 \qquad 1200 \times 50 \qquad 1200 \div 50 \qquad 1215 \div 45$$

a Which two calculations will not help to solve the problem?

b Which two calculations give approximate solutions to the problem?

c Which calculation would you use?

5 Kelly is reading a book that has 217 pages. She reads about 40 pages each evening.

Roughly how many days will it take Kelly to read the book?

Band 2 questions

6 a There are 36 eggs in a tray. A box of eggs contains 12 trays of eggs.

Approximately how many eggs are in a box?

b Approximately how many 62-seater coaches are needed to take a school of 1796 students on a trip?

c A bottle of cola contains 1950 ml. Approximately how many millilitres are there in 11 bottles?

d A bottle of cola contains 1950 ml. 205 ml are needed to fill a cup.

Approximately how many cups can be filled from one bottle?

e A job pays £214 per week. Approximately how much is this in one year (52 weeks)?

f One pint of milk is sufficient for 22 cups of tea.

Approximately how many pints are needed for 485 cups of tea?

Reasoning

Problem solving

Reasoning

Reasoning

Key Stage 3 Mastering Mathematics: Book 3

7 One of the four numbers below is the correct answer for 59×81.

4779   4803   4239   4885

An approximate answer is $60 \times 80 = 4800$.

Without using a calculator, choose the correct answer and explain your choice.

8 For each of these calculations, there is a choice of answers.

Use an approximation to help you select the correct answer.

a 3.2×8.9

    i 284.8   **ii** 28.48   **iii** 54.8

b $72 \div 12.5$

    i 9.45   **ii** 3.76   **iii** 5.76

c $\dfrac{110 \times 94}{55}$

    i 188   **ii** 1880   **iii** 18.8

9 For each of the calculations below:

i estimate the answer

ii work out the correct answer on your calculator

iii compare your estimate with the correct answer.

a $134 \div 8.9$ **b** 79×8.31 **c** $2.3 + 45.9 + 123.7$

d $897 \div 19.25$ **e** 21.3×47.2 **f** $56 \times 72 \times 12$

g $634 \div 3.9$ **h** $\dfrac{47.6 + 16.87}{6.9}$ **i** $\dfrac{87.6 - 11.25}{18.9}$

Band 3 questions

10 Alan works five days every week.

In a typical day he spends about 1 hour 40 minutes travelling to and from work.

a Estimate the number of hours Alan spends travelling in a full working year of 48 weeks.

b Approximately how many days a year does he spend travelling?

11 Ella has a part-time holiday job.

The table shows how long Ella worked at different rates of pay last week.

	Hours worked	Rate of pay
Normal pay	25 hours 20 minutes	£8.15
Overtime	4 hours 45 minutes	£9.60
Sunday	3 hours 10 minutes	£13.20

Which four of these calculations help to estimate Ella's earnings for the week?

a $3 \times 13 = 39$ **b** $25 \times 8 = 200$ **c** $10 \times 13 = 130$ **d** $5 \times 10 = 50$

e $8 \times 10 = 80$ **f** $26 + 5 + 3 = 33$ **g** $40 + 200 + 50 = 290$

12 In these calculations, each box represents an operation (+, −, × or ÷).

Use estimation to find which operations to use to complete the calculations.

a $(37 \boxed{} 21) \boxed{} 223 = 1000$

b $(756 \boxed{} 18) \boxed{} 29 = 1218$

c $27 \boxed{} (36 \boxed{} 18) = 675$

e $476 \boxed{} (2040 \boxed{} 24) = 391$

d $31 \boxed{} (87 \boxed{} 19) = 2108$

f $(3461 \boxed{} 276) \boxed{} 101 = 37$

g $(967 \boxed{} 34) \boxed{} (1023 \boxed{} 654) = 369\,369$

h $(29 \boxed{} 8^2) \boxed{} 9 = 84$

i $(619 \boxed{} 316) \boxed{} 425 \boxed{} 196 = 924$

j $6975 \boxed{} (36 \boxed{} 39) = 93$

13 Look how Tilly estimates the answer to $\sqrt{37.35} \times \sqrt{78}$.

$$\sqrt{37.35} \times \sqrt{78} \approx \sqrt{36} \times \sqrt{81}$$
$$\approx 6 \times 9$$
$$\approx 54$$

a Why did Tilly round the numbers to 36 and 81?

b Use your calculator to work out $\sqrt{37.35} \times \sqrt{78}$ correct to 2 decimal places.

Was Tilly's method accurate?

c Use Tilly's method to estimate the answers to these calculations.

i $\sqrt{15.6}$

ii $\sqrt{8.9} \times \sqrt{4.3}$

iii $\dfrac{\sqrt{103.5}}{\sqrt{38.9} + \sqrt{17.3}}$

3.3 Accuracy

✓ Skill checker

Play a game of rounding '4 in a line'.

You will need:

▶ four 10-sided dice

▶ 2 coloured pens.

Throw the dice and use the scores to give you a number between 0 and 9999.

These dice show 854

> Ignore the 0 on the first dice.

Round your number to one significant figure and place a counter in the matching box on the grid.

The winner is the player to get a line of 4.

The line can be horizontal, vertical or diagonal.

3000	2000	5000	6000	2000	4000
6000	0	7000	1000	9000	8000
8000	2000	9000	6000	3000	4000
3000	10000	1000	9000	10000	6000
4000	9000	5000	9000	2000	1000
10000	1000	8000	2000	7000	5000

Upper and lower bounds

The number of people at a concert was 24 000 correct to the nearest thousand.

How many people could have attended at the concert?

You can use a number line to help you work this out

23 000 23 500 24 000 24 500 25 000

The smallest number that rounds up to 24 000 to the nearest thousand is 23 500. ← | 23 499 rounds to 23 000 to the nearest 1000. |

24 500 rounds up to 25 000 to the nearest thousand.

So the maximum number of people at the concert is 24 499.

When you measure something, it is important to say how accurate your measurement was.

Kyle says the length of a line is 7 cm to the nearest centimetre.

The line could be as short as 6.5 cm as 6.5 cm rounds up to 7 cm to the nearest centimetre.

6.5 cm is called the **lower bound.** ← | 6.4999 cm would round down to 6 cm. |

You can write this as an inequality using l for the length of the line:

$6.5 \leqslant l$ ← | l is greater than or equal to 6.5. |

The line can't quite be as long as 7.5 cm but can get very, very close to it. ← | The line could be 7.499 999... cm long. |

So 7.5 cm is called the **upper bound.**

As an inequality this is written

$l < 7.5$ ← | l is less than 7.5. |

You can write the inequalities together like this:

$6.5 \leqslant l < 7.5$ ← | l is greater than or equal to 6.5 but is less than 7.5. |

Worked example

Stella draws a square with a side length of 21 cm to the nearest centimetre.
a What are the lower and upper bounds of the side length, s, of the square?
b What are the lower and upper bounds of the perimeter, P, of the square?
Give each of your answers as an inequality.

Solution

a Lower bound for s is 20.5 cm ← | 20.5 is $\frac{1}{2}$ cm less than 21 cm. |

Upper bound for s is 21.5 cm ← | 21.5 is $\frac{1}{2}$ cm more than 21 cm. |

20.5   21.5

20   21   22

$20.5 \leqslant s < 21.5$

b Lower bound of perimeter = 4 × 20.5 = 82 cm
Upper bound of perimeter = 4 × 21.5 = 86 cm
$82 \leqslant P < 86$

3.3 Now try these

1 There are 80 people in a cinema to the nearest 10 people.

What is the:

a smallest possible number of people at the cinema?　**b** greatest possible number of people at the cinema?

2 Callum buys some sweets for his younger sister's birthday party.

He says, 'I have 400 sweets to the nearest 100 sweets.'

What is the:

a smallest number of sweets that Callum could have?　**b** greatest number of sweets that Callum could have?

3 Write down the:

i lower bounds　**ii** upper bounds

for the number that

a rounds to 30 to the nearest 10　**b** rounds to 1200 to the nearest 100

c rounds to 3000 to the nearest 1000　**d** rounds to 15 to the nearest integer (whole number)

4 350 is accurate to 2 significant figures.

a Explain why Dan rounded 349 to 350 to 2 s.f.

b Write down two other whole numbers smaller than 349 which will round to 350 to 2 s.f.

5 2.56 is correct to 2 decimal places.

a Explain why Daisy wrote 2.563 as 2.56 to 2 decimal places.

b Write down two more numbers bigger than 2.563 that Daisy would still round to 2.56 to 2 decimal places.

c Write down two numbers less than 2.56 which will round up to 2.56 to 2 decimal places.

d What are the biggest and the smallest numbers that can round to 2.56 to 2 decimal places?

6 a Write these numbers correct to 2 significant figures.

　i 1.24　　　　　　**ii** 1.237　　　　　　**iii** 1.1652

　iv 1.151　　　　　　**v** 1.249　　　　　　**vi** 1.249 99

What do you notice?

b Kate measures the length of a line as 1.2 m correct to 2 significant figures.

　i Write down the lower and upper bounds for the length of the line l.

　　Lower bound = __ metres

　　Upper bound = __ metres

　ii Complete the inequality for l.

　　$\boxed{} \leqslant l < \boxed{}$

7 Brian weighs 67 kg to the nearest kilogram.

a Round these weights to the nearest kilogram.

　67.4 kg, 66.97 kg, 66.52 kg, 67.499 9 kg

b Write down the smallest possible value for Brian's weight.

c Write down the largest possible value for Brian's weight.

d Write Brian's weight, w, as an inequality.

8 A box of soap powder is labelled 4 kg.

a The label is correct to the nearest kilogram.

　What are the minimum and the maximum amounts of soap powder in the box?

b Write this as an inequality.

9 A bottle of apple juice holds 75 cl to the nearest centilitre.

   a What is the largest possible error when measuring to the nearest centilitre?

   b Write down the smallest possible value for the volume of apple juice.

   c Write down the largest possible value for the volume of apple juice.

   d Write the volume of apple juice as an inequality.

10 10 Swiss francs are worth £4.30 to the nearest 10 pence.

   a What is the largest possible error when measuring to the nearest 10 pence?

   b Write down the smallest possible value for 10 Swiss francs.

   c Write down the largest possible value for 10 Swiss francs.

   d Write the value of 10 Swiss francs in pounds as an inequality.

11 Explain why it might not be safe for these people to travel together in the lift.

- David 65 kg
- Brian 92 kg
- Bronwen 74 kg
- Pat 54 kg
- Peter 86 kg
- Bruce 95 kg
- Ahmed 89 kg
- Mark 93 kg

| **Lift** |
| Maximum safe load |
| 8 persons or |
| 650 kg |

Band 3 questions

12 The angles a and b are 100° and 140° (to the nearest degree).

   a Find the upper and lower bounds of a and b.   **b** What is the smallest angle c can be?

13 The measurements of this photograph are accurate to the nearest millimetre.

6.3 cm

8.7 cm

   a Write the upper and lower bounds of each measurement.

   b Work out the smallest possible measurement for the perimeter of the photograph.

   c Work out the largest possible value for the perimeter.

   d Work out the smallest and largest values for the area of the photograph.

14 Carlos is designing a central heating flue duct to take waste fumes out through the wall.

The hole for the duct has to be sealed.

There is a 16.5 cm square plate with a 4.5 cm radius circle removed from it.

The measurements are given accurate to 1 decimal place.

   a Calculate the maximum and minimum areas of the square sheet of metal needed.

   b Calculate the maximum and minimum areas of the circle to be removed.

   c Calculate the maximum area of the metal seal (the metal remaining after the circle has been cut out).

   d Write an inequality to show the upper and lower bounds of the area of the metal seal.

Key words

Here is a list of the key words you met in this chapter.

| Accuracy | Approximate | Decimal | Estimate |
| Lower bound | Rounding | Significant figure | Upper bound |

Use the glossary at the back of this book to check any you are unsure about.

Review exercise: accuracy

Band 1 questions

1 Zac does several calculations.

For each one, he estimates the answer then uses his calculator to do the calculation accurately. Here are his results.

  a   Rough 6, calculator 7.162   **b**   Rough 0.1, calculator 10.29

  c   Rough 450, calculator 489.2   **d**   Rough 24, calculator 2.414

  e   Rough 0.048, calculator 0.0511   **f**   Rough 17.5, calculator 84.23

Which estimates suggest that an error has been made in using the calculator?

2   **a**   Copy these numbers and underline the second significant figure in each of them.

     i   23.7   **ii**   1056   **iii**   0.437   **iv**   0.00257   **v**   759218

  b   Write each of the numbers in part **a** to 2 significant figures.

3 Write the number 17032.9 correct to:

  a   1 significant figure

  b   2 significant figures

  c   3 significant figures

  d   4 significant figures.

4 John orders three portions of fish and chips, two pie and chips and a jumbo sausage.

> **Avonford Fisheries**
> Fish and chips £5.95
> Pie and chips £3.90
> Jumbo sausage £2.25

  a   Round each price to the nearest pound.

  b   Use your answers to estimate the cost of John's order.

  c   John has £30. Is this enough?

5 750 g is a measurement accurate to 2 significant figures.

  a   Explain why 750 is 746 correct to 2 significant figures.

  b   What is the smallest number that will give 750 when rounded to 2 significant figures?

  c   Write down the largest number that will give 750 when rounded to 2 significant figures.

6 George's height is being measured. He is 178 cm tall to the nearest centimetre.

  a   What is the largest possible error when measuring to the nearest centimetre?

  b   Write down the smallest possible value for George's height.

  c   Write down the largest possible value for George's height.

  d   Write George's height as an inequality:

     $\square \leqslant$ George's height $< \square$

Band 2 questions

7 Write these numbers correct to the number of significant figures shown in brackets.

  a   18.34 **(2)**   **b**   41.359 **(3)**   **c**   1246 **(3)**   **d**   0.015 **(1)**

  e   460 **(1)**   **f**   4986 **(2)**   **g**   0.0204 **(2)**   **h**   0.1096 **(3)**

Problem solving

Fluency

Problem solving

Reasoning

Fluency

Reasoning

Problem solving

8 Ari saved regularly every week so that he had £189.50 in a year.

Approximately how much did he save each week?

9 Write each of these measurements as an inequality.

$\boxed{} \leqslant x < \boxed{}$

a 45 cm to the nearest cm
b 124 litres to the nearest litre
c 58 grams to the nearest gram
d 4.1 cm to the nearest mm
e 2.5 km to the nearest metre

10 At a Christmas market, 1794 entrance tickets were sold. The total amount of money made was £16 146.

a Estimate the average amount each person spent.

b At last year's Christmas market, they sold 2057 tickets and made £14 399.

Estimate how much more a ticket to the Christmas market costs this year.

11 Quick checks by rounding the numbers will tell you that three of these answers are wrong.

Which three?

a $9.2 \times 17.5 = 161$
b $45.8 \div 17 = 2.694...$
c $28.9 \times 11.2 = 40.1$
d $3.2 \times 2.9 \times 19.1 = 177.2...$
e $\dfrac{29}{14.7} = 14.3$
f $\dfrac{13.2 \times 21.6}{4.9} = 58.18...$

Band 3 questions

12 Use your calculator to do these calculations.

Give your answers to the degree of accuracy shown in brackets.

a $(11.47 - 3.56)^2$ **(3 s.f.)**
b 3.7^2 **(3 s.f.)**
c $\pi \times 20.82$ **(2 s.f.)**
d 0.025^2 **(2 s.f.)**
e $(9.56 + 3.37)^2 \times (9.56 + 3.37)^2 \div 0.0102$ **(2 s.f.)**

13 This question is about the numbers 123.5678 and 0.123 5678.

a Round these numbers to:

i 3 decimal places
ii 3 significant figures.

b In part **a** which of the numbers gives the same answer?

c Write down another number which is the same when rounded to 3 decimal places and 3 significant figures.

14 Here are six calculations:

a $(49.7 \times 43) \div (12.6 - 7.4)$
b $\sqrt{8.72 + 7.82}$
c $(675.6 - 123.2) \div (17.8 + 12.3)$
d $\sqrt[3]{1.2^2 + 2.8^2 + 3.9^2}$
e $\pi \times 5.2^2$
f $\sqrt{\dfrac{314.16}{\pi}}$

The correct answers, to 1 decimal place, are given below but they have been mixed up.

| 2.9 | 18.4 | 411.0 | 84.9 | 10.0 | 4.1 |

Use estimation to match each answer to the correct calculation.

15 A paperback book is 2.6 cm thick, measured to the nearest millimetre, and contains 378 numbered pages.

a What is the maximum thickness of the book?

b What is the maximum thickness of one sheet of paper in millimetres?

Give your answer to 2 significant figures.

> Take care! Sheets are not the same as pages.

Chapters 1–3

Band 1 questions

Fluency

① Write these fractions in their simplest form.

a $\dfrac{40}{80}$ b $\dfrac{12}{16}$ c $\dfrac{25}{30}$ d $\dfrac{12}{18}$

e $\dfrac{21}{35}$ f $\dfrac{24}{32}$ g $\dfrac{12}{20}$ h $\dfrac{240}{360}$

Problem solving

② Write the correct inequality sign (< or >) between each pair of fractions.

a $\dfrac{3}{4} \square \dfrac{7}{8}$ b $\dfrac{2}{3} \square \dfrac{5}{6}$ c $\dfrac{9}{20} \square \dfrac{3}{7}$ d $\dfrac{8}{9} \square \dfrac{4}{5}$

③ Copy and complete this cross-number puzzle.

Across	**Down**
1 2^4	**2** 4^3
4 7^2	**3** 3^1
5 The square root of 25	**6** 11^2
8 The cube root of 8	**7** The square root of 169
9 11^3	

④ A bus arrives at a bus stop. It is already $\dfrac{3}{4}$ full.

The number of people standing at the stop could fill $\dfrac{1}{3}$ of the bus.

What fraction of a bus load are left at the bus stop?

Fluency

⑤ Here are Ellie's exam marks.

a Copy and complete this statement.

$\dfrac{10}{25} = \dfrac{\square}{100}$

b Write $\dfrac{10}{25}$ as a percentage.

c Write the rest of Ellie's marks as percentages.

d Which is Ellie's

  i best subject

  ii worst subject?

Subject	Mark
French	10 out of 25
English	15 out of 20
Science	21 out of 50
Maths	18 out of 40

Band 2 questions

6 Work out these.

Give each answer as a fraction in its lowest terms.

a $\dfrac{1}{4} + \dfrac{1}{5} + \dfrac{1}{10}$

b $\dfrac{1}{2} + \dfrac{1}{4} - \dfrac{5}{8}$

c $\dfrac{1}{4} - \dfrac{9}{16} + \dfrac{3}{8}$

7 Estimate the volume of this room.

3.21 m

5.86 m

4.09 m

8 Estimate the number of minutes in a year. Give your answer to 1 significant figure.

9 Write each expression as a single power of 2.

a $2^5 \times 2^2$ b $2^8 \div 2^3$ c $(2^3)^2$ d $2^4 \div 2^4$ e $2^4 \div 2^6$ f $\dfrac{2^3 \times 2^5}{2^2}$

10 Work out these.

Give your answers as mixed numbers where appropriate.

a $\dfrac{17}{8} - \dfrac{11}{6}$

b $\dfrac{8}{3} + \dfrac{19}{5}$

c $\dfrac{27}{5} - \dfrac{19}{7}$

11 The answers below were found using a calculator. Write each of the answers

i correct to 2 significant figures   ii correct to 3 significant figures.

a $49.737\,\text{cm}^2$ b £283 721   c $7.8241\,\text{cm}$ d $0.067\,36\,\text{m}$ e $0.000\,484\,2$

f $8.937\,\text{kg}$ g $10.785\,\text{m}$ h £37 694   i $40.038\,\text{cm}^3$ j $0.706\,83\,\text{m}^2$

k $40.96\,\text{kg}$ l 20.81 litres   m $0.9008\,\text{km}$ n $5.942\,\text{m}$ o $10.94\,\text{cm}^2$

12 To get to work, Isobel walks $\dfrac{2}{3}$ km to the bus stop.

She catches the bus to the train station, a distance of $3\dfrac{3}{4}$ km.

Her train journey is $14\dfrac{4}{5}$ km.

Finally, she walks $\dfrac{1}{2}$ km to her office.

What is the total length of Isobel's journey to work?

Give your answer as a mixed number.

13 Write the numbers in these statements in standard form.

a There are 1500 pupils in the school.

b This week's lottery jackpot is worth £3.6 million.

c The distance from London to New York is about 3000 miles.

14 Write these as ordinary numbers.

a A red blood cell has a diameter of 7×10^{-3} mm.

b The Gobi desert covers an area of $1.04 \times 10^6\,\text{km}^2$.

c The total weight of fish in the world's oceans is estimated at 7.6×10^8 tonnes.

d The radius of a uranium atom is 8.68×10^{-15} metres.

e The Nou Camp stadium in Barcelona can hold 1.15×10^5 people.

Band 3 questions

15 Write down a number that lies between each of these pairs of numbers.

    a 2.3×10^4 and 2.3×10^6

    b 1.2×10^3 and 2.0×10^3

16 Calculate the area of each of these shapes.

    a   **b**

17 Sometimes the mixed number $3\frac{1}{7}$ is used as an approximation to π.

Use this value to work out the circumference and area of these circles without a calculator.

    a   **b**   **c**

18 Some fractions and their equivalent decimal values are given below.

Write each decimal correct to 3 significant figures.

    a $\frac{2}{3} = 0.\dot{6}$

    b $\frac{5}{6} = 0.8\dot{3}$

> A dot over a digit shows that the digit recurs, e.g. $0.8\dot{3} = 0.833\,33...$

    c $\frac{5}{11} = 0.\dot{4}\dot{5}$

    d $\frac{5}{37} = 0.\dot{1}3\dot{5}$

> Two dots show that the digits between the dots recur, e.g. $0.\dot{1}3\dot{5} = 0.135135135...$

    e $\frac{5}{12} = 0.41\dot{6}$

    f $\frac{5}{7} = 0.\dot{7}1428\dot{5}$

    g $\frac{11}{12} = 0.91\dot{6}$

    h $\frac{503}{999} = 0.\dot{5}0\dot{3}$

    i $\frac{19}{27} = 0.\dot{7}0\dot{9}$

19 You are told that $T = \dfrac{7.8^2 + 5.79^2}{17.67}$

    a Estimate an approximate value for T by rounding all the numbers to 1 significant figure.

    b Use your calculator to find the true value of T correct to 3 significant figures.

20 A megabyte is one million bytes.

A gigabyte is 1000 megabytes.

A terabyte is 1000 gigabytes.

Write down how many bytes are in a terabyte.

Give your answer in standard form.

21 Simplify these algebraic expressions.

The first one has been done for you.

    a $\frac{x}{3} + \frac{x}{2} = \frac{2x}{6} + \frac{3x}{6} = \frac{5x}{6}$

    b $\frac{m}{4} + \frac{m}{5}$

    c $\frac{d}{2} + \frac{2d}{7}$

    d $\frac{x}{5} + \frac{2x}{9}$

    e $\frac{e}{3} - \frac{e}{5}$

    f $\frac{5h}{6} - \frac{h}{4}$

Reasoning | Problem solving | Reasoning | Fluency | Reasoning

Key Stage 3 Mastering Mathematics: Book 3

Each side of a piece of square card is 21 cm correct to the nearest centimetre.

This means that each side could be anywhere between 20.5 cm and 21.5 cm.

The area of the square could be

- largest possible area $= 21.5 \times 21.5 = 462.25 \, \text{cm}^2$
- smallest possible area $= 20.5 \times 20.5 = 420.25 \, \text{cm}^2$

So the range of area for this square is $462.25 - 420.25 = 42 \, \text{cm}^2$.

a   Another square has sides of 16 cm correct to the nearest cm.

   Find the range of possible values for the area of this square.

b   Can you find a connection between the length of the side of a square and the possible range for its area?

c   Prove that your result is true for any square.

CHAPTER 4

Percentages

▶ **Coming up...**

◆ Percentages review
◆ Using multipliers
◆ Reverse percentages

➡ **Find the magic number**

See if you can find the magic number in the red square.

After following all of the clues you will get back to the magic number.

Be careful: there is only one number that works!

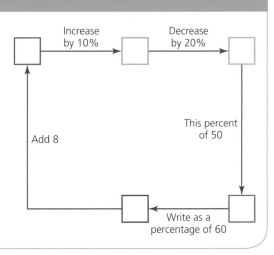

4.1 Percentages review

✔ **Skill checker**

Look at the grid.

a What percentage of the squares are coloured blue (the plain squares)?

b What percentage of the numbers are prime numbers?

c What percentage of the blue (plain) squares are square numbers?

d What percentage of the numbers in the first two rows are even numbers?

e What percentage of the squares containing square numbers are coloured in the yellow and black diagonal stripes?

f Can you think up some of your own questions?

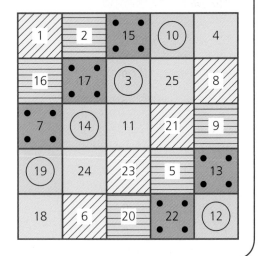

Percentages recap

Recall the important skills you have learnt relating to percentages:

● Percentages add up to 100%.
● Finding a percentage of a quantity, for example 20% of £300.
● Writing one number as a percentage of another, for example writing 6 cm as a percentage of 10 cm.
● Converting between fractions, percentages and decimals.
● How to calculate percentage increases and decreases.
● How to calculate percentage change.

Worked example

There are fifty seats in the school canteen. At 12:15 the canteen is full.

At 12:30, 20% of pupils leave the canteen.

a What percentage of the pupils remain in the canteen?

b How many pupils are left?

c How many pupils remain in the canteen?

d At 12:45 five more pupils enter the canteen. How full is the canteen now? Give your answer as a percentage.

e Write your answer to part **d** as a fraction and a decimal.

At 1:00 the canteen is completely full.

Mr Grimes, who is on duty, finds an extra 15 seats.

f What is the percentage increase in the number of seats available?

g Write the new number of seats as a percentage of the original number.

Solution

a If 20% leave, 80% remain in the canteen.

b 20% of 50 is $\dfrac{1}{5}$ of 50, which is 10 pupils who leave the canteen.

c 80% of 50 is $\dfrac{4}{5}$ of 50, which is 40 pupils who remain.

d $40 + 5 = 45$

The canteen is now $\dfrac{45}{50}$ full.

$$\dfrac{45}{50} = \dfrac{90}{100} = 90\%$$

So the canteen is now 90% full.

e As a fraction the canteen is $\dfrac{45}{50}$ full, which simplifies to $\dfrac{9}{10}$ full. As a decimal this is 0.9.

f The number of seats increases by 15.

Write this as a fraction of the original number and convert to a percentage:

$$\dfrac{15}{50} = \dfrac{30}{100} = 30\%$$

There has been a 30% increase in the number of seats.

g There are now 65 seats.

Write this as a fraction of the original number:

$$\dfrac{65}{50} = \dfrac{130}{100} = 130\%$$

Activity

This is a game for two players.

Player 1 starts with two pots of marbles, each containing 10 marbles.

Player 2 does not watch what Player 1 is doing.

Player 1 makes four moves and describes them, making at least two moves that involve percentages.

For example:

  a I'm transferring 10% of the marbles from pot 1 to pot 2.

  b I'm transferring three marbles from pot 2 to pot 1.

  c I'm transferring 25% of the marbles from pot 1 to pot 2.

  d I'm removing one third of the marbles from pot 1.

Player 2 must try to keep track of how many marbles are in each pot.

After these four moves, if Player 2 gives the correct number of marbles in each pot, they win the game. Otherwise Player 1 wins.

Swap positions and play again.

4.1 Now try these

You can use a calculator in this exercise, except where you see the non-calculator symbol.

Band 1 questions

1 Find these:

  a $22\frac{1}{2}$% of 80 m²   **b** 5% of 56 mm   **c** $7\frac{1}{2}$% of 80 km   **d** $37\frac{1}{2}$% of 48 cm

  e $62\frac{1}{2}$% of 8 mm   **f** 3% of 64 cm²   **g** 74% of 200 kg   **h** 85% of 16 g

2 Briony's season ticket for the train costs £342 a quarter.

  Fares are to increase by 5.5%.

  > A quarter means a quarter of a year, which is 3 months.

  a How much more will Briony's season ticket cost?

  b How much will Briony pay per quarter after the increase?

3 Last year the amount Tim paid for his car insurance was £420.

  This year Tim's insurance premium will increase by 12%.

  How much will Tim pay this year?

4 A mathematics book has 260 pages, 35% of which are on algebra, 25% on geometry and the remainder on arithmetic.

  How many pages are there on each topic?

Band 2 questions

5 Copy and complete this table.

Give all fractions in their simplest form.

The first row has been done for you.

Fraction	Decimal	Percentage
$\dfrac{19}{20}$	0.95	95%
$\dfrac{9}{10}$		
	0.65	
		24%
$\dfrac{31}{40}$		
	0.675	
		42.5%
$\dfrac{6}{5}$		
	2.3	
		180%

6 Alfredo runs a pizza restaurant.

Customers leave feedback about the restaurant on a website.

The scores are shown below.

> **Restaurant Feedback**
> Quality of food 19 out of 20
> Service 8 out of 10
> Cleanliness 17 out of 20

a Write all three scores as percentages.

   i Quality of food   **ii** Service   **iii** Cleanliness

b What is the restaurant's total score out of 50?

c Write the total score as a percentage.

7 a Copy and complete the following to work out 15% of £3900.

   100% is £3900

   1% is £3900 ÷ 100 = £ _____

   15% is 15 × £ _____ = £ _____

b Now copy and complete these:

   i An increase of 15% gives £3900 + £ _____ = £ _____

   ii A decrease of 15% gives £3900 − £ _____ = £ _____

c Steve thinks it would be easier to use a different method.

   Copy and complete Steve's working.

   10% is £3900 ÷ 10 = £ _____

   5% is £ _____ ÷ 2 = £ _____

   15% is £ _____ + £ _____ = £ _____

8 a Copy and complete this table to find 10%, 5% and 1% of £270.

Percentage	100%	10%	5%	1%
Amount	£270			

b Now copy and complete the following:

i 15% of £270 is £____ + £____ = £____

ii 40% of £270 is 4 × £____ = £____

iii 16% of £270 is £____ + £____ + £____ = £____

iv 35% of £270 is 3 × £_____ + £_____ = £_____

v 27% of £270 is _____

vi 110% of £270 is _____

9 Alok's phone bill will be increased by 8% from the first quarter of the year to the second quarter.

His phone bill was £64.50 for the first quarter.

How much will Alok pay for his phone bill in the second quarter?

> A quarter means a quarter of a year, which is 3 months.

10 Twenty four percent of a field is sold to build houses.

If the field was originally 15 acres in size, how large is it after the sale?

> An acre is a measure of area, roughly equal to 4000 m².

Band 3 questions

11 What percentage of each shape is coloured?

a

b

c

d

e

f

g

h

i

12 The interest rate on Samantha's savings account is 2.5%.

If she invests £300, how much simple interest would she receive:

a in one year

b in five years?

> You learnt about simple interest in Year 8, Chapter 12

Problem solving

⑬ James and Chloe did a survey about which British cheese people preferred.

The results are shown in the pie chart below, but one of the numbers has been lost.

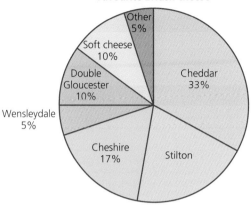

Favourite British cheese

a What percentage said they preferred Stilton?

b James and Chloe asked 180 people altogether.

How many of them said they preferred:

i Double Gloucester?   **ii** Wensleydale?

Reasoning

⑭ Carlo is practising his archery.

He fires 5 arrows, labelled A to E on the diagram.

a Look at where the arrows landed and calculate his total score.

b What is the maximum score with five arrows?

c What percentage of the maximum did Carlo get?

d Carlo says 'If I hadn't fired arrow C, my percentage would have been 70%!'

Is he correct? Explain your answer.

Problem solving

⑮ The bar chart shows the number of hours Freya worked each day one week.

Hours worked each day

a How many hours did Freya work in total this week?

b What percentage of those hours were on Wednesday?

c Freya worked fewer hours on Friday than she did on Thursday.

What was the percentage decrease from Thursday to Friday?

d What was the percentage increase in Freya's hours from Wednesday to Thursday?

e Freya had an important deadline to meet this week.

She had to write a report for her manager by _____ morning.

On which morning do you think she had to deliver her report?

4.2 Using multipliers

✔ Skill checker

Find the new price for these items.

Copy and complete the table.

Item	Old price	Percentage change	New price
Bag of flour	£1	15% increase	
Scarf	£8.50	20% decrease	
Jacket	£49.50	10% off in the sale	
Blueberries	£2.90	Reduced by 30%	
Skirt	£36	Price going up by 25%	
Jeans	£45	Price cut by 40%	
Tin foil	£1.80	5% added to price	

Percentage increase using a multiplier

Worked example

There are three ways to work out percentage increases and decreases.

All three methods are shown below for this question:

Find the amount when £120 is:

a increased by 15%

b decreased by 15%.

Solution

Method 1. Finding the increase or decrease

You have used this method in Year 8.

100% is £120

1% is £120 ÷ 100 = £1.20

15% is 15 × £1.20 = £18

a An increase of 15% gives £120 + £18 = £138

b A decrease of 15% gives £120 − £18 = £102

Method 2. Using a table

You have used this method in Year 8.

Percentage	100%	10%	5%	15%
Amount	£120	£120 ÷ 10 = **£12**	£12 ÷ 2 = **£6**	£12 + £6 = **£18**

a An increase of 15% gives £120 + £18 = £138

b A decrease of 15% gives £120 − £18 = £102

Key Stage 3 Mastering Mathematics: Book 3

Method 3. Using a multiplier

This is a calculator method that you may not have learnt before.

It is usually quicker than the other two methods.

a To increase by 15% multiply by 1.15

$£120 \times 1.15 = £138$

b To decrease by 15% multiply by 0.85

$£120 \times 0.85 = £102$

> Add 15 to 100 and divide by 100
> $$\frac{100 + 15}{100} = 1.15$$

> Why does this work?
> Increasing a quantity by 15% is the same as finding 115% of the quantity.
> To find 115%, multiply by $\frac{115}{100}$ or 1.15.

> Why does this work?
> Decreasing a quantity by 15% is the same as finding 85% of the quantity.
> To find 85%, multiply by $\frac{85}{100}$ or 0.85.

> Subtract 15 from 100 and divide by 100
> $$\frac{100 - 15}{100} = 0.85$$

Worked example

Using a multiplier:

a increase £48 by 25%
b decrease £48 by 25%
c increase 150 kg by 5%
d decrease 150 kg by 5%
e increase 15 cm by $33\frac{1}{3}$%
f decrease 15 cm by $33\frac{1}{3}$%
g increase 6 km by 100%
h increase 150 sandwiches by 200%
i increase 500 litres by 250%

Solution

a To increase £48 by 25%, multiply by 1.25
$£48 \times 1.25 = £60$

b To decrease £48 by 25%, multiply by 0.75
$£48 \times 0.75 = £36$

c To increase 150 kg by 5%, multiply by 1.05
$150 \times 1.05 = 157.5$ kg

d To decrease 150 kg by 5%, multiply by 0.95
$150 \times 0.95 = 142.5$ kg

e To increase 15 cm by $33\frac{1}{3}$%
$33\frac{1}{3}\% = 33.333...\%$
So the multiplier is 1.33333... or $1\frac{1}{3}$.
$15 \times 1.\dot{3} = 20$
or
$15 \times 1\frac{1}{3} = 20$
The answer is 20 cm.

> Some calculators have a button for recurring decimals.

f Decreasing by $33\frac{1}{3}$% is the same as finding $66\frac{2}{3}$% of the number.
So the multiplier is 0.6666... or $\frac{2}{3}$.
$15 \times 0.\dot{6} = 10$
or
$15 \times \frac{2}{3} = 10$
The answer is 10 cm.

> Be careful with multipliers that are recurring decimals.
> Using an incorrect multiplier of 0.6 gives an answer of 9 cm.
> Using an incorrect multiplier of 0.66 gives an answer of 9.9 cm.
> Although these are close to the correct answer, they are not exact!

g To increase by 100% use a multiplier of 2.

   $6 \times 2 = 12$ km

> To find the multiplier, add 100 to 100 and divide by 100:
> $$\frac{100 + 100}{100} = 2$$

h To increase by 200% use a multiplier of 3.

   $150 \times 3 = 450$ sandwiches

> To find the multiplier, add 200 to 100 and divide by 100:
> $$\frac{100 + 200}{100} = 3$$

i To increase by 250% use a multiplier of 3.5.

   $500 \times 3.5 = 1750$ litres

> To find the multiplier, add 250 to 100 and divide by 100:
> $$\frac{100 + 250}{100} = 3.5$$

Worked example

Anneka earns £21 000 per year. She is given a 3% increase.

Using a multiplier, calculate how much she now earns in a year.

Solution

To increase by 3%, use a multiplier of 1.03.

   $£21\,000 \times 1.03 = £21\,630$

4.2 Now try these

Band 1 questions

1 What multiplier would you use to:

a increase by 12%	**b** decrease by 12%	**c** increase by 20%
d decrease by 20%	**e** increase by 7%	**f** decrease by 7%
g increase by 80%	**h** decrease by 80%	**i** increase by 100%
j decrease by 50%	**k** increase by 150%	**l** increase by 300%

2 Use a multiplier to find:

a 20 cm increased by 25%	**b** £400 increased by 30%	**c** £7500 increased by 22%
d 620 metres decreased by 15%	**e** 160 kg decreased by 40%	

3 Jack is selling a computer games console. He originally asks for £80.

After a few days the console has not been sold. Jack reduces the price by 20%.

a Using a multiplier, find the reduced price of the console.

b Calculate the reduction in price.

4 The price of each of these items goes up by 20%.

Find the new prices using a multiplier.

a Textbook £15 **b** Jeans £45 **c** Smart speaker £75 **d** Football ticket £25

5 These items go down in value by the percentage shown. Find the new value of each item using a multiplier.

a Bicycle £300, down 20% **b** Guitar £440, down 25% **c** Model car £30, down 50%

Key Stage 3 Mastering Mathematics: Book 3

Fluency

Problem solving

6 Using a multiplier, find the sale price of each of these items.

SALE 10% off

a €40

b €65

c €32

7 Sasha gets a 3% pay rise. Her salary before the rise was £29 500.

   a Calculate her new salary using a multiplier.

   b What is her salary increase?

Band 2 questions

8 William bought a new bicycle three years ago, costing £300.

Now it has lost 30% of its value.

Using a multiplier, find its new value.

9 The area of sand on a beach is 160 m².

When the tide goes out, the area of sand increases by 400%.

Using a multiplier, find the area of sand when the tide is out.

10 **a** Increase 25 by 100%.

   b Increase 48 by 100%.

   c Increase 1200 by 100%.

   d Copy this sentence and complete the missing word:

      Increasing by 100% is the same as d_____g.

   e Increase 250 by 200%.

   f Increase 2 by 200%.

   g Increase 60 by 200%.

   h Copy this sentence and complete the missing word:

      Increasing by 200% is the same as _____ing.

Band 3 questions

11 Ciaran is thinking about putting some money into a savings account.

Here is an advert for the account.

> **Blackfen Building Society**
> *Young Savers Savings Account*
> Balances below £1000 receive 2.5% simple interest per annum
> Balances £1000 or above receive 3.5% simple interest per annum

Ciaran is trying to decide whether to put £900 or £1000 into the account.

   a If Ciaran put £900 into the savings account, how much simple interest would he receive each year?

   b If Ciaran put £1000 into the savings account, how much simple interest would he receive each year?

Ciaran plans to keep his money in the account for 5 years.

   c Find the amount of interest he would receive over 5 years on both £900 and £1000.

   d What is the difference in the total amount of interest he would receive over 5 years?

⑫ A shopkeeper bought a box of 200 chocolate bars for £50.

    a How much did she pay for each bar?

    b She made a profit of 20% on each bar. How much did she sell each bar for?

    c How much money did she receive from the sale of all the bars?

    d How much profit did she make from selling all the bars of chocolate?

    e The shopkeeper paid £50 for the bars of chocolate and made a profit of 20% on each bar.

       Find 20% of £50.

       What do you notice about your answer to part **d** and this value? Explain your answer.

⑬ A shop has this offer on all its office chairs.

> **Prices reduced by £5 or 10% whichever is greater!**

    a What would be the sale price for a chair which normally cost

       i £20   **ii** £35   **iii** £60   **iv** £74?

    b Emily buys an office chair. The sale price is the same whichever way the discount is given.

       i What is the normal price of the chair Emily buys?

       ii What is the sale price?

⑭ A youth club has some special offers as shown in the diagrams.

    a Using multipliers, work out the offer prices for six activities.

    b If you wanted to spend exactly £10, how could you do it?

Cinema Usually £4.52 25% off	**Salsa Dancing** Normally £4.50 Save 18%	Reduced from £5.07 by $33\frac{1}{3}$% **TEN** **PIN** **BOWLING**
DIVING CLASSES 12% off £4.00 usual charge	Standard price £3.80 Get 15% off **Clay pigeon shooting**	**Abseiling** Normal price £3.90 Now 10% off

⑮ When water is frozen, its volume increases by 4%.

    a 5 litres of water is frozen. How many cm^3 of ice will be made? ←   1 litre = 1000 cm^3

    b A machine makes identical ice cubes, each with a volume of 10 cm^3.

       2.5 litres of water are used to make these ice cubes.

       How many ice cubes are made?

4.3 Reverse percentages

✔ Skill checker

Copy this multiplier trail.

Fill in the shaded squares with the correct multipliers to get from one number to the next. The first one has been done for you.

Give your answers as fractions or decimals.

Start	30	×1⅓	40		50		40		100

	99		110		100		75		150

	66		44		55		60.5		30.25	Finish

Finding the original price or size

Sometimes you know the cost or size of something and the percentage change but not the original cost or size.

Reverse percentages can be used to find the original cost or size of a quantity.

Worked example

A coat costs £45 in a sale. It has been reduced by 10%. What was its original price?

This percentage bar shows what you know and what you need to find out.

Sale price £45 90% of original price	10%
Original price 100%	

90% of the original price is £45

Turn this into an equation:

$$0.9 \times x = 45$$

> 90% is 0.9. Replace the word 'of' with a times sign. Use x for the original price.

$$x = \frac{45}{0.9} = £50$$

The original price of the coat was £50.

Worked example

A multi-storey car park has a total area of 14 400 m².

It is 12.5% bigger than last year after the addition of an extra storey.

a What was the area of the car park last year in m²?

b What is the size in m² of the new storey?

Solution

a The car park is 12.5% bigger than last year, so it is now 112.5% of its original size.

112.5% of the original size is 14 400

$1.125x = 14\,400$ ← Use x for the original size.

$x = \dfrac{14\,400}{1.125} = 12\,800$

Last year the car park had an area of 12 800 m².

b The area of the extra storey is the difference between the new size and the original size.

$14\,400 - 12\,800 = 1600\,\text{m}^2$

The extra storey has an area of 1600 m².

Worked example

The sale price of a pair of designer sunglasses is £96.

a The reduction in the sale is 20%. What percentage of the original price is the sale price?

b Find the original price.

Solution

a $100\% - 20\% = 80\%$

The sale price is 80% of the original price.

b 80% of the original price is £96. As an equation, using x for the original price:

$0.8x = 96$

$x = \dfrac{96}{0.8} = £120$

The original price of the sunglasses was £120.

VAT for shoppers

VAT is a tax added to the price of some goods in shops.

In 2020 VAT was charged at 20%.

Usually the prices in shops already have VAT added.

Worked example

A school bag is priced at £24.

How much VAT was included in the price?

Solution

Look at the diagram below.

Total price including VAT £24 120%	
Price without VAT 100%	20%

The price including VAT is 120% of the price without VAT.

Using x for the price without VAT:

$1.2x = 24$

$x = \dfrac{24}{1.2} = £20$

The price before VAT was £20.

The VAT added was £24 − £20 = £4.

Percentage profit and loss

Worked example

A violin is sold in a music shop for £55 at a percentage profit of 10%.

What did the shop buy it for?

Solution

110% of the original price is £55.

$1.1x = 55$ (where x is the original price).

$x = \dfrac{55}{1.1} = £50$

The violin was bought by the shop for £50.

Worked example

Mr Patterson sells his house at a 15% loss.

The sale price is £425 000.

How much did Mr Patterson buy the house for?

Solution

£425 000 is 85% of the original price.

$0.85x = 425\,000$

$x = \dfrac{425\,000}{0.85}$

$x = 500\,000$

Mr Patterson bought the house for £500 000.

> **Remember**
>
> The original amount is always represented by 100%.

VAT for businesses

① Not all businesses charge VAT, but if a business or self-employed person earns more than a threshold amount (in 2020 this was £85 000 per year), they have to register for VAT. This means that:

   i   they have to charge VAT on all their bills

   ii they can claim back any VAT they pay when they buy anything for the business.

The second point is important, as it is money the business can get back from the taxman. They have to do the calculations first though and work out how much they can claim. Many invoices just give the total. You have to carry out a reverse percentage calculation to find the VAT paid.

Your friend Will is running his own printing business, but he does not understand VAT very well.

Will buys a new printer for the business for £240 including VAT.

Help him to calculate how much VAT he could claim back.

Fill in the blank spaces below. If x is the price before VAT was added, then:

$1.2x = £\_\_\_$

$$x = \frac{£\_\_\_}{1.2} = £\_\_\_$$

To work out the VAT:

$VAT = £240 - £\_\_\_ = £\_\_\_$

The price of the printer before VAT was £___.

The VAT added was £___, so this is the amount Will can claim back.

② A few years ago, VAT was charged at 17.5%. How would Will calculate what to claim back if this happened again?

To find the price before VAT, the equation would be:

$1.175x = £\_\_\_$

$$x = \frac{£\_\_\_}{1.175} = £\_\_\_$$

③ What about if VAT goes up to 22.5%?

$1.225x = £\_\_\_$

$$x = \frac{£\_\_\_}{1.225} = £\_\_\_$$

④ Sally has her own landscape gardening business. She is earning about £35 000 each year and is wondering whether to register for VAT. She does not have to as she is earning way under the government threshold.

She asks you whether she should register anyway and claim back the VAT on the things she has to buy. If she registers though, she will have to charge her customers VAT. Would you advise her to register or not? What sort of information might you need to ask her to help make the decision?

4.3 Now try these

Band 1 questions

1 Find 100% if:

a	20% is 13	**b**	45% is 675 metres	**c**	15% is 24 party hats
d	40% is 388	**e**	25% is 1925 cockroaches	**f**	60% is 534 litres
g	75% is 4425	**h**	95% is 399 cm	**i**	75% is 4875 miles
j	80% is 2000 kg				

2 Sale prices in a department store are 80% of the original price.

Find the original price for each of these items.

a   Towels: sale price £12   **b**   Table lamp: sale price £35

c   Table and chairs: sale price £90   **d**   Cutlery set: sale price £450

3 A bottle of shampoo says it contains 30% extra free.

The bottle contains 780 ml of shampoo.

What volume of shampoo is in a bottle that does not have the extra 30%?

4 House prices in London have risen by 3% in the last month.

a   Taking last month's value as 100%, what percentage is the current value?

b   A house in London is sold for £785 000.

   What was the value of the house one month ago?

   (Round your answer to the nearest pound.)

5 Sale prices in a shoe shop are 70% of the original price.

Find the original price for each of these items.

a   Trainers: £35   **b**   Boots: £42   **c**   Shoes: £45.50

Band 2 questions

6 These prices include VAT at 20%, so they are 120% of the original prices.

Find the price before VAT.

a   £72   **b**   £240   **c**   £2160   **d**   £64.80

7 VAT (value added tax) is 20%. It is added to the original price (100%) of an item.

The prices of the items shown include VAT. For each of these items, find

a   the original price   **b**   the amount of the VAT.

   i   £300   **ii**   £168   **iii**   £204

8 Miguel bought a car for £6800 and later sold it for £6120.

What percentage loss did Miguel make?

9 Ranjeet pays tax at 24%. Find how much money he earns when the amount left after tax is

a   £18 240   **b**   £6399.20   **c**   £91.20

10 These prices include VAT at 20%. Find the price before VAT is added.

a   Printer cartridge: £22.50   **b**   Telephone bill: £103.20

c   Burger and chips: £9.12   **d**   Hooded top: £43.20

Problem solving | Reasoning | Problem solving | Fluency | Problem solving | Fluency | Problem solving

⑪ Martin has some business expenses this month.

On each of these items, VAT has been paid at 20%.

For each item, work out:

i   the cost before VAT was added.   ii   the amount of VAT that was added.

a   He bought some building materials for £180.   b   He received a telephone bill of £135.

⑫ A market stallholder sells fruit and vegetables at a profit of 40%.

Find the price the stallholder paid for these items.

a   Cauliflowers sold for 98p each   b   Apples sold for £1.82 per kg

c   New potatoes sold for £2.80 per bag   d   Bananas sold for £1.05 per kg

e   Mushrooms sold for £3.50 per kg   f   Carrots sold for 56p per kg

Band 3 questions

⑬ Tabitha stays at three different hotels on Friday, Saturday and Sunday.

Her hotel bills are

Grand Salisbury Hotel: Friday £79.20

Best Northern Hotel: Saturday £64.80

Trafalgar Rooms: Sunday £84

a   The hotel bills for Friday and Sunday nights include VAT at 20%.

Find the cost at these two hotels before VAT is added.

b   The hotel bill for Saturday night did not include VAT.

Which was the most expensive hotel Tabitha stayed at?

Which was the cheapest?

⑭ There is roughly 29.94 million km^3 of ice in the ice sheet of Greenland.

The ice, however, is melting. It is thought that the ice sheet has lost roughly 0.2% of its volume in the last 30 years.

How much ice was there in the Greenland ice sheet 30 years ago?

⑮ The VAT rate is 20%.

a   Find a rule for working out the VAT paid on a cost that includes VAT.

b   A restaurant buys a new cooker costing £450 before VAT.

Check your rule on this item by doing the following:

i   Work out the VAT that is paid.

ii   What is the total cost including VAT?

iii   Now use your rule from part a.

Does your answer agree with your answer to b part i.

🔤 Key words

Here is a list of the key words you met in this chapter.

Percentage	Percentage change	Percentage increase	Percentage loss
Percentage profit	Reverse percentage	VAT	

Use the glossary at the back of this book to check any you are unsure about.

Review exercise: percentages

Band 1 questions

1 Wyoming and Colorado are the only rectangular states of the 50 states in the USA.

What percentage of the states are rectangular?

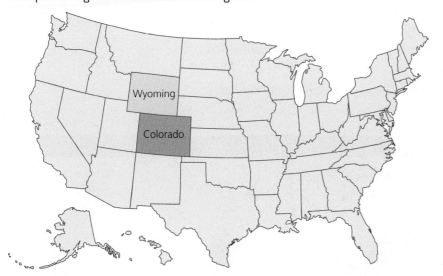

2 Daniel's phone is 85% charged. Write this:

   a as a fraction in its simplest form   **b** as a decimal.

3 A shop is selling goods at 10% off.

Using a multiplier, find the sale price of each of these items.

   a Shoes £30   **b** Jeans £55   **c** Jumper £42

4 Find 100% if:

   a 50% is 16   **b** 25% is 1350   **c** 10% is 64   **d** 70% is 3780 litres

   e 75% is 4.875 cm   **f** 60% is 252 m   **g** 90% is 3060   **h** 45% is 1575 tonnes

   i 85% is 7055 years   **j** 15% is 27

Band 2 questions

5 A valuable painting is bought at auction for £192 000.

It is later sold at a loss for £120 000.

What is the percentage loss?

6 The government awards a 4% pay increase to all public sector workers.

Work out the new salary for:

   a Beatrice, who earned £15 000

   b Bert, who earned £17 000

   c Brett, who earned £24 000

> **Remember**
>
> Depreciate in value means go down in value.

7 Cars depreciate in value as they get older.

By using a multiplier, find the value of each of these cars after one year's depreciation.

   a Peugeot 806 originally £17 500, depreciation 9%

   b Chrysler Neon originally £13 496, depreciation 25%

   c Vauxhall Astra originally £16 140, depreciation 15%

8 The value of these items has increased. Find their new values using a multiplier.

    a An old postage stamp £5, increased by 20%   **b** Antique pottery £150, increased by 65%

    c A diamond ring £1500, increased by 124%   **d** A vintage car £1800, increased by 26%

9 **a** The cost price of a bedroom rug is £120. A carpet shop sells it at a profit of 12%.

       What is the selling price?

    b A book shop buys a maths textbook for £18. A more recent edition has been written by the same author, so the book shop sells the book at a loss of 25%.

       What is the selling price?

    c The cost of some gym equipment is £140. It is sold at a profit of 40%.

       What is the selling price?

    d A pair of trainers is bought for £60. They are sold at a profit of 70%.

       What is the selling price?

Band 3 questions

10 These items are marked with the sale prices.

SALE **20% off**

A   €40

B   €65

C   €32

    a What percentage of the original prices are the sale prices?

    b For each of the sale items find:

       i 1% of the original price   **ii** the original price.

11 Find the original price of these items.

    a Designer label jeans selling at £51.20 after a 20% reduction

    b Designer label shirt selling at £31.50 after a 30% reduction

12 Barbara has just bought an office for her business.

She needs to make a lot of purchases.

The prices below include VAT at 20%.

Find the price of each of these items before VAT was added.

    a A carpet £336   **b** A wall painting £19.20

    c A computer printer £132   **d** Table and chairs £462

13 **a** Ollie's weight increases from 55 kg to 63.25 kg between his 15th and 16th birthdays.

       What is the percentage increase in his weight during this year?

    b During the summer, Ollie's mum and dad both try to lose weight. Look at this table.

	Ollie's mum	Ollie's dad
Weight (start of summer)	76 kg	
Weight (end of summer)		76 kg

Ollie's mum's weight went down by 5%.

What is her weight at the **end** of the summer?

Ollie's dad's weight also went down by 5%.

What was his weight at the **start** of the summer?

14 Amol carried out a survey. He asked twenty pupils in his class about their favourite type of film.

The pie chart shows the results of the survey.

a Find the percentage of pupils who said they preferred each type of film.

Copy and complete this table.

Put the types of film in order. Romance is top as it has the largest number of pupils.

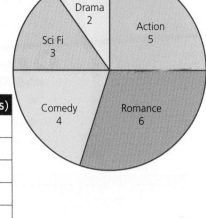

Favourite type of film

Type of film	Number of pupils (out of 20)	Percentage (of 20 pupils)
Romance		

b The following day five more pupils asked Amol if they could be included in the survey.

One of these five said they preferred drama films, one said action, one said romance, one said comedy and one said sci fi.

Copy and complete this table, again listing the types of film in order, from largest number to smallest.

Type of film	Number of pupils (out of 25)	Percentage (of 25 pupils)

c After adding one extra pupil in each category, some of the percentages go up and some go down.

Can you explain why this happens?

15 The concentration of carbon dioxide (CO_2) in the earth's atmosphere is measured in parts per million (ppm).

The concentration of CO_2 in the atmosphere in 1965 was roughly 320 ppm.

By 2015 this had increased by about 25%.

a Using a multiplier, find the concentration of CO_2 in the atmosphere in 2015.

b Scientists warn that the concentration of CO_2 in the atmosphere may increase further.

If the concentration of CO_2 in the atmosphere reaches 500 ppm, what will the percentage increase be, compared with:

i the 2015 concentration   ii the 1965 concentration?

c The 1965 level of 320 ppm was roughly 25% higher than what scientists call **pre-industrial levels**.

Roughly what were pre-industrial levels of CO_2 in the atmosphere?

CHAPTER 5

Ratio and proportion

▶ Coming up...

- ◆ Ratio and proportion review
- ◆ Direct proportion
- ◆ Inverse proportion

→ Proportion crossword

Clues

Across

1 I need 2 eggs to make 14 cookies.
How many cookies could I make with 4 eggs?

2 To cover 50 yards of footpath a workman needs 110 paving slabs.
How many slabs would he need to cover 40 yards?

5 A piece of string is 99 cm long. It is cut into 9 equal sections. Four of them are put end to end.
What is the total length of these four sections in centimetres?

7 Each jailer in a prison carries an identical bunch of keys. Two of the jailers are patrolling the prison. In total they have 42 keys. There are six jailers currently on their tea break.
How many keys do they have between them?

9 Twenty tea bags need the leaves from 325 tea plants.
How many tea plants must be plucked to make 8 tea bags?

11 There are 380 rooms in a hospital and usually 20 cleaners clean them all.
Today only 8 cleaners are working. How many rooms can they clean?

13 The weight of five identical chocolate eggs is 315 g. How many grams do two eggs weigh?

Down

1 It requires 17 grams of sugar to make a single fondant fancy.
How many grams would I need for 13 fondant fancies?

3 Seven men with exactly the same weight are chosen for a TV advert. Together they weigh 294 kg.
How much, in kilograms, do two of them weigh?

4 Eleven identical pot plants cost £44. A restaurant buys four of these plants. How much do they spend?

6 A man has swum the English Channel 19 times, a total distance of 380 miles. By the end of next year he hopes to have swum the channel another 5 times. How many miles will that be **altogether**?

8 Ten identical parts for a machine cost £190. How much will fifteen of these parts cost?

10 It takes a robot 392 hours to build 28 electric cars. How long would it take the robot to build 24 of them?

11 Lena comes from Poland. She takes a holiday to England and changes 2880 Polish zloty into £600. By the end of her holiday she has just £2.50 left. How many Polish zloty would she get for this?

12 A runner runs a marathon at a steady pace. After 2 hours she has completed 14 miles.
How many miles has she run after 3 hours?

5.1 Ratio and proportion review

✔ Skill checker

Ratio clues in the clouds

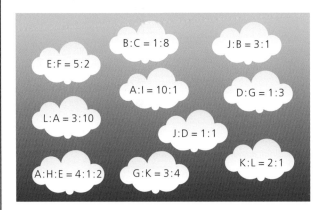

Can you find the values of all the letters using the clues in the clouds?

The value of I has been given.

$A =$	$B =$	$C =$	$D =$
$E =$	$F =$	$G =$	$H =$
$I = 2$	$J =$	$K =$	$L =$

Recap: finding an equivalent ratio

To find an equivalent ratio, multiply or divide each part of the ratio by the same number.

$4 : 1 : 15$ and $12 : 3 : 45$ are equivalent ratios. ← *Each part of the first ratio is multiplied by 3.*

Worked example

Complete these equivalent ratios by filling in the empty boxes.

a $3 : 7 = \boxed{} : 28$

b $30 : 40 = 3 : \boxed{} = \boxed{} : 80$

c $7 : 9 = \boxed{} : 45$

d $8 : 36 = \boxed{} : 9 = \boxed{} : 27$

e $10 : \boxed{} = 55 : 44$

Solution

a $3 : 7 = 12 : 28$

b $30 : 40 = 3 : 4 = 60 : 80$

c $7 : 9 = 35 : 45$

d $8 : 36 = 2 : 9 = 6 : 27$

e $10 : 8 = 55 : 44$

Recap: splitting in a given ratio

A charity divides £2600 between a rescue puppy centre and a donkey sanctuary in the ratio 8 : 5.

How much money does each of these animal homes receive?

Solution

Add the number of parts in the ratio:

$$8 + 5 = 13$$

Divide the total amount of money by this number of parts:

$$£2600 \div 13 = £200$$

The rescue puppy centre receives £200 × 8 = £1600

The donkey sanctuary receives £200 × 5 = £1000

> As a check: £1600 + £1000 = £2600, the original amount of money being shared.

Activity

Proportion

Freda the painter has been asked to paint the art room in a school.

She makes a paint colour called terracotta by mixing three different paint colours: orange, red and pink.

a The art room has a surface area of 96 m².

One litre of paint covers 12 m².

How much terracotta paint must Freda make?

b The instructions for terracotta paint are:

Mix 5 litres of orange paint, 2 litres of red paint and 1 litre of pink paint.

What is the ratio of orange : red : pink paint Freda must use?

c How many litres of each colour will Freda need? ←

> Divide the total amount of paint needed in your ratio from part b.

d One tin of paint contains 2 litres.

How many tins of each colour must Freda buy?

5.1 Now try these

Band 1 questions

1 Simplify these ratios:

    a   21 : 3   **b**   6 : 24   **c**   3 : 27   **d**   14 : 35   **e**   63 : 56   **f**   100 : 65

    g   46 : 69   **h**   15 : 35 : 10   **i**   38 : 2 : 12   **j**   100 : 24 : 10

2 Find the number that goes in the box to make an equivalent ratio.

    a   4 : 5 = ☐ : 40   **b**   1 : 4 = 5 : ☐   **c**   1 : 9 = ☐ : 36

    d   5 : 4 = 45 : ☐   **e**   8 : 3 = ☐ : 27   **f**   9 : 7 = 81 : ☐

    g   25 : 6 = 75 : ☐   **h**   1 : 6 : 5 = ☐ : ☐ : 25   **i**   3 : 11 : 2 = ☐ : 44 : ☐

    j   41 : 2 : 6 = ☐ : 8 : ☐   **k**   12 : 22 = ☐ : 11 = 36 : ☐

Problem solving

3 For each shape:

 a Work out the fraction of the shape that is coloured.

 b Work out the ratio of the coloured area to the white area.

Fluency

4 Split £30 in these ratios:

a 1:1	**b** 1:2	**c** 1:4	**d** 1:5	**e** 1:9	**f** 1:14
g 2:1	**h** 2:3	**i** 2:13	**j** 3:2	**k** 3:7	**l** 4:1
m 4:11	**n** 5:1	**o** 5:7			

Band 2 questions

Fluency

5 Write these ratios in their simplest form.

 a 4.5 kg : 250 g **b** 750 ml : 3.5 litres **c** 5 metres : 75 cm **d** 48 cm : 1.68 metres

6 Write these ratios in their simplest form using whole numbers.

 a 1.1 : 1.2 **b** 1.5 : 2 **c** $7\frac{1}{2} : 10$

 d 9.5 : 10 **e** $6\frac{1}{4} : 8$ **f** $5\frac{3}{4} : 2\frac{1}{4}$

Problem solving

7 A carpenter buys 192 metres of timber to build 32 windows. How many metres of timber would the carpenter need to build

 a 1 window?

 b 19 windows?

Fluency

8 Gemma has 3 cats, 2 dogs and a tortoise.

 Melissa has 2 cats and a dog.

 Find these ratios in their simplest form.

 a The number of cats Gemma has to the number of cats Melissa has.

 b The number of dogs Gemma has to the number of dogs Melissa has.

 c The total number of pets Gemma has to the total number Melissa has.

9 I have a photo measuring 4 cm by 6.4 cm.

The photo can be enlarged, for example by doubling the height and width to 8 cm by 12.8 cm.

Picture frames are on sale in the shop IDEA with these dimensions:

a   10 cm by 16 cm   **c**   7.5 cm by 12 cm

b   25 cm by 40 cm   **d**   12 cm by 18 cm

Which of these frames would be suitable for my photo? There may be more than one answer.

10 Look at the three flags.

a

b

c

For each one work out:

i   the fraction of the flag that is white

ii   the ratio of the areas green to white to black.

For the flag in part **c**, the heights of the green and black stripes are both 25 cm. The height of the white stripe is 10 cm.

11 Eleanor is making ice cream. She uses this recipe.

> 320 ml double cream
> 300 ml milk
> 140 g caster sugar
> 1 vanilla pod
> 4 egg yolks
> **Serves 4**

Find how much cream, milk and sugar Eleanor would need to make ice cream for:

a   8 people   **b**   1 person   **c**   3 people   **d**   6 people.

12 Tajikistan is a country in central Asia. The currency is called somoni.

Two British pounds is roughly equivalent to 27 Tajik somoni.

Copy and complete this table to help you answer the following questions.

British pounds	1	2	100	
Tajik somoni		27		540

a   How many Tajik somoni would you get for £1?

b   How many Tajik somoni would you get for £100?

c   How many British pounds could be bought for 540 Tajik somoni?

d   Roughly how many pence is one somoni worth?

Problem solving

13 Shaun's salary changes each month, but his expenses are fixed. Each month he has to spend:

- £800 on rent
- £240 on food
- £100 on bills
- £200 on his train fare.

Anything that is left is Shaun's **disposable income**.

a Find the ratio of his spending on rent to his spending on train fares, giving your answer in its simplest form.

b Find the ratio of his spending on rent to his spending on food, giving your answer in its simplest form.

c In January Shaun earns £2340.

Find the ratio of his rent to his disposable income for January in its simplest form.

d In February Shaun earns £1540.

Find the ratio of his rent to his disposable income for February in its simplest form.

e In March Shaun moves to a different flat. His food bill remains at £240 per month. His total monthly expenses also remain the same. His monthly rent, bills and train fare are now in the ratio 14 : 3 : 5.

Find how much Shaun now pays each month for his:

   i rent   **ii** bills   **iii** train fare.

14 There are roughly 250 billion stars in the Milky Way galaxy.

On average, there is 1 planet orbiting each star.

Astronomers are interested in how many planets are similar to Earth, because intelligent life may live there.

They have estimated that there could be 40 billion planets similar to Earth.

a What is the ratio of Earth-like planets to non-Earth-like planets? Give your answer in its simplest form.

b Of these 40 billion Earth-like planets, 10 billion could be orbiting stars that are similar to the Sun.

What fraction of Earth-like planets are orbiting Sun-like stars?

c What is the ratio of Earth-like planets orbiting Sun-like stars to Earth-like planets orbiting non-Sun-like stars? Give your answer in its simplest form.

d Suppose that on three planets out of every one billion Earth-like stars orbiting Sun-like stars there is intelligent life.

On how many planets in the Milky Way galaxy can we expect intelligent life?

Reasoning

15 Look at this model of the letter H.

It is made from two cuboids standing upright and a smaller cube between them.

The base of each cuboid is a square with side length 2 cm.

The height of each cuboid is three times its width.

The cube in the centre has a side length of 2 cm.

Find:

a The ratio of the volume of one cuboid to the cube.

b The ratio of the total height of the model to its total width.

The model is placed into a tray of red paint so that the base of each cuboid is painted red. The rest of the surface area remains blue.

c What fraction of the surface area is now painted red?

d What is the ratio of red to blue surface area?

5.2 Direct proportion

2 cost
£_____

5 cost
£_____

30 cost
£_____

100 cost
£_____

**Chocolates
£3.64 for 28**

10 cost
£_____

15 cost
£_____

8 cost
£_____

12 cost
£_____

Using a graph to show direct proportion

You learnt about conversion graphs in Year 8. They are often used to convert between two quantities that are **directly proportional**. If two quantities are directly proportional, their conversion graph is a straight line passing through the origin $(0, 0)$.

If the two quantities are x and y, there is a formula linking them in the form:

$y = kx$ ←

> The value of k depends on the variables. The constant of proportionality for converting from pounds to euros is different from the constant of proportionality for converting from pounds to dollars, for example.

k is a number called the **constant of proportionality**.

There is a special mathematical symbol for direct proportion: $\propto$.

y is directly proportional to x can be written $y \propto x$.

Worked example

A lorry travels at a constant speed of 56 mph (miles per hour) on a motorway.

a Copy and complete the table below.

Time taken (hours)	1	2		10
Distance travelled (miles)	56		280	

b Plot a graph of distance travelled against time taken.

Plot time on the x-axis using values from 0 to 10 hours.

Plot distance on the y-axis using values from 0 to 600 miles.

c Find a formula linking the distance travelled and the time taken.

Use D for the distance travelled and T for the time taken.

d What is the constant of proportionality?

Solution

a

Time taken (hours)	1	2	5	10
Distance travelled (miles)	56	112	280	560

c The formula is $D = 56T$

d The constant of proportionality is 56.

b

Finding a formula

If two quantities are directly proportional and you are given a pair of values, you can find the formula.

Worked example

In electrical circuits, if the resistance is constant, the current I is directly proportional to the voltage V.

In the circuit shown, the resistance is constant. The ammeter marked A measures the current I.

When $I = 0.2$, $V = 10$.

a Write a formula connecting I and V.

b Find I when $V = 100$.

Solution

a Since I and V are directly proportional, $I \propto V$, or $I = kV$

When $I = 0.2$, $V = 10$. Use this information to calculate the value of k.

$0.2 = k \times 10$

$k = 0.2 \div 10$

$k = 0.02$

So the formula is

$I = 0.02\,V$

b When $V = 100$,

$I = 0.02\,V$

$I = 0.02 \times 100$

$I = 2$

5.2 Now try these

Fluency

① Jo is on holiday in France.

She takes this graph with her to help convert between British pounds (£) and euros (€).

a Convert £65 into euros.

b Convert €105 into pounds.

c Copy and complete this conversion table

British pounds (£)	25	50	70			
Euros (€)				21	77	126

d Explain how you can use the graph to convert £250 into euros.

② A quantity p is directly proportional to another quantity q. When q is 7, p is 21.

a Find the value of p when q is 42.

b Find the value of p when q is 10.

c Write an equation connecting p and q.

③ Two quantities x and y are connected by the equation $y = kx$.
When $x = 5$, $y = 10$.

a Find the value of k.

b Find the value of x when $y = 8$.

c Draw a graph of y against x.

④ This graph shows the relationship between x and y.

a Complete this statement: y is directly _____ to x.

b Find the constant of proportionality.

c What is the value of y when $x = 1.5$?

Reasoning

⑤ Seema does an experiment. She hangs different weights on a spring and measures the length of the spring.

The table shows how the length of the spring varies with the weight hanging on it.

Weight (g)	50	100	150	200	250
Length of spring (cm)	10	20	30	40	50

a Draw a pair of axes.

Use values from 0 to 250 grams on the horizontal axis and from 0 to 50 cm on the vertical axis.

Plot the points and join them with a straight line.

b The length of the spring is 24 cm.

Use your graph to find the weight hanging on it.

c Seema says, 'If you double the weight, the length of the spring doubles as well.' Is she right?

Key Stage 3 Mastering Mathematics: Book 3

Band 2 questions

6 r is proportional to s.

    a Write this in symbols.

    b When $s = 5$, $r = 40$.

       Find the constant of proportionality.

    c Write down a formula connecting r and s.

    d **i** Find r when $s = 10$.   **ii** Find s when $r = 7$.

7 You are told that $a \propto b$ and also that $b \propto c$.

    a When $c = 8$, $b = 5$.

       When $b = 10$, $a = 0.2$.

       What are the constants of proportionality for a to b and for b to c?

    b Show that a is proportional to c.

    c How is the constant of proportionality for a to c related to values you found in part **a**?

8 The table shows some values for two variables d and e.

    Is d directly proportional to e?

d	$\dfrac{1}{2}$	$\dfrac{1}{5}$	$\dfrac{1}{10}$
e	$\dfrac{5}{16}$	$\dfrac{1}{8}$	$\dfrac{5}{80}$

9 You are told that $a \propto b$ with a constant of proportionality k.

    Is $b \propto a$ and, if so, what is the constant of proportionality?

> You could use some of the examples from previous questions and see if they work the other way round.

10 Cardboard can be recycled.

    The value of this cardboard is in direct proportion to its weight.

    One tonne of cardboard has a value of £45.

    A cardboard box has a weight of 50 g.

    Max works in a recycling centre.

    How many cardboard boxes does he need to have a value of £900?

Band 3 questions

11 Assume the time, T days, for a journey through space is directly proportional to the distance travelled, D kilometres.

    a Write this as a formula using a constant of proportionality k.

    b It takes about 4 days to travel the 400 000 km to the Moon.

       Use this information to find the value of k.

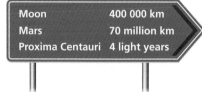

Moon	400 000 km
Mars	70 million km
Proxima Centauri	4 light years

    c Use your formula with the value of k from part **a** to work out the time taken for a journey to Mars, 70 million km away.

    d The nearest star is Proxima Centauri, roughly 4 light years away.

       One light year is roughly 10 million million kilometres. Using standard form:

$$1 \text{ light year} \approx 1 \times 10^{13} \text{ km}$$

> You learnt about standard form in Chapter 1.

       Use your formula with the value of k from part **a** to work out the time taken for a journey to Proxima Centauri.

    e Do you think humans are ever likely to travel to Mars? What about to stars like Proxima Centauri?

Fluency

Problem solving

Reasoning

Problem solving

⑫ When reading from a graph, it can be difficult to be accurate.

a Jordan reads from a graph that 30 minutes of tennis burns 240 calories.

Calculate how many calories Jordan would burn doing 1 hour of tennis every day for a week.

b Andrew thinks that Jordan has read the graph incorrectly and that 30 minutes of tennis burns 220 calories.

Using Andrew's reading, how many calories would Jordan burn doing 1 hour of tennis every day for a week?

c What is the difference in the results based on the two different readings of the graph?

⑬ Tom sells packs of playing cards on the internet.

For each pack of cards he sells, he makes 80p profit.

a Write a formula connecting the profit he makes (P) and the number of packs of cards he sells (d).

b One month, Tom sells 13 packs of cards.

How much profit does he make?

c Tom wants to buy a magic trick that costs £30.

How many packs of cards does he need to sell to have enough to buy the trick?

⑭ Here is a sign in a post office:

> £1 will buy
> Canadian $1.70
> 1.20 Swiss francs
> €1.10
> US$1.30

a Find the cost in pounds (£) of:

    i a bicycle costing €150   **ii** a pair of jeans costing US$28

    iii an ice cream costing 2 Swiss francs   **iv** a cable car ride costing Canadian $29.

b Jake has £190.

Approximately how many euros can he buy?

⑮ The time it takes Nora's kettle to boil is proportional to the amount of water in it.

The amount of electricity used is proportional to the time taken.

The cost of the electricity used is proportional to the amount used.

Nora puts 0.8 litres of water into her kettle.

a Use the graph below to find the time taken for it to boil.

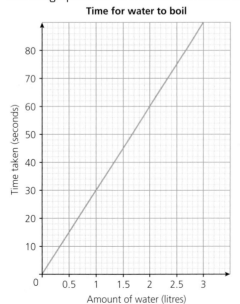

Time for water to boil

b What is the formula linking the time taken to the amount of water? Use the letter T for the time taken and V for the volume of water.

c The number of units of electricity used can be calculated using this formula:

$$E = 0.45T$$

where T is the time in seconds.

Find how many units of electricity Nora uses.

d Electricity costs 1.2p per unit.

Find how much it costs Nora to boil her kettle. Give your answer to the nearest penny.

e Find a formula to calculate the cost of boiling the kettle from the amount of water in it. Use the letter C for the cost and V for the volume of water.

5.3 Inverse proportion

✔ Skill checker

Oh dear – somebody has made a mess of their homework again!

Copy and complete, replacing all the splodges with numbers or operations ($\times$ or $\div$).

1 $3x = 18$ $x = 18 \div$ ✦ $x =$ ✦	2 $\dfrac{x}{4} = 17$ $x = 17 \times$ ✦ $x =$ ✦
3 $5x = 95$ $x =$ ✦ $\div$ ✦ $x =$ ✦	4 $\dfrac{x}{6} = 12$ $x =$ ✦ $\times$ ✦ $x =$ ✦
5 $2x = 10$ $x =$ ✦ ✦ ✦ ← Complete the two numbers and the operation between them: is it × or ÷ ? $x =$ ✦	6 $\dfrac{x}{✦} = 12$ $x = 3$ ✦ ✦ ← The first splodge is an operation × or ÷. The second is a number. $x =$ ✦

Introduction to inverse proportion

Inverse proportion means there is a connection between two variables: as one variable increases, the other decreases by the same proportion.

For example, if one variable is doubled, the other will be halved.

In the previous section you learnt the sign $\propto$ means 'is proportional to'. Where a and b are inversely proportional,

$$a \propto \frac{1}{b}$$

Using a constant k, we can write

$$a = \frac{k}{b}$$

Rearranging this we find that

$$ab = k$$

In other words, if two quantities are inversely proportional, multiplying the two quantities together gives a constant value.

> **Note**
>
> If a and b are inversely proportional
>
> a is proportional to $\dfrac{1}{b}$.
>
> $\dfrac{1}{b}$ is called the reciprocal of b.

Worked example

A science student is studying Boyle's law for a gas.

Boyle's law states that

$$P \propto \frac{1}{V}$$

where P is the pressure and V is the volume of the gas. Pressure is measured in newtons per square metre ($N\,m^{-2}$) and volume in cubic centimetres (cm^3).

She tests the gas using four different volumes.

a In her first test, the volume used is $6\,cm^3$. The pressure measured is $60\,N/m^2$.

    Find the constant of proportionality and write down the formula linking P and V.

b In the second test the pressure is reduced to $30\,N/m^2$.

    What is its new volume?

c In her third test, the student adjusts the volume to $9\,cm^3$.

    Use your formula to find the pressure of the gas now.

d In the fourth test she adjusts the pressure to $50\,N/m^2$.

    Use the formula to find the volume.

Solution

a $P \propto \frac{1}{V}$ means that $P = \frac{k}{V}$

    When $V = 6$, $P = 60$.

    $60 = \dfrac{k}{6}$ gives $k = 60 \times 6 = 360$.

    The formula is $P = \dfrac{360}{V}$ or $PV = 360$

b   Use the formula

    $PV = 360$

    When $P = 30$

    $30 \times V = 360$

    $V = 360 \div 30$ ← Divide both sides by 30.

    $V = 12$

    At $30\,N/m^2$ the volume is $12\,cm^3$.

c $PV = 360$

    $P \times 9 = 360$

    $P = 360 \div 9$ ← Divide both sides by 9.

    $P = 40$

    If the volume of the gas is $9\,cm^3$, the pressure becomes $40\,N/m^2$.

d $PV = 360$

    $50 \times V = 360$

    $V = 360 \div 50$

    $V = 7.2$

    At $50\,N\,m^{-2}$ the volume is $7.2\,cm^3$.

Looking for inversely proportional relationships

Worked example

The table shows values for two variables, c and d.

c	8	12	24
d	30	20	10

Martin thinks that c is inversely proportional to d.

Is Martin correct?

Explain how you know.

Solution

If c and d are inversely proportional, then $c \propto \dfrac{1}{d}$.

Another way of writing this is $c = \dfrac{k}{d}$ and re-arranging this leads to $cd = k$.

In other words, if c and d are inversely proportional, then multiplying c by d should give a constant value. Using the paired values of c and d in the table:

$$8 \times 30 = 240$$
$$12 \times 20 = 240$$
$$24 \times 10 = 240$$

In each case, the answer is the same, 240, so c and d are indeed inversely proportional.

Remember

▶ If two variables are inversely proportional, it means that as one variable is increased, the other is decreased at the same rate.

▶ When two variables, x and y, are inversely proportional, $xy = k$ where k is a constant.

5.3 Now try these

Band 1 questions

1 Sarah and Claire are planning a party, but they are not sure how many people will turn up.

They make 60 cupcakes.

   a There are 20 people altogether at the party.

      How many cupcakes do they get each?

   b Claire thinks that if there had been more people, they would have had more cakes each.

      Give an example to show that Claire is wrong.

   c How many people could be at the party so that the cakes could be shared equally without having to cut the cakes?

      List all the possible answers.

2 Five of Sam's colleagues decide to buy him a leaving gift that will cost them £6 each.

   a What is the value of the leaving gift?

   b In the end, only four people contribute towards the gift.

      How much do the four colleagues each need to pay?

3 Here is a table showing values for two variables, a and b.

Show that a and b are inversely proportional.

a	100	200	70
b	14	7	20

4 $c \propto \dfrac{1}{d}$

Copy and complete this table of values.

c	16	8		32
d	2		8	

Reasoning

Problem solving

Fluency

5 j is inversely proportional to k.

Which of these could be correct formulas connecting j and k?

$$jk = 500$$

$$j = \frac{500}{k}$$

$$j = 500\,k$$

$$\frac{j}{k} = 500$$

Band 2 questions

6 v and w are inversely proportional.

Copy and complete the table

v	0.2	0.3		24
w	6		12	

7 A new section of motorway needs to be covered in tarmac. It would take six workmen 12 days.

a If eight workmen are employed instead of six, how long will it take them?

b How long will it take if 12 workmen are employed?

c How long would it take one workman working alone?

d How many workmen would be needed to complete the job in just one day?

8 A farmer has enough feed to keep 80 cows for five days.

a How long would the same amount of feed last if the farmer had

i 40 cows   **ii** 100 cows   **iii** 50 cows?

b The farmer decides to retire from farming.

She keeps one cow as a pet.

She has enough feed left over to keep 60 cows for six days.

How long will the feed last for her one pet cow?

c Why might your answer to part **b** not be quite right?

9 A campsite has enough food to feed 120 scouts for 35 days.

a How long will the food last if there are 15 fewer scouts?

b How long will the food last if there are 20 extra scouts?

10 The frequency of a vibrating guitar string is inversely proportional to its length.

a A guitar string 0.7 metres long vibrates at a frequency of 6 times each second.

What frequency would a string 0.3 metres long vibrate at?

b What length of string vibrates 7 times every two seconds?

11 In a factory, six pipes are used to fill a large tank with water.

The six pipes take 12 hours to fill the tank from when it is empty.

a How long will the tank take to fill if only four pipes are used?

b The factory's owner is considering buying two extra pipes.

How much time would having two extra pipes save?

c Write a formula connecting the time taken, t hours, and the number of pipes, n.

Band 3 questions

12 Luca says, 'The exterior angle of a regular polygon is inversely proportional to the number of sides'.

Investigate whether Luca is right.

For example, pentagons have five sides.

The exterior angles of a regular pentagon are 72°.

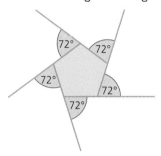

Use a table to help you decide.

13 y is inversely proportional to x.

a Complete this table of values.

x	1		4		12
y	12	4		2	

b Draw a graph of y against x using values of x from 0 to 12 and values of y from 0 to 12.

c Use your graph to answer the following questions.

Find the value of y when:

i $x = 0.5$ **ii** $x = 0.1$

d Does the graph pass through the coordinate axes? Describe the curve as it approaches both axes.

e Do all inverse proportion graphs look like this?

14 In the table, the variables p and q are inversely proportional.

Some values for p and q are given using algebraic expressions.

p	$2x$	$4x$	$4x^2$	$4xy$
q	$8x$			

a Find an expression for pq in terms of x.

b Copy and complete the table.

15 A farmer needs to build a rectangular fence around part of his field.

The length is l and the width is w metres.

The fenced-off section needs to have an area of 100 square metres.

a Make a table of some possible values for l and w.

b Add another row to your table, giving the length of fencing the farmer needs.

c What is the minimum length of fencing needed?

Key words

Here is a list of the key words you met in this chapter.

Direct proportion   Inverse proportion   Proportion   Ratio

Use the glossary at the back of this book to check any you are unsure about.

Review exercise: ratio and proportion

Band 1 questions

Problem solving

1 If six teenagers can plant 108 trees in a day, how many trees can ten teenagers plant in a day?

Reasoning

2 Aunt Lucy decides to give her nephew and niece, Harry and Lily, £540 between them.

Because Lily is older than Harry, Aunt Lucy decides that the money must be divided so that Lily gets £5 for every £4 that Harry gets.

How much does each child get?

Problem solving

3 Eight workers can plaster a block of flats in six days.

    a How many men are needed to plaster the flats in four days?

    b How many days would it take one man to plaster the block of flats on his own?

Reasoning

4 The number of windows in a church, a school and a house are in the ratio $3 : 7 : 1$.

There are 154 windows altogether and of these, 42 are in the church.

How many windows are there in the school and in the house?

Fluency

5 In an electrical circuit, for a fixed voltage, the current I is inversely proportional to the resistance R.

When the current is 40 amps, the resistance is 280 ohms.

    a Write a formula connecting I and R.

    b Use your formula to calculate the resistance when the current is 60 amps.

6 It will take four workers five hours to repair a road.

The boss wants it finished in two hours or less.

How many workers are needed?

7 Copy and complete this table of values for the variables p and q, given that p is inversely proportional to q.

p	3		25	30
q		10	6	

Band 2 questions

Reasoning

8 You are going on holiday to Mars.

Dave the spaceman and his dog are going as well.

The gravitational pull on Mars is weaker than on Earth.

This means that things weigh less on Mars.

Dave weighs 1000 N on Earth.

He only weighs 400 N on Mars.

    a Use this information to draw a conversion graph between weight on Earth and weight on Mars.

    b Dave's dog Pluto weighs 250 N on Earth.

       Use your graph to find how much Pluto weighs on Mars.

c Pzork the Martian weighs 360 N on Mars.

Use your graph to find how much Pzork weighs on Earth.

d A Mars buggy weighs about 6000 N on Mars.

Explain how to find its weight on Earth.

9 Use the values in the table to find out whether w and y are inversely proportional or not.

Explain how you know.

w	52.5	35	21	14
y	4	6	10	15

10 A pump can empty a swimming pool in six hours.

How long would it take to empty the pool using:

a two pumps

b three pumps

c 12 pumps?

Band 3 questions

11 A recycling company knows that the weight of newspaper can be estimated when it is stacked up.

A 30 cm stack of newspaper weighs approximately 15 kg.

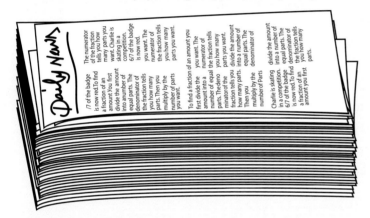

Melody says that you can estimate the weight of newspaper in kilograms by finding half of the height of the stack of newspaper in centimetres.

a Copy and complete this word formula.

Weight in kilograms = _____ × _____

b Write a formula connecting the weight W and the height H of stacks of newspapers.

c Use your formula to estimate the weight of a stack of newspapers 70 cm high.

12 When newspaper is compacted using a machine, the weight in kilograms can be estimated based on the volume in cubic metres (m^3).

$5\,m^3$ of compacted paper weighs 2400 kg.

a Calculate the weight of $1\,m^3$ of compacted paper.

b Write a formula connecting the weight W and the volume V.

c A recycling bank can hold $6.5\,m^3$ of compacted paper.

How much will this paper weigh?

⓭ A pedometer is an instrument that counts how many steps you take.

This chart shows the equivalent number of steps you would make when taking part in three activities.

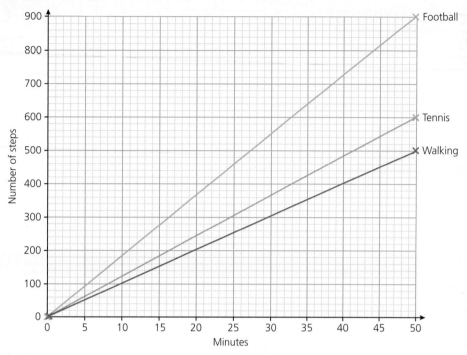

a Oliver takes part in a tennis match which lasts 40 minutes.

How many steps is that equivalent to?

b Naomi does 30 minutes each of walking, tennis and football.

How many steps is that equivalent to in total?

c Priya needs an extra 1500 steps to achieve her weekly target.

How many minutes of football should she play?

⓮ A ship travels s kilometres in t hours. s is directly proportional to t with equation $s = kt$.

When $t = 5, s = 120$.

a Find the value of s when

i $t = 10$

ii $t = 1$.

b Find the constant of proportionality, k.

c What does the constant of proportionality tell you?

⓯ The circumference of a circle is directly proportional to the diameter of the circle.

What is the constant of proportionality?

> **Remember**
>
> In Year 8 you learnt how to calculate the circumference of a circle.

Chapters 4–5

Band 1 questions

Fluency

1 Find these:

   a 11% of 600 mm

   c $7\frac{1}{2}$% of 2000 kg

   e 41% of 94 km

   g 87% of 60 mm

   b 5% of 480 cm²

   d 27% of 87 tonnes

   f 7% of 56 cm

   h 17% of 99 g

2 Copy and complete this table.

Give all fractions in their simplest form.

The first row has been done for you.

Fraction	Decimal	Percentage
$\frac{17}{20}$	0.85	85%
$\frac{7}{10}$		
	0.55	
		14%
$\frac{21}{40}$		
	0.875	
		62.5%
$\frac{11}{5}$		

Reasoning

3 There were 15 000 women and 18 000 men living in the town of Allerton.

The population increased over the next few years.

The number of women increased by 10%.

The number of men increased by only 4%.

   a How many men and how many women lived in Allerton after this increase?

   b What was the total increase as a percentage of the original population?

④ Joshua surveyed all the people in his class about how they get to school.

The results are shown in the pie chart.

Travel to school survey

a What percentage of pupils said they walk to school?

b There are 30 pupils in Joshua's class. How many of them said:

    i car   **ii** walk   **iii** cycle   **iv** bus?

Band 2 questions

⑤ What multiplier would you use to:

a increase by 12%   **b** decrease by 20%   **c** increase by 7%

d decrease by 80%   **e** increase by 400%?

⑥ Use a multiplier to find:

a 40 kg increased by 25%   **b** 120 cm increased by 30%   **c** 2200 metres increased by 22%

d £310 decreased by 15%   **e** 670 decreased by 40%

⑦ These items go down in value by the percentage shown. Find the new value of each item using a multiplier.

a Exercise equipment £250, down 30%

b Scooter £45, down 20%

c Electric piano £640, down 25%

⑧ Rebecca is thinking about putting some money into a savings account.

Here is an advert for the account.

> **Hilltown Building Society**
> *Live Savers Savings Account*
> Balances below £500:
> ● 1.5% simple interest per annum
> Balances £500 or above:
> ● 1.75% simple interest per annum

Rebecca is trying to decide whether to put £450 or £500 into the account.

a If Rebecca put £450 into the savings account, how much simple interest would she receive each year?

b If Rebecca put £500 into the savings account, how much simple interest would she receive each year?

Rebecca plans to keep her money in the account for 3 years.

c Find the amount of interest she would receive over 3 years on both £450 and £500.

d What is the difference in the total amount of interest she would receive over 3 years?

9 A carton of orange juice says it contains 20% extra free.

The carton contains 396 ml of juice.

What volume of juice is in a carton that does not have the extra 20%?

10 In a building supplies shop, all prices include VAT at 20%.

   i What is the price of these items before VAT is added?

   ii How much VAT is added?

   a Shovel £42

   b Timber £11.76 per metre

   c 100 Nails £4.80

   d Sand £38.40 per tonne

Band 3 questions

11 Look at this model of a letter L.

The front face is painted blue, while the rest is yellow.

What is the ratio, in its simplest form, of blue to yellow paint used?

12 The table shows some values for two variables F and L.

Is F inversely proportional to L? Explain your answer.

F	2	6	7
L	12	4	3

13 The graph shows how a taxi company works out the fare for a journey, using the distance travelled.

Are the distance travelled and cost for the journey directly proportional, inversely proportional, or neither? Explain your answer.

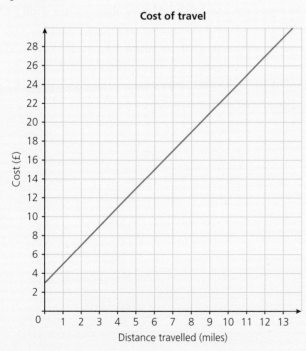

14 In the table, the variables C and S are inversely proportional.

Some values for C and S are given using algebraic expressions.

a What is $C \times S$?

b Copy and complete the table.

C	$5x$		$2xy$	
S	$4y$	$4x$		y

15 Mrs Abraham's class and Mr Benjamin's class do PE at the same time on Thursdays. The two classes have to share the PE hall.

The PE hall has an area of $200\,\text{m}^2$.

Sometimes one class uses more space than the other.

Look at this graph of the space used by Mrs Abraham's class against the space used by Mr Benjamin's class.

a One Thursday Mr Benjamin's class arrives first. He lets his class use $140\,\text{m}^2$. Mrs Abraham's class is left with $60\,\text{m}^2$, as shown by the point marked in the diagram.

Mr Benjamin's class allows Mrs Abraham's class to use an additional $20\,\text{m}^2$ of space. How much space is each class using now?

b Mrs Abraham says 'When the space for our class goes up, the space for Mr Benjamin's class goes down. So, the space for our class is inversely proportional to the space for Mr Benjamin's class.'

Is this correct? Explain your answer.

Using measures

Coming up...

- Speed as a compound measure
- Density as a compound measure
- Conversion between metric units of area and volume

→ Guess the formula

① The units for speed are metres per second (m/s).

Which one of the following is the correct formula for speed?

speed = distance × time	**speed = $\dfrac{\text{distance}}{\text{time}}$**	**speed = $\dfrac{\text{time}}{\text{distance}}$**

② The units for density are grams per centimetre cubed (g/cm³).

Which one of the following is the correct formula for density?

density = $\dfrac{\text{mass}}{\text{volume}}$	**density = mass × volume**	**density = $\dfrac{\text{volume}}{\text{mass}}$**

③ The units for pressure are newtons per square metre (N/m²). ← A newton is a unit of force.

Which one of the following is the correct formula for pressure?

pressure = force × area	**pressure = $\dfrac{\text{area}}{\text{force}}$**	**pressure = $\dfrac{\text{force}}{\text{area}}$**

6.1 Speed

✔ Skill checker

Substitute the numbers into the formulas.

a $A = BC$
Find A if $B = 3$ and $C = 6$.

b $P = QR$
Find P if $Q = -7$ and $R = 6$.

c $Z = \dfrac{X}{Y}$
Find Z if $X = 12$ and $Y = 4$.

d $m = np$
Find m if $n = 5$ and $p = 3.5$.

e $s = \dfrac{r}{t}$
Find s if $r = 20$ and $t = 2.5$.

f $a = fg$
Find a if $f = 1.5$ and $g = 10.5$.

g $k = \dfrac{F}{r}$
Find k if $r = 16$ and $F = 2$.

h $c = pe$
Find c if $p = \dfrac{1}{5}$ and $e = 7$.

i $d = \dfrac{q}{n}$
Find d if $q = \dfrac{1}{8}$ and $n = \dfrac{1}{4}$.

Speed as a compound measure

A compound measure is a measure involving two or more quantities.

An example is speed, which involves distance and time.

$$\text{speed} = \frac{\text{distance}}{\text{time}}$$

If distance is measured in kilometres and the time is in hours, then the unit for speed will be kilometres per hour (km/h).

If distance is measured in metres and the time is in seconds, then the unit for speed will be metres per second (m/s).

Other possible units for speed are miles per hour, centimetres per second, kilometres per minute, etc.

Other examples of compound measures are:

● Density, often measured in grams per cubic centimetre
● Pressure, often measured in newtons per square metre.

You will learn about density in section 6.2.

Worked example

Converting units of time

a   Convert 6.5 minutes to minutes and seconds.

b   Convert 3 hours 15 minutes to hours and minutes.

Solution

a   6.5 minutes $= 6\frac{1}{2}$ minutes, or 6 minutes 30 seconds.

b   3 hours 15 minutes is $3\frac{1}{4}$ hours, or 3.25 hours.

> **Remember**
>
> 3.25 hours **does not mean** 3 hours 25 minutes!

Worked example

Working with the formula for speed

Jason leaves London on a motorbike at 06:00 and travels to his parents' house 432 km away.

He arrives at 10:00.

a   Find his average speed

   i   in kilometres per hour   ii   in kilometres per minute   iii   in metres per second.

b   Write the unit 'metres per second' another way.

Solution

a   His journey takes from 6 o'clock to 10 o'clock so it lasts 4 hours.

   i $\text{average speed} = \frac{\text{distance}}{\text{time}} = \frac{432 \text{ kilometres}}{4 \text{ hours}} = 108 \text{ kilometres per hour}$

   ii   For an answer in kilometres per minute, use a distance in kilometres and a time in minutes.

   $\frac{\text{distance}}{\text{time}} = \frac{432 \text{ kilometres}}{240 \text{ minutes}}$ [4 hours = 4 × 60 = 240 minutes]

   $= 1.8 \text{ kilometres per minute}$

   iii   For an answer in metres per second, use a distance in metres and a time in seconds.

   $\frac{\text{distance}}{\text{time}} = \frac{432\,000 \text{ metres}}{14\,400 \text{ seconds}}$ [432 kilometres = 432 × 1000 = 432 000 metres]

   [4 hours = 4 × 60 × 60 = 14 400 seconds]

   $= 30 \text{ metres per second}$

b   Another way of writing 'metres per second' is m/s.

Using a formula triangle

For all compound measures, you may find it helpful to use a formula triangle.

Using the formula

$$\text{speed} = \frac{\text{distance}}{\text{time}}$$

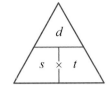

begin labelling the triangle from the bottom left, then the top, then the bottom right.

To use the triangle:

● To find the speed, cover up s with your finger.

The formula is $s = \dfrac{d}{t}$

● To find the distance, cover up d with your finger.

The formula is $d = s \times t$

● To find the time, cover up t with your finger.

The formula is $t = \dfrac{d}{s}$

If you are not sure of the formula for a compound measure, you may be able to construct it using the units.

For example, speed is measured in metres per second (or miles per hour, etc.), so its formula is distance over time.

Worked example

a A truck travels 126 miles in 2 hours 15 minutes on a motorway.

What is the average speed of the truck while it is on the motorway?

b The truck leaves the motorway and travels a further 100 miles at a speed of 50 miles per hour.

How long does it take for this part of the journey?

c For the final part of its journey, the truck travels at an average speed of 40 miles per hour. It takes $1\frac{1}{2}$ hours to reach its final destination.

What distance did the truck travel for this third part of the journey?

Solution

a Convert 2 hours 15 minutes to a time in hours.

15 minutes is $\frac{1}{4}$ hour or 0.25 hours, so 2 hours 15 mins = 2.25 hours.

Using the triangle and covering s you find that $s = \dfrac{d}{t}$

$s = \dfrac{126}{2.25} = 56$ miles per hour

b In this part of the question you are finding the time, so cover t in the triangle.

$t = \dfrac{d}{s} = \dfrac{100}{50} = 2$ hours

c Find the distance d for the third part of the journey. Covering d in the triangle gives $d = s \times t$.

$d = 40 \times 1.5 = 60$ miles

6.1 Now try these

1 Change the units for these amounts of time.

a Convert 2 hours to minutes.

b Convert $2\frac{1}{4}$ hours to minutes.

c Convert 2.75 hours to minutes.

d Convert 2 hours 25 minutes to minutes.

e Convert 2 minutes to seconds.

f Convert $2\frac{1}{2}$ minutes to seconds.

g Convert 2.5 minutes to seconds.

h Convert 2 minutes 20 seconds to seconds.

i Convert 3 days to hours.

j Convert $2\frac{1}{3}$ days to hours.

k Convert 1.25 days to hours.

l Convert 2 days and 6 hours to hours.

2 Calculate the average speed for each of these objects, giving your answer with appropriate units.

a A cricket ball travelling 60 metres to the edge of the cricket ground in 5 seconds.

b A paper plane flying 4 metres in 3.2 seconds.

c A leaf falling 10 metres from a tree, taking 16 seconds to reach the ground.

d A jet plane travelling 800 miles from London to Madrid in Spain in 2 hours 30 minutes.

e A rocket taking $8\frac{1}{2}$ minutes to travel 255 km into orbit.

3 A sprinter runs 200 m in 20 seconds.

How fast, on average, was the sprinter running:

a in metres per second

b in kilometres per hour?

4 a Kamala drives a distance of 280 km in 4 hours.

Work out Kamala's average speed.

b A worm moves 8 metres in 32 minutes.

Work out the worm's average speed in:

i metres per minute

ii centimetres per second.

c Julia swims for 1 hour. She completes 58 lengths, each 25 metres.

What is her average speed?

5 Work out the average speed of each of these ships and boats.

a A speedboat travelling 12 km in $\frac{1}{4}$ hour.

b A cargo ship travelling 19 200 km from Shanghai, China to the UK in 50 days.

c A cruise ship covering 384 km in 12 hours.

6 Anna's train leaves Edinburgh at 10:26 in the morning and arrives in London at 2:56 that afternoon. The total distance for the journey is 337.5 miles.

What is the train's average speed in miles per hour?

7 The national speed limit for cars on most roads is 60 miles per hour.

A bird can fly at 45 metres per second.

Which is faster, the car or the bird?

Explain your answer.

Key Stage 3 Mastering Mathematics: Book 3

Fluency

Problem solving

Reasoning

8 The official world land speed record is 1223.7 kilometres per hour.

It was set on 15 October 1997 by Andy Green in the jet-engine car Thrust SSC.

What was Thrust SSC's average speed in metres per second?

9 A black mamba snake of Eastern Africa can move at up to 5 m/s.

What is its average speed in miles per hour?

(Use the fact that 8 kilometres is approximately 5 miles.)

10 Sound travels 1 kilometre in 3 seconds.

Alana sees a fork of lightning.

> Alana sees the lightning almost instantaneously because light travels very, very quickly.

Five seconds later she hears the thunder.

How many metres away is the lightning?

Band 3 questions

11 A light year is the distance that light travels in one year.

The speed of light is 300 million metres per second.

How many kilometres are there in one light year?

12 Jackson is riding a motorbike at 35 miles per hour.

Carol is driving her car at 12.5 metres per second.

Convert both of these speeds into kilometres per hour, using the fact that 5 miles is approximately 8 kilometres.

Who is travelling faster?

13 Chuck and Simone live 2 km from school.

This travel graph represents their journey to school one day.

a How far does Chuck travel in:

   i 2 minutes

   ii 5 minutes?

b What is Chuck's speed in:

   i metres per minute

   ii kilometres per hour?

c What is Simone's speed in:

   i metres per minute

   ii kilometres per hour?

d One of them cycles and the other walks. Who cycles?

Distance from home

14 Ryan is doing a research project on birds. He learns that most birds can fly, but others are described as flightless.

Here is some information Ryan finds about how fast some birds can travel.

a A swallow can fly 100 m in 7.2 seconds.

b A penguin can swim 2 km in $\frac{1}{4}$ hour.

c An ostrich can run 200 m in 12 seconds.

   Ryan works out the speed of each of these birds in:

   i metres per second

   ii kilometres per hour.

Copy and complete the table below.

	Speed (metres per second)	Speed (kilometres per hour)
Swallow		
Penguin		
Ostrich		

⑮ Paula has her own private aeroplane.

She makes a five-leg tour of England, Wales and Scotland, starting in Penzance.

The map shows the first leg of her tour, from Penzance to Swansea.

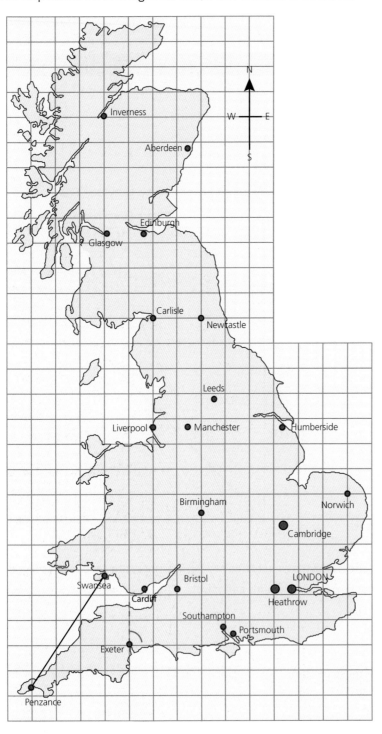

1 cm represents 50 km

a Copy and complete the table below.
For one leg of the journey you will need to measure the distance with a ruler and convert to kilometres.

b On which stretch of the journey does she have the highest average speed?

c How far does Paula fly in total and what is her total flying time?

d What is her average speed for the entire tour?

Leg	Start	End	Distance (km)	Time	Average speed (km/h)
1	Penzance	Swansea	200	20 minutes	
2	Swansea	Carlisle	370		370
3	Carlisle	Newcastle		30 minutes	
4	Newcastle	Aberdeen		45 minutes	324
5	Aberdeen	Penzance	814		407

6.2 Density

✔ Skill checker

Answer the questions relating to these formula triangles.

①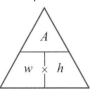

a What is the formula for A?

b What is the formula for w?

c What is the formula for h?

②

a What is the formula for P?

b What is the formula for V?

c What is the formula for T?

③ There is a formula linking pressure, force and area: $\text{pressure} = \dfrac{\text{force}}{\text{area}}$

Which of these formula triangles is correct?

a	b	c
		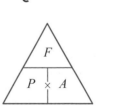

④ There is a formula linking force F, mass m and acceleration a: $F = ma$

Which of these formula triangles is correct?

a	b	c
		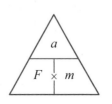

Density as a compound measure

The formula for density is:

$$\text{density} = \frac{\text{mass}}{\text{volume}}$$

If the mass is measured in grams and the volume is in cm³, then the unit for density will be grams per cubic centimetre (g/cm³).

If the mass is measured in kilograms and the volume is in m³, then the unit for density will be kilograms per cubic metre (kg/m³).

Other possible units for density are kilograms per cm³, grams per m³, etc.

Worked example

Working with the formula for density

a   A metal block has a volume of 1000 cm³.

   It has a mass of 8.5 kg.

   Using the formula
   $$\text{density} = \frac{\text{mass}}{\text{volume}}$$
   find the density of the block in:

   i   kilograms per cm³

   ii   grams per cm³

b   A brick has a density of 1.8 grams per cubic centimetre.

   Its volume is 1470 cm³.

   Find the mass of the brick.

Solution

a   i $\text{density} = \dfrac{\text{mass}}{\text{volume}}$

   $= \dfrac{8.5}{1000}$ ← To get an answer in kg/cm³ use a mass in kg and a volume in cm³.

   $= 0.0085$ kilograms per cm³ ← This unit can also be written as kg/cm³.

   ii   8.5 kg = 8500 g

   $\text{density} = \dfrac{\text{mass}}{\text{volume}}$

   $= \dfrac{8500}{1000}$ ← To get an answer in g/cm³ use a mass in g and a volume in cm³.

   $= 8.5$ grams per cm³ ← This unit can also be written as g/cm³.

b   Using the formula
   $$\text{density} = \frac{\text{mass}}{\text{volume}}$$

   $1.8 = \dfrac{\text{mass}}{1470}$

   $\text{mass} = 1.8 \times 1470 = 2646\,\text{g} = 2.646\,\text{kg}$

Worked example

Working with the formula triangle

Using the formula, $\text{density} = \dfrac{\text{mass}}{\text{volume}}$, you can construct the triangle:

a A plastic toy has a mass of 815 g and a volume of 3260 cm³.

Calculate its density.

b A larger toy made from the same plastic material has a volume of 5000 cm³.

Find its mass.

Solution

a Looking for density, construct the triangle and cover up D.

You divide the mass by the volume. So

$$\text{density} = \frac{815}{3260}$$
$$= 0.25 \text{ g/cm}^3$$

b Since the larger toy is made from the same plastic material, it also has a density of 0.25 g/cm³.

It has a volume of 5000 cm³. To find the mass using the triangle, cover up m.

You multiply the density and the volume. So

$$\text{mass} = 0.25 \times 5000$$
$$= 1250 \text{ g} = 1.25 \text{ kg}$$

Activity

Look at this domino trail.

The right-hand end of the first (green) domino matches the left-hand end of the second (pink) domino.

Fill in the empty boxes with the correct numbers and units.

6.2 Now try these

Band 1 questions

1 Calculate the density in g/cm³ for each of these items:

   a   A piece of copper with a volume of 50 cm³ and a mass of 450 g.

   b   A litre of water with a volume of 1000 cm³ and a weight of 1 kg.

   c   A block of plastic with a mass of 1.84 kg and a volume of 2000 cm³.

   d   A tonne of recycled cardboard with a volume of 1 400 000 cm³.

2 Find the density of these foods in grams per cm³.

   The volume of each food container is 500 cm³.

   a   **b**   **c**

3 A block of metal A has a mass of 130 g and has volume 26 cm³.

   A block of metal B weighs 24 000 kg and has volume 2 m³.

   Use the formula

$$density = \frac{mass}{volume}$$

   to calculate the density of each block.

Key Stage 3 Mastering Mathematics: Book 3

Fluency

4 The mass of the block of oak shown is 390 g.

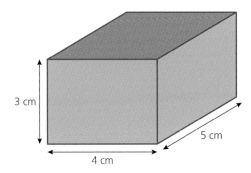

3 cm

5 cm

4 cm

a Calculate the density of the oak in g/cm³.

b Find the mass in kilograms of a cube of oak with a side length of 20 cm.

Band 2 questions

5 A gold bar has a mass of 965 grams.

Gold has a density of 19.3 g/cm³.

a Find the volume of the gold bar.

b A fraudster makes a second bar out of a different metal. It has exactly the same size and shape, but its density is 15 g/cm³.

Find the weight of this metal bar.

6 Peter is investigating two objects in his classroom.

He says 'The first object is much lighter than the second, so it must have a lower density.'

Is he right? Explain your answer.

7 Water has a density of 1 gram per cm³ or 1000 kg per m³.

An object will float on water if its density is lower than the density of water.

a Decide whether these objects will float on water or sink.

i A rock, mass 4.5 kg, volume 2000 cm³

ii An ice cube, mass 24.84 g, volume 27 cm³

iii An iceberg, mass 74 520 kg, volume 81 m³

iv A tree trunk, mass 6500 kg, volume 10 cubic metres

v A 1000 tonne oil spill with a volume of 1250 cubic metres

b Do you think density is the only factor that will decide whether an object floats? Explain your answer.

Problem solving

Reasoning

8 This is a density column. It is made using liquids of different densities.

The liquid with the lowest density rises to the top, while the densest liquid remains at the base of the column.

— Cooking oil
— Raisin
— Water
— Washing-up liquid
— Honey

a The densities of the four liquids are:

$1.05\,\text{g/cm}^3$ $0.9\,\text{g/cm}^3$ $1\,\text{g/cm}^3$ $1.45\,\text{g/cm}^3$

Match each of the four liquids with the correct density.

b An object carefully placed into the density column may sink through some of the liquids but float on top of others.

For example, the raisin shown has a density greater than oil, so it sinks through the oil layer. Since it has a density lower than water it will come to rest at the top of the water layer.

Decide where each of these items will come to rest.

     i   A piece of screwed-up tissue paper with density $0.25\,\text{g/cm}^3$

     ii   A glass marble with a volume of $1\,\text{cm}^3$ and a mass of 2.5 grams

     iii A nut with a mass of 0.51 grams and a volume of $0.5\,\text{cm}^3$

     iv A small ice cube with a side length of 0.5 cm and a mass of 0.115 g

9 Look at the table below listing the planets in our solar system, their masses and volumes.

Planet		Mass (kg)	Volume (m³)	Density (kg/m³)
Mercury		3.3×10^{23}	6.08×10^{19}	5427
Venus		4.87×10^{24}	9.29×10^{20}	
Earth		5.97×10^{24}		5514

Mars			1.63×10^{20}	3933
Jupiter		1.9×10^{27}	1.43×10^{24}	
Saturn		5.68×10^{26}		687
Uranus			6.83×10^{22}	1271
Neptune		1.02×10^{26}	6.23×10^{22}	

a   Copy and complete the table.

b   Which planet in our solar system has the lowest density?

c   Which has the highest density?

d   How many of the planets would float in a giant pool of water?

e   Do you know why the four planets closest to the sun (Mercury, Venus, Earth and Mars) have higher densities than the other planets?

10   Human fat has a density of 0.9 grams per cm^3.

The lean (non-fat) components of the human body have an overall density of 1.1 grams per cm^3.

a   The table below shows the mass and volume of the fat and non-fat components of Lucy's body.

Copy the table and complete the four blank boxes.

	Mass (g)	Volume (cm^3)
Fat Density 0.9 g/cm^3	16 560	
Non-fat Density 1.1 g/cm^3		50 400
Totals		

b   What percentage of Lucy's body mass is fat?

c   Work out the overall density of Lucy's body.

11 The stone shown has a mass of 53 grams and a volume of 20 cm³.

The jar of stones weighs 7 lb and has a volume of 3000 cm³.

a Work out the density of the single stone in grams per cubic centimetre.

b Find the density of the jar of stones in the same units.

Use the conversion 1 lb = 454 grams.

c Which object has the highest density?

Can you explain this?

12 A balloon filled with the gas **helium** will rise to the ceiling or, if you are outdoors, into the sky!

It does this because the overall density of the balloon filled with helium is lower than the density of air.

The density of air is 1.2754 kg/m³.

The density of helium is 0.178 kg/m³.

a Ali fills a balloon with helium. If the volume of the balloon is 0.056 18 m³, find the mass of helium inside the balloon.

b Ali's helium balloon rises to the ceiling and stays there for several days.

Each day 10% of the original mass of helium leaks out. This means that:

▸ the mass of helium in the balloon goes down by 10% each day; and

▸ the volume of the balloon goes down by 10% each day.

The mass of the balloon when empty (**before** it was blown up with helium) was 10 grams or 0.01 kg.

Copy and complete this table. Round all your decimal answers to 3 decimal places.

	Mass of balloon (kg)	Mass of helium (kg)	Total mass (kg)	Volume (m³)	Overall density (kg/m³) (Total mass ÷ volume)
Start	0.01			0.05618	
After 1 day	0.01	90% of original mass = _____		90% of original volume = _____	
After 2 days	0.01	80% of original mass = _____		80% of original volume = _____	
After 3 days					
After 4 days					
After 5 days					

c Continue adding extra rows to your table until the overall density goes above the density of air.

After how many days does the balloon fall to the floor?

6.3 Converting between metric units of area and volume

✔ Skill checker

Copy and complete the following.

① There are 100 cm in 1 metre.

To convert from metres to centimetres multiply by 100.

To convert from centimetres to metres _____ by 100.

Examples: 5.5 m = _____ cm

659 cm = _____ m

② There are 10 mm in 1 cm.

To convert from centimetres to millimetres _____ by 10.

To convert from millimetres to centimetres divide by _____.

Examples: 7.4 cm = _____ mm

25.9 mm = _____ cm

③ There are 1000 m in 1 km.

To convert from kilometres to metres _____ by 1000.

To convert from metres to kilometres _____ by _____.

Examples: 19 km = _____ m

25 700 m = _____ km

Units of area

Worked example

Converting 1 cm² to mm²

Look at this diagram. It shows there are 10 millimetres in 1 centimetre.

1 cm

Now look at this diagram showing 1 square centimetre (1 cm²).

1 cm

1 cm

It has been divided into square millimetres.

How many square millimetres make up one square centimetre?

Solution

There are ten rows of ten.

So there are 100 square millimetres in one square centimetre.

1 cm² = 100 mm²

To convert from square centimetres to square millimetres multiply by 10² or 100.

To convert from square millimetres to square centimetres divide by 10² or 100.

Converting between metric units of volume

Worked example

Converting 1 cm³ to mm³

Now look at this picture of 1 cubic centimetre (1 cm³).

1 cm
1 cm
1 cm

It has been divided into cubic millimetres.
How many cubic millimetres make up one cubic centimetre?

Solution

In the top layer (coloured orange) there are 100 cubic millimetres.

In the entire cube there are 10 layers of 100.

$$10 \times 100 = 1000$$

So there are 1000 mm³ in 1 cm³.

$$1 \text{ cm}^3 = 1000 \text{ mm}^3$$

To convert from cubic centimetres to cubic millimetres multiply by 10^3 or 1000.
To convert from cubic millimetres to cubic centimetres divide by 10^3 or 1000.

Worked example

a   How many centimetres make up one metre?

b   How many square centimetres make up one square metre?

c   How many cubic centimetres make up one cubic metre?

d   How many square centimetres make up five square metres?

e   How many cubic centimetres make up five cubic metres?

Solution

a $1 \text{ m} = 100 \text{ cm}$

b $1 \text{ m}^2 = 10\,000 \text{ cm}^2$ (ten thousand) ← *Because $100^2 = 10\,000$*

c $1 \text{ m}^3 = 1\,000\,000 \text{ cm}^3$ (one million) ← *Because $100^3 = 1\,000\,000$*

d   There are 10 000 cm² in one square metre.

   So, to convert from square metres to square centimetres multiply by 10 000.

   $5 \times 10\,000 = 50\,000$

   There are 50 000 cm² in 5 m².

e   There are 1 000 000 cm³ in one cubic metre.

   So, to convert from cubic metres to cubic centimetres multiply by 1 000 000.

   $5 \times 1\,000\,000 = 5\,000\,000$

   So there are 5 000 000 cm³ in 5 m³.

Worked example

a   Convert an area of 0.07 m² to cm².

b   Convert a volume of 168 000 cm³ to m³.

Solution

a $1 \text{ m}^2 = 10\,000 \text{ cm}^2$

   $0.07 \times 10\,000 = 700$

   So 0.07 m² = 700 cm²

b $1 \text{ m}^3 = 1\,000\,000 \text{ cm}^3$

   $168\,000 \div 1\,000\,000 = 0.168$

   So 168 000 cm³ = 0.168 m³

Summary

	To convert
1 cm = 10 mm	From cm to mm: multiply by 10.
	From mm to cm: divide by 10.
$1 \, cm^2 = 100 \, mm^2$	From cm^2 to mm^2: multiply by 100.
	From mm^2 to cm^2: divide by 100. ⬚ 100 is 10^2
$1 \, cm^3 = 1000 \, mm^3$	From cm^3 to mm^3: multiply by 1000.
	From mm^3 to cm^3: divide by 1000. ⬚ 1000 is 10^3
1 m = 100 cm	From m to cm: multiply by 100.
	From cm to m: divide by 100.
$1 \, m^2 = 10\,000 \, cm^2$	From m^2 to cm^2: multiply by 10 000.
	From cm^2 to m^2: divide by 10 000. ⬚ 10 000 is 100^2
$1 \, m^3 = 1\,000\,000 \, cm^3$	From m^3 to cm^3: multiply by 1 000 000.
	From cm^3 to m^3: divide by 1 000 000. ⬚ 1 000 000 is 100^3
1 km = 1000 m	From km to m: multiply by 1000.
	From m to km: divide by 1000.
$1 \, km^2 = 1\,000\,000 \, m^2$	From km^2 to m^2: multiply by 1 000 000.
	From m^2 to km^2: divide by 1 000 000. ⬚ 1 000 000 is 1000^2
$1 \, km^3 = 1\,000\,000\,000 \, m^3$	From km^3 to m^3: multiply by 1 000 000 000.
	From m^3 to km^3: divide by 1 000 000 000. ⬚ 1000^3

6.3 Now try these

Band 1 questions

1 True or false?

Correct any false statements.

  a   1 cm = 10 mm   **b** $1 \, cm^2 = 10 \, mm^2$ **c** $1 \, cm^3 = 10 \, mm^3$

  d   1 m = 100 cm   **e** $1 \, m^2 = 100 \, cm^2$ **f** $1 \, m^3 = 100 \, cm^3$

  g   1 km = 1000 m   **h** $1 \, km^2 = 1000 \, m^2$ **i** $1 \, km^3 = 1000 \, m^3$

2 Copy and complete each statement. The first one has been done for you.

  a $4 \, m^2 = 40\,000 \, cm^2$ **b** $60 \, m^2 = $ _____ cm^2 **c**   _____ $cm^2 = 400 \, mm^2$

  d $0.1 \, km^2 = $ _____ m^2 **e** $3 \, m^3 = $ _____ cm^3 **f** $55 \, m^3 = $ _____ cm^3

  g   _____ $cm^3 = 250 \, mm^3$ **h** $9.3 \, km^3 = $ _____ m^3

3 The school playground is 500 square metres. How many square centimetres is this?

4 A shipping container can hold 50 cubic metres of cargo. How many cubic centimetres is this?

5 Convert each of these quantities into the units given.

   a   78 mm² into cm²   **b**   1650 cm² into m²   **c**   26 000 mm² into cm²

   d   1 350 000 m² into km²   **e**   6400 mm² into cm²   **f**   1900 cm² into m²

6 Jake has been asked to paint three red squares on the school playground for a game.

Each square should measure 1 metre by 1 metre.

How many square centimetres of paint does Jake use?

7 **a**   Find the volume of each of these cuboids in cubic centimetres.

   b   Convert your answers to cubic millimetres.

8 Priti wants to carpet two rectangular rooms.

One of the rooms measures 3.5 m by 1.8 m.

The other is 480 cm by 290 cm.

How many square metres of carpet will she need?

9 A swimming pool is 2 m deep and has a base area of 435 m².

   a   Find the volume of the pool in m³.

   b   Find the volume of the pool in cm³.

10 A volcano erupts.

3.2 cubic kilometres of the mountain is blown away by the blast.

What is this in cubic metres?

Band 3 questions

11 The edge of one dice is 1.2 cm in length.

   a   Find the volume of one dice in cubic centimetres.

   b   Find the volume of one dice in cubic millimetres.

   c   Find the volume of three dice in cubic millimetres.

Key Stage 3 Mastering Mathematics: Book 3

⑫ Reuben's homework is below. There is one mistake in each of his answers.

Can you correct his work?

Question 1. Convert 5.8 m² to cm²

Step 1   1 m = 100 cm

1 m² = 100 × 100 × 100 = 1 000 000 cm²

Step 2   5.8 m² = 5.8 × 1 000 000 = 5 800 000 cm²

Question 2. Convert 152 mm³ to cm³

Step 1   1 cm = 10 mm

1 cm³ = 10 × 10 × 10 = 1000 mm³

Step 2   152 mm³ = 152 × 1000 = 152 000 cm³

⑬ Convert each of these measurements into the units given.

  a   1.2 m² into mm²   b   0.001 km² into cm²   c   50 million mm² into m²

  d   613 000 000 cm² into km²   e   0.000 04 km² into mm²   f   71 550 mm² into m²

⑭ Convert each of these measurements into the units given.

  a   4 million mm³ into km³   b   0.0002 m³ into mm³   c   875 cm³ into km³

  d   18 450 mm³ into m³   e   27 cm³ into m³   f   0.001 69 km³ into mm³

⑮ The table gives the volumes of three 3-D shapes.

  a   Which shape has the largest surface area? Show working to explain your answer.

  b   Which shape has the largest volume? Show working to explain your answer.

Shape	Surface area	Volume
A	70 m²	1.15×10^7 cm³
B	750 000 cm²	8.96 m³
C	65 000 000 mm²	9.25×10^9 mm³

Key words

Here is a list of the key words you met in this chapter.

Centimetre   Compound measure   Density   Kilometre
Mass   Metre   Metric unit Millimetre
Speed   Volume

Use the glossary at the back of this book to check any you are unsure about.

Review exercise: using measures

Band 1 questions

1 **a** Convert $4\frac{1}{4}$ minutes to seconds.

    b Convert 3.25 hours to minutes.

2 **a** Patrick walks 16 km in 4 hours. What is his average speed?

    b Aoife travels by train a distance of 329 km in 3 hours 30 minutes. Work out the train's average speed in kilometres per hour.

    c Adam drives 120 miles in 1 hour 45 minutes. Find Adam's average speed.

3 The distance from London to Budapest is 1450 km.

A flight from London to Budapest takes 4 hours. At what average speed does the aeroplane fly?

4 A train travels 440 km in 2 hours 20 minutes.

Find the average speed of the train in km/h.

5 Convert each of these quantities into the units given.

    a $0.003\,km^3$ into m^3 **b** $17\,cm^3$ into mm^3 **c** $0.6\,m^3$ into cm^3

    d $0.236\,km^3$ into m^3 **e** $0.000\,054\,cm^3$ into mm^3

Band 2 questions

6 Ivan and Sue are travelling from their homes to the same meeting.

Ivan leaves his home at 08:00. He travels 35 miles at an average speed of 28 miles per hour.

Sue leaves her home at 07:10. She travels 48 miles in 2 hours.

    a How long does it take Ivan to reach the meeting?

    b At what speed does Sue travel?

    c Who travels fastest?

    d Who reaches the meeting first?

7 The volume of a gold chain is $5\,cm^3$. The density of gold is $19.3\,g/cm^3$. Find the mass of this chain.

8 A cheese has a density of 1.2 grams per cubic centimetre and a mass of 360 g. Find the volume of this block of cheese.

9 The table below shows the density, mass and volume of three different objects.

Copy and complete the table, giving the correct units for each number.

Object	Mass	Volume	Density
A	30 kg	$1200\,cm^3$	
B		$220\,m^3$	$85\,g/m^3$
C	10.2 g		$15\,g/cm^3$

10 The diagram shows a marble paperweight in the shape of a hemisphere. It has a radius of 4 cm.

    a Find the volume of the hemisphere using the formula $V = \frac{2}{3}\pi r^3$ where r is the radius.

    b The density of marble is 2.7 g/cm³.

       Calculate the mass of the paperweight.

       Give your answer correct to 3 significant figures.

11 An aeroplane flies at 1080 kilometres per hour.

    a How far would it travel, at this speed, in

       i 6 minutes   **ii** 1 minute   **iii** 15 seconds   **iv** 5 seconds?

    b Using the fact that 5 miles is approximately 8 kilometres, convert the aeroplane's speed into miles per hour.

12 **a** Find the area of each of these rectangles in square centimetres.

    b Convert your answers to square millimetres.

13 **a** Find the volume of each of these cuboids in cubic centimetres.

    b Convert your answers to cubic millimetres.

⑭ The block of wood shown has a volume of 1120 cm³ and a mass of 840 grams.

The density of water is 1 gram per cm³.

Would the block of wood float in a large tub of water? Explain your answer.

Band 3 questions

⑮ Gwyneth and Alun go on a cycling holiday to Bufi's Rock, shown on the map.

It is a small island and they cycle around it from Friday to Monday.

They keep a record of their journeys, but they forget to fill in some of the information.

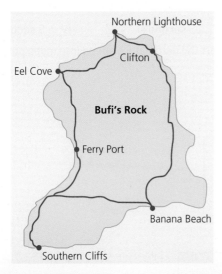

	From	To	Distance (km)	Time	Average speed (km per h)
Friday	Ferry Port	Southern Cliffs	18 km	1 h 15 mins	
	Southern Cliffs	Banana Beach		45 mins	25.3
Saturday	Banana Beach	Clifton	32.5 km		13
Sunday	Clifton	Northern Lighthouse		Half an hour	12.6
	Northern Lighthouse	Eel Cove	10.5 km		14
Monday	Eel Cove	Ferry Port	12 km	$\frac{3}{4}$ hour	

a Copy and complete the table.

b How far did Gwyneth and Alun cycle altogether?

c What was their average cycling speed for the whole trip?

d On which stretch of the journey did Gwyneth and Alun reach their highest speed?

Why do you think their speed was higher on this stretch?

CHAPTER 7

Equations, expressions and formulas

▶ Coming up...

- ◆ Solving equations (review)
- ◆ Using the laws of indices
- ◆ Expanding brackets
- ◆ Formulas

→ Magic square

a   Copy out the grid below, replacing each equation with its solution.

$c - 7 = 10$	$s - 9 = 15$	$6 + f = 7$	$p + 5 = 13$	
$k + 8 = 31$		$10x = 70$	$3n = 42$	
$5r = 20$			$g - 8 = 12$	$z + 15 = 37$
$g - 2 = 8$		$t - 10 = 9$	$10j = 210$	$14h = 42$
$12y = 132$	$\dfrac{p}{3} = 6$	$\dfrac{a}{5} = 5$		$4h = 36$

The solutions to these equations form a **magic square**. The rows, columns and diagonals all add up to the same total.

b   What is this total?

c   Can you make up some equations that could be used in the empty boxes to complete the magic square?

✔ Skill checker

Find the number that each symbol represents.

The numbers given are the row and column totals.

✓	🚲	🚲	**23**
✓	🛡	🛡	**21**
✓	🚲	🛡	**22**
33	**17**	**16**	

✦	●	🕷	🚌	**23**
●	🚌	🕷	⊘	**16**
✦	🕷	🕷	🕷	**35**
20	**15**	**27**	**12**	

Solving equations with an unknown on one side

Remember that an **equation** says that one expression is equal to another.

For example:

$$12x + 6 = 30$$
$$32 - 5y = 22$$

> x and y are called **UNKNOWNS**.

Solving an equation means finding the value of the **unknown** that makes the equation true – this is the **solution** to the equation.

> The solution may be a positive whole number, a negative or a fraction.

You can use the **balance method** to solve an equation.

> Apply the same operation to both sides of the equation to keep it balanced.

Worked example

Solve:

a $12x + 6 = 30$

b $32 - 5y = 22$

Solution

a

$-6 \Big(\begin{array}{c} 12x + 6 = 30 \\ 12x = 24 \end{array} \Big) -6$

> Imagine a pair of old-fashioned scales, ⚖ ; to keep them balanced you add or subtract the same amount to both sides.

$\div 12 \Big(\begin{array}{c} 12x = 24 \\ x = 2 \end{array} \Big) \div 12$

> You can check your answer by substituting it back into the equation.
> $12 \times 2 + 6$
> $= 24 + 6$
> $= 30 \checkmark$

b Method 1

$$32 - 5y = 22$$

-32 ⟶ -32 ← Subtract 32 from both sides.

$$-5y = -10$$

$\div -5$ ⟶ $\div -5$ ← Divide both sides by –5.

$$y = 2$$

Check:
$32 - 5 \times 2 = 32 - 10 = 22$ ✓

Method 2

$$32 - 5y = 22$$

$+5y$ ⟶ $+5y$ ← Add 5y to both sides to make the y term positive.

$$32 = 22 + 5y$$

-22 ⟶ -22 ← Subtract 22 from both sides.

$$10 = 5y$$

$\div 5$ ⟶ $\div 5$ ← Divide both sides by 5.

$$y = 2$$

Worked example

Solve:

a $\dfrac{15}{c} = 5$ **b** $\dfrac{x}{8} - 2 = 3$

Solution

a

$$\dfrac{15}{c} = 5$$

$\times c$ ⟶ $\times c$ ← Multiply both sides by c to get the unknown in the numerator.

$$15 = 5c$$

$\div 5$ ⟶ $\div 5$ ← Divide both sides by 5.

$$c = 3$$

Check: $\dfrac{15}{3} = 5$ ✓

b

$$\dfrac{x}{8} - 2 = 3$$

$+2$ ⟶ $+2$ ← Add 2 to both sides.

$$\dfrac{x}{8} = 5$$

$\times 8$ ⟶ $\times 8$ ← Multiply both sides by 8.

$$x = 40$$

Check: $\dfrac{40}{8} - 2$

$= 5 - 2$

$= 3$ ✓

Worked example

You can use bar diagrams to help you solve equations.

Solve:

a $4x + 5 = 19$

b $4x + 7 = 2x + 23$

Solution

a

$x = 3.5$

b $4x + 7 = 2x + 23$

$x = 8$

Worked example

Solve these equations.

a $5(7x + 5) = 4(7x + 8)$

b $\dfrac{3}{5x - 1} = \dfrac{4}{2x + 1}$

Solution

a

$$5(7x + 5) = 4(7x + 8)$$

Expand the brackets on both sides.

$$35x + 25 = 28x + 32$$

Subtract $28x$ from both sides. Subtract the smaller x term to get a positive x term on one side.

$$35x + 25 - 28x = 32$$

$$35x - 28x = 32 - 25$$

Subtract 25 from both sides.

$$7x = 7$$

Simplify.

$$x = 1$$

b $\dfrac{3}{5x - 1} = \dfrac{4}{2x + 1}$

Multiply both sides by $(5x - 1)$:

$$3 = \frac{4(5x - 1)}{2x + 1}$$

Multiply both sides by $(2x + 1)$:

$$3(2x + 1) = 4(5x - 1)$$

This technique – multiplying by both denominators can be done in one step. It is known as cross-multiplying.

Proceed with the method used in part **a**. Expand the brackets.

$$6x + 3 = 20x - 4$$

Subtract $6x$ from both sides and add 4 to both sides.

$$3 + 4 = 20x - 6x$$

$$7 = 14x$$

$$x = \frac{7}{14} = \frac{1}{2}$$

Problem solving using equations

Worked example

One cinema ticket costs £c.

Bronagh buys five tickets and one large box of popcorn, which is £3.50.

She gets £4 change from £60.

a Write an equation for c and solve it to find the cost of one ticket.

b Check your answer.

Solution

a The price of one cinema ticket is c, so the cost of 5 tickets is $5c$.

The cost of the tickets and popcorn is $5c + 3.5$.

Bronagh gets £4 change from £60, so the total cost is £56.

$5c + 3.5 = 56$ ← Subtract 3.5 from both sides.

$5c = 52.5$ ← Divide both sides by 5.

$c = 10.5$

The cost of each ticket is £10.50. ← The final answer is an amount of money and must have 2 decimal places. In the working, however, this isn't necessary. The £ sign only needs to be given with the final answer.

b Check that Bronagh bought 5 tickets for £10.50 each and popcorn for £3.50:

$5 \times 10.5 + 3.5$

$= 52.5 + 3.5$

$= 56$

The amount she spends is £56, which agrees with her getting £4 change from £60.

Worked example

At the start of the week, Jamie and Holly both have the same amount of credit on their school meal cards. This week:

Jamie has 5 school meals and has £1 credit left.

Holly has 2 school meals and has £8.80 credit left.

a Find the cost of one school meal.

b How much credit did Jamie and Holly start with?

Solution

a Let c represent the cost of one meal in pence. Work in pence because whole numbers are easier to work with.

Jamie's credit = Holly's credit

$5c + 100 = 2c + 880$

$3c + 100 = 880$

$3c = 780$

$c = 260$

So a school meal costs 260p or £2.60.

b Substitute $c = 260$ into the expression for Jamie's credit.

$5c + 100 = 5 \times 260 + 100$

$\qquad\qquad = 1400$

So Jamie's starting credit was 1400p or £14.

Check that Holly's credit is also 1400p:

$2c + 880 = 2 \times 260 + 880$

$\qquad\qquad = 1400$

Activity

Gulnaz has got her maths homework wrong.

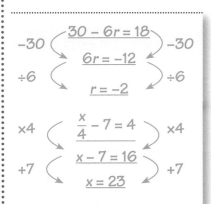

▶ How can you show Gulnaz that she has the wrong answers without solving the equations?

▶ Where has Gulnaz gone wrong?

▶ Work out the correct solutions to both equations.

7.1 Now try these

Band 1 questions

1 Solve these equations.

Show a check for **one** of your answers by substituting into the equation.

a $m + 4 = 11$

b $p - 6 = 10$

c $5 + d = 7$

d $y - 8 = 22$

e $4b = 12$

f $\dfrac{d}{2} = 3$

g $-4j = 12$

h $\dfrac{1}{2}x = 5$

i $\dfrac{x}{2} = \dfrac{5}{2}$

j $\dfrac{2}{3}x = 8$

2 Solve these equations.

Show a check for **one** of your answers by substituting into the equation.

a $2a + 3 = 5$

b $4d + 1 = 9$

c $2 + 2c = 8$

d $6c + 2 = 20$

e $6m + 4 = 16$

f $3d - 2 = 10$

g $2k - 10 = 8$

h $7 - 4l = 15$

i $6 - 2m = 0$

j $18 - 5p = 8$

3 Solve these equations.

Show a check for **one** of your answers by substituting into the equation.

a $\dfrac{x}{6} + 3 = 9$

b $3 = 4 - \dfrac{4}{p}$

c $4 + \dfrac{d}{3} = 19$

d $\dfrac{7}{q} - 24 = 4$

e $\dfrac{2}{f} - 7 = 3$

f $\dfrac{3}{a} + 4 = 10$

4 Solve each of these equations.

Show a check for **one** of your answers by substituting into the equation.

a $2r = 4.2$

b $s + 6.2 = 11$

c $5.4 = 8 - t$

d $4u - 5.6 = 10$

e $9.5 = 7.1 + 3y$

f $15 - 3n = 1.2$

Band 2 questions

5 **a** Match each of these equations with its solution.

i $3x - 2 = 10$

ii $5x - 1 = 24$

iii $4x + 11 = 17$

iv $2x + 5 = 10$

v $3x - 33 = 0$

$x = 5$	$x = 1\dfrac{1}{2}$	$x = 3$	$x = 4$	$x = 11$	$x = 2\dfrac{1}{2}$

b Which value of x is not used?

Write an equation with this value of x as its solution.

6 Jo has a pencils and Humza has b pencils.

Write in words the meaning of each of these equations.

The first one has been done for you.

   a $a + b = 12$ In total Jo and Humza have 12 pencils

   b $a - b = 4$

   c $a = 8$

   d $a = 2b$

7 Tim is buying some fish and chips in Calais.

Chips €1   Fish €

He pays €13 for three portions of fish and four portions of chips.

   a   Write down an equation to show this information.

       Use f to represent the cost of one portion of fish.

   b   Solve your equation to work out the price of one portion of fish.

   c   Check your answer.

8 Steve buys five pens in a shop for £1.20.

   a   Write an equation for this information using p pence as the cost of one pen.

   b   Solve your equation to find the cost of one pen.

Band 3 questions

9 Three prizes are given from a prize fund, with these conditions.

   ● The first prize is twice the third prize.

   ● The second prize is £5 more than the third prize.

   a   Find the values of the prizes when the total prize money is:

       i   £65   **ii**   £37.

   b   It is decided that the first prize must be at least £5 more than the second prize.

       Investigate the total prize money needed to meet all three conditions.

10 Both of these rectangles have a perimeter of 30 cm.

   a

   b

Find the length and width of each rectangle.

11 Each obtuse angle of this parallelogram is 32° more than each acute angle.

Let one obtuse angle be x.

Form an equation for x and solve it.

Find all the angles of the parallelogram.

12 Sunita has 11 metres of wire netting.

She says, 'I'm making a run for my guinea pig. I'll make it against the garden wall.'

She makes the run 3 metres wide.

The length of the run is x metres.

Form an equation for x and solve it.

13 Solve these equations by filling in the blanks on the bar diagrams.

a $3x + 7 = 31$

b $5x + 8 = 23$

14 Write down using algebra all the steps in the solution of the equation below.

$5x + 7 = 3x + 29$

15 Solve these equations.

Show a check for **one** of your answers by substituting into the equation.

a $2n + 1 = n + 3$

b $3b - 2 = 4 + b$

c $5k - 1 = 2k + 2$

d $4m - 3 = 5 + 2m$

e $10 + 2f = 15 - 3f$

16 Solve these equations by expanding the brackets first.

Choose **one** of your solutions to check by substituting back into the original equation.

a $4(x + 1) = 28$

b $4(a + 2) = 18$

c $5(b - 7) = 16$

d $10(7 - c) = 26$

e $13 = 5(2d - 4)$

f $6(3e + 5) = 14$

17 Jenny and Simon are both thinking of numbers.

Jenny says:	Simon says:
I think of a number.	I think of a number.
I multiply by 6.	I double it.
I add 7.	I subtract 6.
My answer is 19.	My answer is 18.

  a   **i**   Write down an equation for Jenny's number.

        ii   Solve your equation.

  b   **i**   Write down an equation for Simon's number.

        ii   What number was Simon thinking of?

18 Jamie and Holly are allowed the same amount of screen time one afternnon.

Jamie spends 1 hour playing computer games and watches some TV.

Holly only watches TV. She watches TV for four times longer than Jamie.

  a   How long does Jamie spend watching TV?

  b   How long does Holly spend watching TV?

19 Jack says:

> One small tile weighs $\frac{1}{2}$ kilogram.
> Eight small tiles and 6 large tiles weigh 16 kg.
> What is the weight of one large tile?

Write an equation to solve Jack's puzzle.

20 Solve these equations by expanding the brackets first.

Show a check for **one** of your answers by substituting into the equation.

  a $7x + 4 = 4(3x + 1)$

  b $2(x + 4) = 5(x + 1)$

  c $5(7x + 7) = 7(4x + 6)$

21 Solve these equations by cross-multiplying first.

  a $\dfrac{1}{2x + 4} = \dfrac{1}{x + 1}$

  b $\dfrac{3}{6x + 9} = \dfrac{4}{7x + 7}$

> These are harder to check. For one of the equations, substitute your answer into both sides of the equation.

  c $\dfrac{6}{4x + 1} = \dfrac{5}{5x - 5}$

7.2 Using the laws of indices

✔ Skill checker

Write the following in index form.

The first one has been done for you.

  a $6 \times 6 \times 6 \times 6 \times 6 = 6^5$ **b** $5 \times 5 \times 5 \times 5 \times 5 \times 5$ **c** 4×4

  d $3 \times 3 \times 3$ **e** $8 \times 8 \times 8 \times 8$ **f** $10 \times 10 \times 10 \times 10 \times 10 \times 10$

The laws of indices

$$a^n = a \times a \times a \times \dots \times a$$

So, for example:

$$a^5 = a \times a \times a \times a \times a$$

5 factors of a

These are the **laws of indices**:

Law 1 $a^x \times a^y = a^{x+y}$

> For example $a^2 \times a^3 = a^{2+3} = a^5$
> $a^2 \times a^3 = (a \times a) \times (a \times a \times a) = a \times a \times a \times a \times a = a^5$

Law 2 $a^x \div a^y = a^{x-y}$

> For example $a^5 \div a^3 = a^{5-3} = a^2$
> $a^5 \div a^3 = \dfrac{a \times a \times a \times a \times a}{a \times a \times a} = \dfrac{a \times a}{1} = a^2$

Law 3 $(a^x)^y = a^{xy}$

> For example $(a^2)^3 = a^{2 \times 3} = a^6$
> $(a^2)^3 = (a \times a) \times (a \times a) \times (a \times a) = a^6$

Law 4 $a^1 = a$

Law 5 $a^0 = 1$

> For example $5^1 = 5$
> and $3^0 = 1$
> $3^3 = 3 \times 3 \times 3 = 27$
> $3^2 = 3 \times 3 = 9$ — Subtracting 1 from the index means dividing by 3.
> $3^1 = 3$
> Following this pattern:
> $3^0 = 1$

Worked example

Simplify these expressions.

a $2a^3b^7 \times 4ab^5$

b $\dfrac{12a^4b^3}{4ab^2}$

c $(2c^2)^3$

Solution

a First, work out the numbers: $2 \times 4 = 8$

Next use the rules of indices: $a^x \times a^y = a^{x+y}$

$a^3 \times a = a^3 \times a^1 = a^4$

$\quad b^7 \times b^5 = b^{12}$

So

$2a^3b^7 \times 4ab^5 = 8a^4b^{12}$

b First, work out the numbers: $12 \div 4 = 3$

Next use the rules of indices: $a^x \div a^y = a^{x-y}$

$\dfrac{a^4}{a} = \dfrac{a^4}{a^1} = a^3$

$\dfrac{b^3}{b^2} = b^1 = b$

So

$\dfrac{12a^4b^3}{4ab^2} = 3a^3b$

c First, work out the numbers: $2^3 = 8$

Next use the rules of indices: $(a^x)^y = a^{xy}$

$(c^2)^3 = c^6$

So $(2c^2)^3 = 8c^6$

7.2 Now try these

Band 1 questions

Fluency

1 Write these in index form.

The first one has been done for you.

a $a \times a = a^2$

b $b \times b \times b \times b$

c $c \times c \times c \times c \times c$

d $d \times d \times d$

e $f \times f \times f \times f \times f \times f$

f $g \times g \times g \times g \times g \times g$

2 Write these expressions as single powers.

a $a^6 \times a^3$

b $b^7 \times b^2$

c $c^5 \times c^4$

d $d^{50} \times d$

e $e^6 \div e^4$

f $f^6 \div f^2$

g $g^{10} \div g^{10}$

h $h^{50} \div h^{49}$

i $i^3 \times i^4$

j $j^2 \times j^2$

k $k^{15} \times k^{20}$

l $l^5 \times l$

m $m^5 \div m^2$

n $n^5 \div n$

o $p^{50} \times p^{49}$

p $q^{100} \div q^{100}$

Reasoning

3 Copy and complete these algebra pyramids.

The value in each brick is found by multiplying the values in the two bricks underneath it.

a

b

4 Copy and complete these algebra pyramids.

The value in each brick is found by multiplying the values in the two bricks underneath it.

a

b

c

Band 2 questions

Fluency

5 Jake simplifies $4x^3 \times 5x^2$ like this:

$$4x^3 \times 5x^2 = 4 \times 5 \times x^3 \times x^2$$
$$= 20x^5$$

Use Jake's method to simplify these expressions.

a $6a^3 \times 3a^5$

b $9b^7 \times 6b^5$

c $3c^5 \times 2c^9$

d $30d^{40} \times 20d^{60}$

6 Simplify these expressions.

a $2a^5 \times 5a^7$

b $3b^4 \times 2b$

c $6c^3 \times 2c^{10}$

d $5d^4 \times 2d^0$

7 Simplify these expressions.

a $5a^2b \times 3ab$

b $7bc^2 \times 6b^5c^3$

c $4c^3d^2 \times 3cd$

d $3de \times 2d^2e^6$

e $9ef^6 \times 4e^2f^3$

f $10f^{100}g^{50} \times 7f^{75}g^{25}$

8 Laila simplifies $\dfrac{12b^5}{4b^3}$ like this:

$$\dfrac{12}{4} = 3$$

$$\dfrac{b^5}{b^3} = b^2$$

So $\dfrac{12b^5}{4b^3} = 3b^2$

Use Laila's method to simplify these expressions.

a $\dfrac{15a^6}{3a^4}$ **b** $\dfrac{24b^8}{8b^3}$ **c** $\dfrac{150c^{27}}{15c^9}$ **d** $\dfrac{125d^{10}}{5d}$

e $\dfrac{3ef^3}{ef^2}$ **f** $\dfrac{12fg^2}{3fg}$ **g.** $\dfrac{8g^{10}}{4g^{10}}$ **h** $\dfrac{4gh^6}{2gh^0}$

9 Simplify these expressions involving negative indices.

a $a^{-3} \times a^5$ **b** $b^7 \times b^{-2}$ **c** $c^{-3} \times c^{-2}$

d $d^{-4} \div d^5$ **e** $e^6 \div e^{-2}$ **f** $f^{-5} \div f^{-3}$

> The usual rules of indices can be used with negative indices.

10 Simplify these expressions.

a $3a^{-2}b \times 3ab$ **b** $7bc^2 \times 3b^5c^{-3}$ **c** $-4c^{-3}d^2 \times 5c^{-2}d^{-3}$

d $10d^{-2}e^{-1} \times 2d^{-4}e^{-7}$ **e** $2ef^{-6} \times 2e^{-2}f^{-3}$

11 Simplify these expressions.

a $\dfrac{18a^{-6}}{3a^2}$ **b** $\dfrac{40b^6}{8b^{-2}}$ **c** $\dfrac{50c^{-7}}{5c^{-3}}$ **d** $\dfrac{12d^{-8}}{2d}$ **e** $\dfrac{6ef^{-1}}{3ef^{-2}}$

12 Simplify these expressions.

a $(x^3)^4$ **b** $(a^{-2})^3$ **c** $(2c^2)^3$ **d** $(y^3)^{-5}$

e $(z^{-2})^{-6}$ **f** $(3d^{-2})^2$ **g** $(2c^2)^3 \times 7c^2$ **h** $(3e^4)^{-2} \times 2e^2f^2$

7.3 Expanding brackets

✔ Skill checker

A	D	E	G	I
$16x - 8$	$25 - 15x$	$5x + 10$	$12x + 32$	$8x + 12$
L	N	P	R	S
$36x + 24$	$24x + 12$	$3 - 3x$	$3x - 18$	$7x + 7$

Expand the brackets and write down the corresponding letter from the table.
What countries do you spell?

① $5(2 + x)$, $3(4 + 8x)$, $4(3x + 8)$, $2(18x + 12)$, $2(8x - 4)$, $4(3 + 6x)$, $5(5 - 3x)$

② $4(2x + 3)$, $3(x - 6)$, $5(2 + x)$, $3(8 + 12x)$, $8(2x - 1)$, $6(2 + 4x)$, $-5(3x - 5)$

③ $7(1 + x)$, $3(1 - x)$, $4(4x - 2)$, $2(4x + 6)$, $12(2x + 1)$

④ $2(6x + 16)$, $-3(6 - x)$, $-5(-x - 2)$, $-5(-2 - x)$, $2(12x + 6)$, $3(12x + 8)$, $-8(1 - 2x)$, $-6(-2 - 4x)$, $5(-3x + 5)$

Expanding a single set of brackets

Worked example

Expand $x(x + 5)$.

> The phrases **expanding brackets** and **multiply brackets out** mean the same thing.

Solution

$x(x + 5)$
$= (x \times x) + (x \times 5)$
$= x^2 + 5x$

> Multiply x outside the brackets by everything inside.

Expanding double brackets

When you expand a pair of brackets you multiply every term in the second bracket by every term in the first bracket then simplify your answer.

$(x + 5)(x - 3)$

So $(x + 5)(x - 3) = (x \times x) + (x \times -3) + (5 \times x) + (5 \times -3)$
$= x^2 - 3x + 5x - 15$
$= x^2 + 2x - 15$

You can remember FOIL:

F stands for First: Multiply the first term in each set of brackets: $x \times x = x^2$

O stands for Outer: Multiply the outer terms: $x \times -3 = -3x$

I stands for Inner: Multiply the inner terms: $5 \times x = 5x$

L stands for Last: Multiply the last terms: $5 \times -3 = -15$

Add these four terms:

$x^2 - 3x + 5x - 15$
$= x^2 + 2x - 15$

Alternatively, you can use a multiplication grid:

	x	5
x	x^2	$5x$
-3	$-3x$	-15

$x^2 - 3x + 5x - 15$
$= x^2 + 2x - 15$

Worked example

Expand the following:

a $(x-4)(x-2)$

b $(x+4)^2$

c $(x-4)(x+2)(x+3)$

Solution

a **Method 1:** Using FOIL to expand $(x-4)(x-2)$.

First: $x \times x = x^2$

Outer: $x \times -2 = -2x$

Inner: $-4 \times x = -4x$

Last: $-4 \times -2 = 8$

Add the four terms:

$(x-4)(x-2) = x^2 - 2x - 4x + 8$

$\qquad\qquad\quad = x^2 - 6x + 8$

Method 2: Using a grid.

	x	-4
x	x^2	$-4x$
-2	$-2x$	8

> Put the contents of one bracket along the top and the other down the side then multiply each pair.

> When you expand a pair of brackets, take care with the signs.

$(x-4)(x-2) = x^2 - 4x - 2x + 8$

$= x^2 - 6x + 8$

> Add the results.

b $(x+4)^2$ means $(x+4)$ multiplied by itself.

> You can use FOIL or the grid to help.

$(x+4)^2 = (x+4)(x+4)$

$= x^2 + 4x + 4x + 16$

$= x^2 + 8x + 16$

c **Step 1:** Expand $(x-4)(x+2)$.

$(x-4)(x+2) = x^2 - 4x + 2x - 8$

$= x^2 - 2x - 8$

Step 2: Multiply the result by $(x+3)$.

$(x^2 - 2x - 8)(x+3)$

You can use a grid to help you.

	x^2	$-2x$	-8
x	x^3	$-2x^2$	$-8x$
3	$3x^2$	$-6x$	-24

$(x^2 - 2x - 8)(x+3) = x^3 + 3x^2 - 2x^2 - 6x - 8x - 24$

$= x^3 + x^2 - 14x - 24$

Remember

FOIL only works when there are two terms inside each set of brackets, so it can't be used here.

7.3 Now try these

Band 1 questions

1 Expand the brackets.

  a $x(x-5)$ **b** $2x(x+2)$ **c** $x(3x-5)$ **d** $4x(2x+5)$

  e $x(5-x)$ **f** $2x(2+x)$ **g** $x(1-3x)$ **h** $4x(11+2x)$

2 You can use a grid to help you expand (multiply out) a pair of brackets.

  a **i** Copy and complete this grid to expand $(x+5)(x+4)$.

	x	4
x	x^2	
5		20

     ii Add together the four terms inside the grid and simplify your expression.

  b Use these grids to help you expand the expressions.

     i $(x+2)(x+3)$

	x	2
x		
3		

     ii $(x+2)(x+1)$

	x	2
x		
1		

     iii $(x+1)(x-2)$

	x	1
x		
-2		

     iv $(x-3)(x+2)$

	x	-3
x		
2		

3 The expression in the top brick of each of these algebra pyramids is found by multiplying together the expressions in the two bricks beneath it.

Copy and complete each algebra pyramid.

Expand and simplify the expression in each of the top bricks.

a

b

c

④ Expand these expressions.

   a $(x+2)(x+6)$ **b** $(x+3)(x+7)$ **c** $(x+2)(x-6)$ **d** $(x-3)(x-7)$

⑤ Expand the brackets in these expressions.

   Simplify your answers.

   a $(a+2)(a+3)$ **b** $(b+1)(b+4)$ **c** $(c-3)(c+5)$ **d** $(d+4)(d-6)$

   e $(e+7)(e-1)$ **f** $(f-3)(f-4)$ **g** $(g-2)(g+2)$

Band 2 questions

⑥ Vaya and Sarah have both expanded the expression $(b+3)^2$.

   Vaya says, 'The answer is b^2+9'.

   Sarah says, 'No, it is b^2+6b+9'.

   a Who is right?

   b How would you show the other person that she is wrong?

   c Expand and simplify these expressions.

      i $(n+3)^2$ **ii** $(x-3)^2$ **iii** $(y-30)^2$

⑦ **a** Expand $(x+5)^2$.

   b Use your answer to part **a** to work out 25^2.

      What value of x should you use?

   c Use this method to calculate:

      i 15^2 **ii** 105^2 **iii** 1005^2

   d Use a similar method to work out 52^2.

⑧ Meena's Dad poses her a problem.

   He says, 'Meena, what is $\left(3\frac{1}{2}\right)^2$?'

   Meena replies, 'That is easy, I have a special trick for squaring halves.

   One more than 3 is 4. You do 3 times 4 and then add $\frac{1}{4}$. The answer is $12\frac{1}{4}$.'

   a Is Meena correct?

   b Check Meena's method for these fractions.

      i $\left(1\frac{1}{2}\right)^2$ **ii** $\left(2\frac{1}{2}\right)^2$ **iii** $\left(5\frac{1}{2}\right)^2$ **iv** $\left(10\frac{1}{2}\right)^2$

   c By writing $\left(1\frac{1}{2}\right)^2$ as $\left(1+\frac{1}{2}\right)^2$ and multiplying out the brackets show how the rule works.

   d By using x to represent any positive integer, show this rule always works.

Band 3 questions

⑨ **a** Follow these instructions.

      Step 1: Think of two numbers that add up to 1.

      Step 2: Square the larger number and add this to the smaller number.

      Step 3: Square the smaller number and add this to the larger number.

   b Repeat for other pairs of values that add up to 1.

   c Use algebra to explain your results.

Hint

If one number is x, the other is $1-x$.

Problem solving

Reasoning

10 a Expand these expressions.

    i $(a+3)(a-3)$ **ii** $(a+b)(a-b)$

    iii $(2c+7)(2c-7)$ **iv** $\left(d-\dfrac{1}{2}\right)\left(d+\dfrac{1}{2}\right)$

    What do you notice?

b Expressions in the form $a^2 - b^2$ are often called the difference of two squares.

    Why do you think this is?

c Factorise these expressions.

    i $a^2 - 16$ **ii** $a^2 - 36$ **iii** $a^2 - 64$ **iv** $a^2 - 1$ **v** $a^2 - \dfrac{1}{9}$

d Show how you would use the difference of two squares to work out these calculations without using a calculator.

    i $26^2 - 16^2$ **ii** $378^2 - 376^2$ **iii** $1025^2 - 1024^2$

11 Find as many different expressions as you can for the blue area in this square.

Show algebraically that your expressions are equivalent.

12 Look at the diagram.

a What is the area of the large square, in terms of a and b?

    Expand the brackets in your expression for the area.

b **i** What is the area of the yellow square in terms of c?

    ii What is the area of one of the blue triangles, in terms of a and b?

    iii Using your answers from **bi** and **bii,** find a second expression for the area of the large square in terms of a, b and c.

c Now you should have two expressions for the area of the large square.

    Can you prove Pythagoras' theorem?

13 Copy and complete these algebra pyramids.

The expression in the top brick is found by multiplying the expressions in the two bricks underneath it.

What rules should you use to find the expressions in the bottom bricks?

a

b

$x^2 + 5x + 6$	
$(x+2)$	$(x+?)$

c

$x^2 + 8x + 12$	
$(x+2)$	?

d

e

$x^2 + 11x + 10$	
$(x+?)$	$(x+?)$

f

14 Look at this shape.

(x + 6) cm

(x + 3) cm

3 cm

(x + 4) cm

   a **i**   Divide the shape into two rectangles with a horizontal line.

       ii   Find the area of each rectangle in terms of x.

      iii Add these two expressions to find the total area of the shape in terms of x, simplifying your answer.

   b **i**   Divide the shape into two rectangles with a vertical line.

       ii   Find the area of each rectangle in terms of x.

      iii Add these two expressions to find the total area of the shape in terms of x, simplifying your answer.

   c Check that the simplified answers you got in parts **a** and **b** are the same.

15 Expand the following sets of brackets and simplify your answers.

   a $x(x + 1)(x + 2)$

   b $x(x - 2)(x + 4)$

   c $(x + 6)(x - 1)(x + 2)$

   d $(2x - 1)(x + 1)(x - 1)$

   e $(x - 1)(x + 1)(2x - 1)$

16 This pattern is called Pascal's triangle.

Each number in Pascal's triangle is the sum of the two numbers above it.

Pascal's triangle can be used to help you expand brackets.

For example, expanding $(x + 1)^2$ take the numbers from Row 2:

$(x + 1)^2 = 1x^2 + 2x + 1$

$= x^2 + 2x + 1$

Expanding $(x + 1)^3$ take the numbers from Row 3:

$(x + 1)^3 = 1x^3 + 3x^2 + 3x + 1$

$x^3 + 3x^2 + 3x + 1$

Use Pascal's triangle to expand $(x + 1)^4$.

			1				Row 0
		1		1			Row 1
	1		2		1		Row 2
1		3		3		1	Row 3
1	4		6		4	1	Row 4

1   5   10   10   5   1   Row 5

1   6   15   20   15   6   1   Row 6

7.4 Formulas

✔ Skill checker

The letters a to j have the values shown in the table.

a	b	c	d	e	f	g	h	i	j
1	2	3	4	5	6	7	8	9	10

① What is this part of the body?

   $bc; g - f; a + b; b^2 + a$

② What is this thing to wear?

   $j - h; a^2; \sqrt{f + j}; c + d; \dfrac{j}{b}$

③ What is this type of food?

   $\sqrt{d}; a + d; g - b; \sqrt{3j + f}$

Substituting into a formula

You can substitute numbers into formulas. These may include negative numbers and decimals.

Worked example

v^2 is the subject of the formula $v^2 = u^2 + 2as$.

Find v when $u = -3$, $a = 9.8$ and $s = 20$.

Solution

$v^2 = u^2 + 2as$

$v^2 = (-3)^2 + 2 \times 9.8 \times 20$ ← Substitute the values given into the formula.

$v^2 = 9 + 392$

$v^2 = 401$

$v = 20.02$ or -20.02 to 2 d.p. ← Square root both sides of the formula to find v. Remember that there are two answers when you square root a number, one positive and one negative.

Rearranging a formula

You can rearrange a formula to make another letter the subject.

You must do the same thing to both sides of the formula to get the variable you want by itself on one side of the formula. ← This is similar to solving an equation.

$v^2 = u^2 + 2as$

Make s the subject.

Subtract u^2 $u^2 + 2as = v^2$ Subtract u^2

   $2as = v^2 - u^2$

Divide by $2a$ $s = \dfrac{v^2 - u^2}{2a}$ Divide by $2a$

Make u the subject.

$u^2 + 2as = v^2$

Subtract $2as$ $u^2 = v^2 - 2as$ Subtract $2as$

Square root $u = \pm\sqrt{v^2 - 2as}$ Square root ← Remember the $\pm$ sign when taking the square root. On its own, the $\sqrt{}$ sign means only the positive root.

Substituting negative numbers into a formula

Worked example

Work out the value of a when $b = -2$ using the formula

$$a = \frac{3b^2 - 6}{b + 4}$$

Substitute -2 in place of b.

Remember

Take care when substituting a negative number into a formula.

Solution

$a = \dfrac{3(-2)^2 - 6}{(-2) + 4}$ $(-2)^2$ means -2×-2 which is equal to 4.

$a = \dfrac{3(4) - 6}{2}$

$a = \dfrac{6}{2} = 3$

Be careful squaring a negative number on the calculator.

Always keep the negative number in brackets, with the power of 2 outside the brackets.

Try these on the calculator:

The wrong way: -2^2 ✗   (Gives the answer -4)

The correct way: $(-2)^2$ ✓   (Gives the answer 4)

Working with formulas

Worked example

The area of this trapezium is $48\,\text{cm}^2$.

Work out the height of the trapezium.

Solution

The formula for the area of a trapezium is $A = \dfrac{1}{2}h(a+b)$ where

- a and b are the lengths of the parallel sides; and
- h is the distance between the parallel sides.

$$48 = \frac{1}{2}h(5+7)$$

> Substitute the values for A, a and b into the formula.

$$\frac{1}{2}h \times 12 = 48$$

> It is usual to work with the variable on the LHS of the equation.

$$6h = 48$$

$$h = 8$$

So the height of the trapezium is 8 cm.

Worked example

The formula for the perimeter of a rectangle is

$$P = 2(l+w)$$

Rearrange the formula to make l the subject.

Solution

Look at how Beth and David rearrange the formula. These methods are both correct.

🔑 Activity

Substitute the numbers below into the formulas given and complete the cross-number puzzle.

a	b	c	d	e	f	g	h	i	j
1	2	3	4	5	6	7	8	9	10

Across

1. $(de)^2 - 9$
3. $(j + e)^2$
5. eg
6. $a + 2a + 3a + 4a + 5a + 6a$
7. gh
9. $5d^2$
10. $gj^2 + 8$
11. e^2
12. $4(13 + j)$
14. $10d + 1$
15. $e(d + f + 1)$
17. $j(e + j) + c^2$
18. $2j^2 + 2j + 2$

Down

2. $100j - ei$
4. $b^2 e (j + 1)$
8. $100f + 10g + e$
9. $111h + 1$
11. $6f^2 - 1$
13. $2(e^3 + 1)$
14. $14c - 1$
16. $7h - d$

7.4 Now try these

Band 1 questions

1 Find the value of $4a + 9b - c$ when

a $a = 3, b = 3$ and $c = 4$

b $a = 4, b = -4$ and $c = 5$

c $a = 0.2, b = 0.3$ and $c = 0.4$

d $a = 0.1, b = -0.2$ and $c = 0$.

2 In rugby union, the formula to calculate the total score is

$S = 5t + 2c + 3g$

where t is the number of tries scored, c is the number of conversions and g is the number of goal kicks.

a   What is the total score when

   i $t = 2, c = 1$ and $g = 8$

   ii $t = 10, c = 7$ and $g = 12$

b   In one match, England score two tries, one conversion and four goal kicks.

Tonga score three tries, three conversions and one goal kick.

Who wins?

③ This swimming pool is a rectangle *l* metres long and *w* metres wide.

a Copy and complete this formula for the perimeter of the pool:

$P = \underline{\hspace{2cm}} + \underline{\hspace{2cm}}$

b Copy and complete this formula for the area of the surface of the pool in terms of *l* and *w*.

$A = \underline{\hspace{2cm}}$

c Find the perimeter and surface area of the pool when

   i $l = 11$ and $w = 2$ **ii** $l = 9$ and $w = 4$ **iii** $l = 7$ and $w = 6$

④ Make *x* the subject in each of these formulas.

  a $y = 2x$ **b** $y = \dfrac{x}{2}$ **c** $y = x + 3$ **d** $y = x - 3$

Band 2 questions

⑤ **a** Change the subject of this formula to *B*:

    $A = 180 - B - C$

b Change the subject of this formula to *w*:

    $P = 2(l + w)$

c Change the subject of this formula to *R*:

    $V = IR$

⑥ Jenny lets out holiday flats during the summer.

The formula she uses to work out the charge is

Cost = rate × number of weeks + deposit + £25 per person.

The rate is £275 per week and the deposit is £150.

a Write out the formula using *C* to stand for the cost, *W* for the number of weeks and *N* for the number of people.

b Find the cost when:

   i   four people stay for two weeks

   ii   two people stay for three weeks.

c Three people have £1050 to spend.

   How long can they stay?

⑦ Joe, Mary, Ben and Myra are trying to find the value of $5b^2 - 3c$ when $b = 4$ and $c = 2$.

They all get different answers.

Joe says, 'The answer is 34.'

Mary says, 'No, it's 48!'

Ben says, 'I think it's 74.'

Myra says, 'You are all wrong! It's 2884.'

Who has the right answer?

Explain where the others have gone wrong.

8 An electrician charges £15 per hour plus a call-out charge of £25.

    a   Write a formula for his total charge, £c, for a job lasting h hours.

    b   Calculate c when:

        i $h = 2$ **ii** $h = 3\frac{1}{2}$

    c   Rearrange your formula to make h the subject.

    d   Find how many hours he worked when his total charge is:

        i   £115   **ii**   £145   **iii**   £77.50.

9 A Greek mathematician named Hero showed that the area of a triangle, of sides a, b and c could be calculated using this formula.

$$A = \sqrt{s(s-a)(s-b)(s-c)}$$

where $s = \frac{1}{2}(a+b+c)$.

    a   Look at these two triangles.

         The side lengths are in centimetres.

         a   **b**

        i   Use Pythagoras' theorem to check that they are right-angled.

        ii   Use the formula $A = \frac{1}{2}bh$ to find their areas.

        iii   Check that Hero's formula gives the same answers.

    b   Now use Hero's formula to find the areas of these non-right-angled triangles:

        i $a = 4$ cm, $b = 6$ cm and $c = 8$ cm   **ii** $a = 6.7$ cm, $b = 9.3$ cm and $c = 12.9$ cm

10 The picture shows a model of a garden swing seat.

The frame is made out of thin wire.

The lengths are in centimetres.

Each end is in the shape of a right-angled triangle.

    a   Write down a formula for the perimeter P of each triangle.

    b   Write down a formula for the total length T of wire. Simplify your expression.

    c   The back, sides and seat are made out of cardboard.

         Write a formula for the area A of cardboard.

11 The path of an object orbiting the sun is an ellipse, not a circle.

The formula for the area of an ellipse is $A = \pi ab$ where a and b are the lengths shown in the diagram.

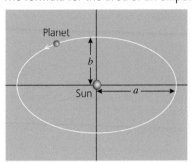

For Pluto, $a = 5.9 \times 10^9$ km and $b = 5.7 \times 10^9$ km. ← Pluto is no longer classed as a planet, but is a **dwarf planet**.

a Find the area inside Pluto's orbit.

b Compare this with the area of a circle of radius 5.8×10^9 km.

12 This tent frame is made from aluminium tubing.

The measurements are in metres.

The length x is called the 'size' of the tent.

a Write down the formula for the total length L of tubing needed.

b **i** The size of a tent is 1.8 m.

How much tubing is needed?

ii A tent uses 25 m of tubing.

What is its size?

iii A tent uses 30 m of tubing.

What is its size?

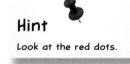

13 **a** Change the subject of this formula to h:

$V = \pi r^2 h$

b Change the subject of this formula to b:

$A = \frac{1}{2} h(a + b)$

c Change the subject of this formula to l:

$A = l^2$

14 Look at these three dot patterns.

Find a formula for the number of lines, l, joining m red dots to n blue dots.

How many lines come from each dot?

Hint

Look at the red dots.

Key words

Here is a list of the key words you met in this chapter.

Equation	Expand	Expression	Formula
Index	Indices	Substitute	

Use the glossary at the back of this book to check any you are unsure about.

Key Stage 3 Mastering Mathematics : Book 3

Problem solving

Fluency

Problem solving

Band 1 questions

1 Solve these equations.

Choose **one** of your answers to check by substituting into the equation.

  a $a + 11 = 15$ **b** $6 + b = 8$ **c** $x + 5 = 15$

  d $d - 7 = 13$ **e** $a - 4 = 4$ **f** $q - 5 = 15$

2 Solve these equations.

Choose **one** of your answers to check by substituting into the equation.

  a $999z + 999 = 999$ **b** $5x + 6 = 16$ **c** $3a - 7 = 14$

  d $10 + 3f = 19$ **e** $12 + 7g = 33$

3 Solve these equations.

Choose **one** of your answers to check by substituting into the equation.

  a $\dfrac{x}{3} = 20$ **b** $\dfrac{3}{4}x = 100$ **c** $\dfrac{g}{5} = 5$ **d** $\dfrac{t}{9} = 4$ **e** $\dfrac{x}{2} = 5$

  f $10 + \dfrac{f}{2} = 14$ **g** $\dfrac{m}{3} - 11 = 21$ **h** $2 - \dfrac{a}{3} = 6$ **i** $3 - \dfrac{m}{2} = 15$ **j** $4 + \dfrac{a}{5} = 16$

4 **a** Change the subject of this formula to h:

      $V = lwh$

  b Change the subject of this formula to a:

      $m = \dfrac{a + b + c + d}{4}$

5 Simplify these expressions.

  a $a^3 \times a^4$ **b** $3b^5 \times 4b$ **c** $2c^3 \times 5c^4$

6 Simplify these expressions.

  a $a^4b \times ab$ **b** $2bc^3 \times 5b^2c^5$

Band 2 questions

7 Expand the brackets in these expressions.

  a $(a + 3)(a + 5)$ **b** $(b + 5)(b + 5)$ **c** $(c + 3)(c - 2)$

  d $(d - 2)(d - 1)$ **e** $(e - 1)(e + 1)$ **f** $(f - 3)(f - 3)$

8 Look at the isosceles triangle shown.

  a Two of the angles are $75°$.

      Form an equation and solve it to find the size of the third angle marked x.

  b The perimeter of the triangle is $11\,\text{cm}$.

      The two equal sides are $4\,\text{cm}$ in length.

      Form an equation and solve it to find the length of the base.

9 Kate buys two apples, at 24p each, and four bananas.

She spends £1.28 altogether.

  a Write an equation for this information, using b pence as the cost of one banana.

  b Solve your equation to find the cost of one banana.

Fluency   Reasoning   Problem solving

10 The length of a rectangle is 4 times its width.

The perimeter is 50 cm.

Find the area of the rectangle.

11 Peter is four times as old as his daughter Tara.

In five years' time their ages will total 50 years.

a Copy and complete this table

	Peter's age	Tara's age
Now	$4x$	x
In 5 years		

b Form an equation and solve it.

c State Peter's and Tara's present ages.

Band 3 questions

12 Paul thinks of a number, x.

> I think of a number.
> I multiply it by 4 and add 2.
> The answer is four more than twice my number.

a Write down expressions for:

   i 'multiply my number by 4 and add 2'

   ii 'four more than twice my number'.

b Form an equation.

c Solve your equation to find Paul's number.

13 Solve these equations by filling in the blanks on the bar diagrams.

a $2x + 7 = 19$

b $4x + 6 = 2x + 39$

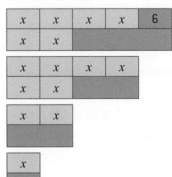

14 Solve these equations.

a $3p - 2 = 2p + 1$

b $12 - 3c = 18 - 5c$

c $7x - 8 = 4x + 4$

d $2x + 9 = 3x - 5$

e $15 - x = 23 - 2x$

15 Simplify these expressions.

a $\dfrac{12a^2}{2a}$　　　　　　　　**b** $\dfrac{b^8c^4}{b^5c^2}$　　　　　　　　**c** $\dfrac{24b^6c^3}{4b^4c^3}$

16 Solve these equations.

a $6(5x+4)=3(4x+2)$　　　　　　**b** $2(5x+7)=4(2x+7)$

c $3(6x+2)=10(5x+7)$　　　　　　**d** $2(6x+10)=5(4x+8)$

e $\dfrac{6}{5x+9}=\dfrac{10}{9x-3}$　　　　　　**f** $\dfrac{1}{8x+1}=\dfrac{1}{10x+1}$

g $\dfrac{10}{4x+10}=\dfrac{8}{3x+9}$

17 Find the value of $2x^2-y$ when:

a $x=1$ and $y=2$　　**b** $x=2$ and $y=6$　　**c** $x=5$ and $y=10$　　**d** $x=10$ and $y=1$

18 **a** Change the subject of this formula to r:

$A=\pi r^2$

b Change the subject of this formula to V:

$x=\sqrt[3]{V}$

c Change the subject of this formula to h:

$t=\sqrt{\dfrac{h}{5}}$

Band 1 questions

Fluency

1. Solve these equations.

   Choose **one** of your answers to check by substituting your answer into the equation.

   a $11j - 11 = 22$ **b** $5d + 3 = 18$ **c** $2s - 6 = 4$ **d** $2n - 4 = 8$ **e** $6b + 5 = 17$

2. Solve these equations.

   Choose **one** of your answers to check by substituting your answer into the equation.

   a $4c - 5 = 11$ **b** $2x + 5 = 45$ **c** $3y - 8 = 28$ **d** $9z + 35 = 125$ **e** $2b - 7 = 7$

   f $100c + 500 = 1500$ **g** $3t - 12 = 3$ **h** $4k + 8 = 24$ **i** $6h - 5 = 1$

3. Solve these equations.

   Choose **one** of your answers to check by substituting your answer into the equation.

   a $\dfrac{r}{4} = 10$ **b** $\dfrac{y}{7} = 1$ **c** $\dfrac{n}{5} + 7 = 15$ **d** $8 - \dfrac{a}{3} = 12$ **e** $\dfrac{3}{s} - 1 = 17$

Reasoning

4. Ollie leaves his house at 07:30.

   He drives 52 miles to work at an average speed of 39 miles per hour.

   At what time does Ollie arrive at work?

Fluency

5. Harish runs 400 metres in 56 seconds.

   Calculate Harish's average speed in metres per second. Round your answer to 2 decimal places.

6. The density of concrete is $2400 \, \text{kg/m}^3$. Work out the mass of a concrete patio step with a volume of $2.7 \, \text{m}^3$.

7. The mass of $5 \, \text{m}^3$ of lead is $56\,750 \, \text{kg}$. Find the density of lead.

8. The distance from New York to Los Angeles is 2457 miles.

   A flight between the two cities takes 6 hours 30 minutes.

   Find the average speed of the aeroplane.

Problem solving

9. A wind speed of 333 km per hour was recorded in Greenland in 1972.

   How fast is this in metres per second?

Fluency

10. **a** Find the volume of each of these cuboids in cubic centimetres.

5 cm 6 cm 3 cm

4 cm 8 cm 5 cm

    b Convert your answers to cubic millimetres.

Band 2 questions

⑪ Find the value of $5a(a-b)$ when

  a $a = 2$ and $b = 5$
  b $a = 0$ and $b = -20$
  c $a = 4$ and $b = 3$
  d $a = 1$ and $b = -4$.

⑫ Here are some materials and their densities.

Material	Density (g/cm³)
Gold	19.3
Cardboard	0.71
Copper	9
Plastic	0.92
Stone	2.65
Water	1
Ice cube	0.92
Oil	0.85
Lead	11.35
Cheese	1.2
Oak	0.75
Air	0.001275
Mahogany	0.96
Peanut	0.95

I am thinking of one of the materials in the table. Which one?

Here are some clues.

Its density is greater than a peanut

It floats in water

It is not a liquid

It doesn't float in oil

⑬ Solve this equation by filling in the blanks on the bar diagram.

$3x + 6 = 39$

Band 3 questions

⑭ Solve these equations.

  a $5x - 5 = 2x + 4$
  b $5x + 1 = 6x - 1$
  c $1 + 4r = 2r + 5$
  d $6x - 10 = 4x$
  e $3 + 3w = 10 - 4w$

⑮ Solve these equations.

  a $10(8x + 7) = 10(6x + 6)$
  b $6(x + 7) = 10(x + 3)$
  c $9(9x + 9) = 8(4x + 4)$
  d $\dfrac{10}{9x + 3} = \dfrac{4}{2x - 6}$
  e $\dfrac{8}{3x + 10} = \dfrac{10}{4x - 3}$

16 Look at this shape.

(x + 2) cm

(2x + 4) cm

2x cm

(x + 4) cm

a **i** Divide the shape into two rectangles with a horizontal line.

    ii Find the area of each rectangle in terms of x.

    iii Add these two expressions to find the total area of the shape in terms of x, simplifying your answer.

b **i** Divide the shape into two rectangles with a vertical line.

    ii Find the area of each rectangle in terms of x.

    iii Add these two expressions to find the total area of the shape in terms of x, simplifying your answer.

c Check that the simplified answers you got in parts **a** and **b** are the same.

d If the shape is divided into two rectangles using a vertical line, there is a larger rectangle on the left and a smaller one on the right.

The area of the smaller rectangle is 10 cm^2.

Find the value of x.

17 **a** Change the subject of this formula to v:

$s = vt$

    b Change the subject of this formula to r:

$C = 2\pi r$

18 **a** Change the subject of this formula to l:

$$t = 2\pi \sqrt{\dfrac{l}{g}}$$

    b Change the subject of this formula to a:

$h^2 = a^2 + b^2$

Graphs

▶ **Coming up...**

- ◆ The gradient of a line
- ◆ The equation $y = mx + c$
- ◆ Plotting quadratic graphs

➔ **Who wants to be a straight-lines pro?**

Answer all eight questions correctly to show you are an expert on straight lines.

① What is the gradient of this line?

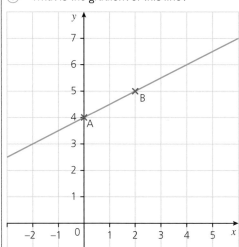

2

0

$\dfrac{1}{2}$

4

② What can you say about these two lines?

$y = 2x + 3$

$y = 2x - 1$

They are both curves

They both have the same gradient

They both have the same y-intercept

They have nothing in common

③ Point A lies on the line $y = 2x - 3$.

A is the point $(1, ?)$

−2

2

−3

−1

④ Which of these points lies on the line $y = 2x + 1$?

$(0, 3)$

$(1, 4)$

$(2, 5)$

$(3, 6)$

⑤ What is the equation of this line?

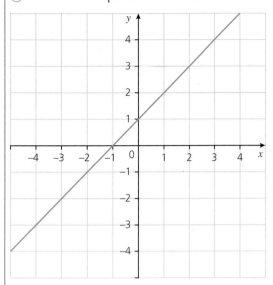

y = x − 1

y = x + 1

y = −x − 1

y = −x + 1

⑥ What is the y-intercept of this line?

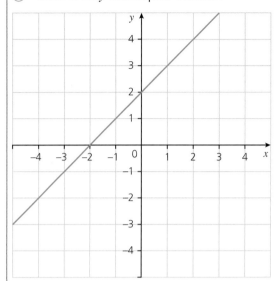

−2

2

1

−1

⑦ Which of the following is NOT a property of this line?

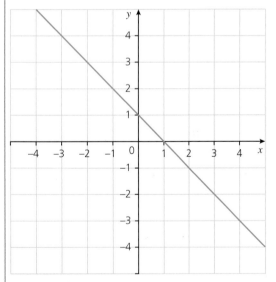

It has a negative gradient

It has a y-intercept of 1

It has a gradient of −1

It has the equation y = x + 1

⑧ Which of these could be the equation of this line?

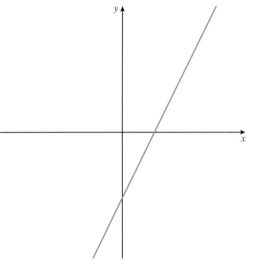

y = 2x + 2

y = 2x − 2

y = −2x + 2

y = −2x − 2

8.1 The gradient of a line

✔ Skill checker

a Copy and complete this table of values for the two straight lines with these equations:

Line 1: $y = x + 1$

Line 2: $y = -x + 1$

Line	x	−2	−1	0	1	2
1	$y = x + 1$				$1 + 1 = \mathbf{2}$	
2	$y = -x + 1$					

b Copy this grid and plot the two straight lines.

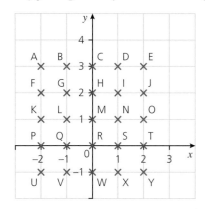

c Also plot these lines on your graph:

Line 3: $x = -1$

Line 4: $x = 1$

Line 5: $y = 1$

Line 6: $y = 3$

d Now crack this code to find the secret word.

i Where do lines 1 and 6 intersect?   **ii** Where do lines 4 and 5 intersect?

iii Where do lines 1 and 4 intersect?   **iv** Where do lines 2 and 3 intersect?

v Where do lines 1 and 2 intersect?   **vi** Where do lines 2 and 6 intersect?

Calculating the gradient

The gradient of a line is the steepness of the line.

To find the gradient of a straight line, choose any two points that lie on the line.

❶ Find the change in the y coordinates.

❷ Find the change in the x coordinates.

❸ The gradient is the change in y divided by the change in x.

> The letter m is used for the gradient.

Worked example

Find the gradient of the line shown.

Solution

The points $(1, 3)$ and $(3, 7)$ on the line have been chosen.

Subtracting the y coordinates gives $7 - 3 = 4$.

Subtracting the x coordinates gives $3 - 1 = 2$.

$$\text{Gradient} = \frac{\text{change in } y}{\text{change in } x}$$

$$= \frac{4}{2} \, 2$$

> Be consistent here: use
> – the second y coordinate minus the first; and
> – the second x coordinate minus the first.

If the line slopes down from left to right the gradient is negative.

Worked example

Find the gradient of the line shown.

Solution

The two points marked are $(0, 4)$ and $(2, 0)$.

Subtracting the y coordinates gives $0 - 4 = -4$.

Subtracting the x coordinates gives $2 - 0 = 2$.

$$\text{Gradient} = \frac{\text{change in } y}{\text{change in } x}$$

$$= \frac{-4}{2} = -2$$

Parallel lines

Parallel lines have the same gradient.

Worked example

a The line L_1 shown in the diagram passes through the points A(18, 32) and B(1, 1).

The line L_2 passes through the points C(9, 11) and D(3, 0).

Are the two lines parallel?

b The line L_3 shown in the diagram passes through the points E(0, 20) and F(16, 16).

The line L_4 passes through the points G(3, 22) and H(7, 21).

Are the two lines parallel?

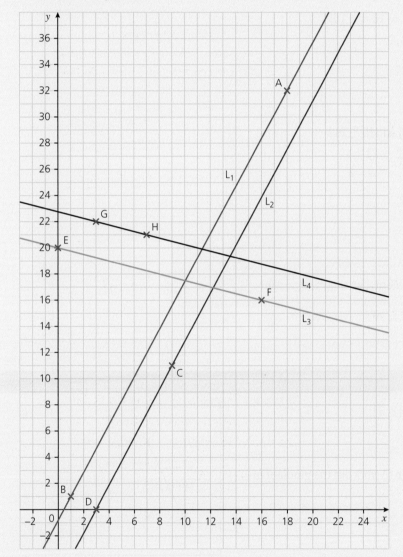

Solution

a For the line L_1, use the points A(18, 32) and B(1, 1).

Subtracting the y coordinates gives $32 - 1 = 31$.

Subtracting the x coordinates gives $18 - 1 = 17$.

$\text{Gradient} = \dfrac{\text{change in } y}{\text{change in } x} = \dfrac{31}{17} = 1.82 \ (2 \text{ d.p.})$

For the line L_2, use the points $C(9, 11)$ and $D(3, 0)$.

Subtracting the y coordinates gives $11 - 0 = 11$.

Subtracting the x coordinates gives $9 - 3 = 6$.

$$\text{Gradient} = \frac{\text{change in } y}{\text{change in } x}$$

$$= \frac{11}{6} = 1.83 \text{ (2 d.p.)}$$

The lines L_1 and L_2 do not have the same gradients, so although they appear to be parallel lines, they are not.

b For the line L_3, use the points $E(0, 20)$ and $F(16, 16)$.

Subtracting the y coordinates gives $20 - 16 = 4$.

Subtracting the x coordinates gives $0 - 16 = -16$.

$$\text{Gradient} = \frac{\text{change in } y}{\text{change in } x}$$

$$= \frac{-4}{16} = -0.25$$

For the line L_4, use the points $G(3, 22)$ and $H(7, 21)$.

Subtracting the y coordinates gives $22 - 21 = 1$.

Subtracting the x coordinates gives $3 - 7 = -4$.

$$\text{Gradient} = \frac{\text{change in } y}{\text{change in } x}$$

$$= \frac{1}{-4} = -0.25$$

The lines L_3 and L_4 have the same gradients, so they are parallel.

8.1 Now try these

1 P is the point $(1, 1)$ and Q is the point $(2, 3)$.

    a Write down the change in y, RQ.

    b Write down the change in x, PR.

    c Use your answers to parts **a** and **b** to work out the gradient of the line PQ in the diagram.

Strictly, this is a line segment, not a line!

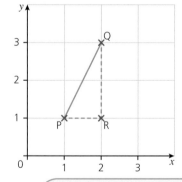

2 Work out the gradient of the line joining each of these pairs of points.

    a $(5, 7)$ and $(7, 11)$

    b $(-4, 2)$ and $(2, 4)$

    c $(7, 9)$ and $(12, -1)$

    d $(-8, -2)$ and $(-3, -7)$

Again, these are line segments, not lines. A line continues forever in both directions.

3 Work out the gradient of the line PQ shown in each of these diagrams.

a

Q(8, 15)

P(6, 7)   R

b

P(2, 6)

R   Q(4, 0)

c

P(2, 2)   Q(5, 2)

4 For each of the lines **a** to **g** in these diagrams:

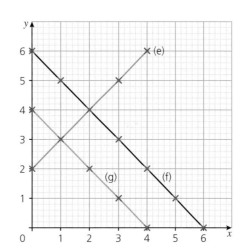

i write down the coordinates of two points marked on the line

ii calculate the gradient of the line.

Band 2 questions

5

a Find the coordinates of two points which lie on each of these lines:

> You can use a table of values to help.

   i $y = x$

   ii $y = 2x$

   iii $y = 3x$

b Use your coordinates to draw a graph of all the lines on the same axes. Label each line.

c Calculate the gradient of each line.

d What do you notice about the gradients of the lines?

e What is the gradient of the line $y = 20x$?

6 **a** Copy and complete these tables:

   i for the equation $y = 3x - 2$

x	-1	0	1	2	3
$y = 3x - 2$		$3 \times 0 - 2$ $=$ _____			$3 \times 3 - 2$ $= 7$

ii for the equation $y = 2x - 2$

x	-1	0	1	2	3
$y = 2x - 2$	$(2 \times -1) - 2$ $= -4$	$2 \times 0 - 2$ $= \underline{}$			

b Draw the graphs of the two lines on the same axes. **c** Find the gradient of each line.

7 For each line segment in this diagram

a Write down the coordinates of two points on the line segment. **b** Calculate the gradient.

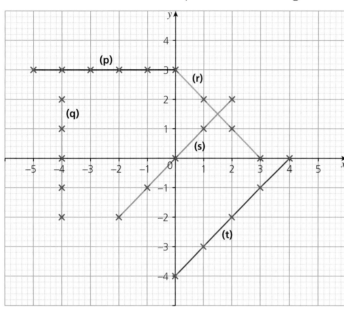

8 a Copy and complete these tables for the lines $y = 2x + 2$ and $y = 2x - 1$.

x	-2	-1	0	1	2	3
$y = 2x + 2$	$(2 \times -2) + 2$ $= -2$					

x	-2	-1	0	1	2	3
$y = 2x - 1$	$(2 \times -2) - 1$ $= -5$					

b Draw and label these two lines on the same axes.

c What can you say about the gradients of these two lines?
How can you tell this from your graph?

d Draw and complete similar tables for $y = 2x$ and $y = 2x + 4$.

Band 3 questions

9 Look at these road signs.

a Which hill is steepest? **b** Which hill is least steep?

10 Draw x and y axes.

Use the same scale on each axis and take values from −2 to 6.

a Plot the points A(−2, −2), B(−1, 5), C(3, 6) and D(2, −1).

b Work out the gradient of the lines AB, BC, DC and AD.

c What type of quadrilateral is ABCD?

11 The shape shown is a rectangle.

a What are the coordinates of point B ?

b What is the gradient of the line AB?

c What is the gradient of the line AC?

12 Fill in the blanks in each sentence with the words on one of these cards:

| one pair | two pairs | no pairs |

a A square has ____ of sides that have the same gradient.

b A rectangle has ____ of sides that have the same gradient.

c A trapezium has ____ of sides that have the same gradient.

d A rhombus has ____ of sides that have the same gradient.

e A kite has ____ of sides that have the same gradient.

f A parallelogram has ____ of sides that have the same gradient.

8.2 The equation of a straight line

✔ Skill checker

a Draw x and y axes using values from −6 to 6.

Plot these lines.

$x = 1$	$x = -1$	$x = 1.5$	$x = -1.5$
$y = -x - 1$	$y = x - 1$	$y = -x + 0.5$	$y = x + 0.5$
$y = 1$	$y = -1$	$y = -x - 0.5$	$y = x - 0.5$
$y = 1.5$	$y = -1.5$	$y = -x + 1$	$y = x + 1$

b Which famous flag have you drawn?

c Can you shade it in with the correct colours?

The equation of a straight line

Straight lines have an equation of the form $y = mx + c$.

▸ The value of m represents the gradient or 'steepness' of the line.

▸ The value of c tells you where the line crosses the y-axis. This is called the **y-intercept**.

Special cases are:

▸ Horizontal lines which have an equation of the form $y = a$ where a is a number.

▸ Vertical lines which have an equation of the form $x = b$ where b is a number.

Worked example

Here are the equations of ten lines.

Write down which ones are parallel.

a $x = 7$ **b** $y = 3 + 7x$ **c** $y = 2x + 3$ **d** $y = -5$

e $y = 2x - 4$ **f** $x = -2$ **g** $y = 5 - x$ **h** $y = -x$

i $y = 7x + 5$ **j** $y = 4$

Solution

a and **f** are parallel   These are both vertical lines ◀──

> Vertical lines have an infinite gradient!

b and **i** are parallel   These both have a gradient of 7

c and **e** are parallel   These both have a gradient of 2

d and **j** are parallel   These are both horizontal lines

g and **h** are parallel   These both have a gradient of -1

Worked example

Match the lines in this diagram with the correct equations.

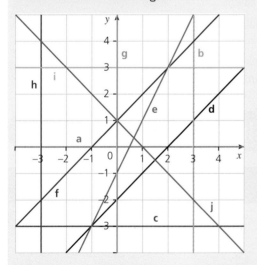

$x = 3$	$x = -3$	$x = 0$	$y = 3$	$y = -3$
$y = 0$	$y = x + 1$	$y = x - 2$	$y = 2x - 1$	$y = 1 - x$

Solution

Line **a** is the x-axis. Its equation is $y = 0$

Line **b** is a vertical line with equation $x = 3$

Line **c** is a horizontal line with equation $y = -3$

Line **d** has a gradient of 1 and a y-intercept of -2. The equation of the line is $y = x - 2$

Line **e** has a gradient of 2 and a y-intercept of -1. The equation of the line is $y = 2x - 1$

Line **f** has a gradient of 1 and a y-intercept of 1. The equation of the line is $y = x + 1$

Line **g** is the y-axis. Its equation is $x = 0$

Line **h** is a vertical line. Every point on the line has an x-coordinate of -3. The equation of the line is $x = -3$

Line **i** is a horizontal line. Every point on the line has a y-coordinate of 3. The equation of the line is $y = 3$

Line **j** has a gradient of -1 and a y-intercept of 1. The equation of the line is $y = -x + 1$ or $y = 1 - x$

 Activity

Links to sequences

① A sequence has the position-to-term formula $2n - 1$.

    a   Copy and complete this table.

n	1	2	3	4	5
$2n - 1$	$(2 \times 1) - 1$ $= 1$				

    b   Copy this graph and plot the remaining points.

    c   The sequence with the formula $2n - 1$ is an arithmetic sequence.

            Arithmetic sequences are sometimes called **linear** sequences. Why?

    d   Draw a line through the points on your graph.

            What is the equation of the line you have drawn?

Think about the pattern made by the points on the graph.

② Repeat for the sequence with the position-to-term formula $\frac{1}{2}n + 2$.

    a   Construct a table to find the first 5 terms of the sequence.

    b   Plot a graph of term against n for the first 5 terms.

    c   Draw a line through the points.

            Find the equation of this line.

8.2 Now try these

Reasoning

1 For each of the following sets of points,

    a plot them on graph paper and draw a straight line through them.

    b find the equation of the line.

       i $(-5, -5), (-4, -4), (-3, -3), (-2, -2)$

       ii $(9, 6), (8, 5), (7, 4), (6, 3)$

       iii $(4, 3), (3, 4), (2, 5), (1, 6)$

2 **a** Draw the lines with these equations on the same axes.

       $y = 2x + 2$ $y = x + 4$ $y = 2x - 3$

       $y = 4 + 2x$ $y = x + 2$ $y = x - 3$

    b Which lines have the same gradient?

       What do you notice about their equations?

    c Which pairs of lines have the same y-intercept?

       What do you notice?

    d A line has a gradient of 3 and y-intercept of -5.

       What is its equation?

Fluency

3 **a** Draw the graphs of these lines on the same axes.

       Take values of x and y from 0 to 5.

       i $x = 4$ **ii** $x = 2$ **iii** $y = 5$ **iv** $y = 3$

    b Which of the lines are parallel to the x-axis?

       Which of the lines are parallel to the y-axis?

    c What are the equations of the x-axis and y-axis?

Reasoning

4 **a** Find the missing coordinates on these straight lines.

       i $(0, 0), (1, 1), (2, 2), (3, \boxed{}), (\boxed{}, 4), (5, \boxed{})$

       ii $(6, 0), (5, 1), (4, 2), (3, \boxed{}), (\boxed{}, 4), (1, \boxed{})$

       iii $(-1, 1), (0, 2), (1, 3), (2, \boxed{}), (\boxed{}, 5), (4, \boxed{})$

       iv $(-2, 5), (-1, 5), (0, 5), (1, 5), (\boxed{}, 5), (3, \boxed{})$

> **Hint:** you can do this by writing the x-coordinates as one sequence of numbers and the y-coordinates as another.

    b Find an equation for each line.

> **Hint:** begin by taking any two points on the line and finding the gradient between them.

5 **a** Draw x and y axes from 0 to 8.

       On your axes draw the pattern formed by these lines.

       i $x = 2$ **ii** $x = 5$ **iii** $y = 2$ **iv** $y = 5$ **v** $y = x$ **vi** $x + y = 7$

    b Draw more lines on your diagram to form eight triangles of the same size.

    c Write down the equations of the lines you drew in part **b**.

6 Write down the gradient and the coordinates of the y-intercept for each of these lines.

    a $y = 2x + 3$ **b** $y = 3x - 4$ **c** $y = x + 4$

    d $y = x - 1$ **e** $y = 4x$ **f** $y = \dfrac{1}{2}x$

    g $y = 7 - 2x$

Band 2 questions

7 Find the gradient and y-intercept for each of these lines.

    Then write down the equation of the line.

a   **b**   **c**

d   **e**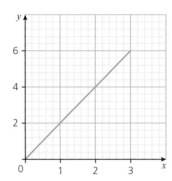

8 For each of these equations of straight lines.

    i   Rearrange the equation into the form $y = mx + c$.

    ii   Write down the gradient and the coordinates of the y-intercept.

    a $y = 2(x + 1)$ **b** $y = \dfrac{1}{2}(2x - 5)$ **c** $2y = 6x - 5$

    d $x + y = 2$ **e** $2x - y = 7$

9 Here are the equations of three lines:

    $y = x$ $y = 3 - x$ $y = x + 3$

    Answer these questions **without** plotting the lines on a graph.

    a   Which of these lines are parallel?

    b   What is the gradient of the two parallel lines?

    c   Which of the lines have the same y-intercept?

Reasoning

10 Ella and Dominic are doing a physics experiment.

They are investigating how forces stretch springs.

Dominic hangs a weight of 1 newton (N) on the end of a spring and measures its length in millimetres.

They then take it in turns to add more weights, each time measuring the length, L mm, of the spring and the force, F N, until there is a total weight of 8 N hanging on it.

Ella and Dominic display their results in a table.

Force, F (N)	0	1	2	3	4	5	6	7	8
Length of spring, L (mm)		36	48	59	71	83	100	106	117

a   Plot the graph of force against length, with force along the horizontal axis.

Draw a line of best fit.

b   One of the results is wrong.

Which one do you think it is?

Suggest the correct value for this result.

c   Dominic forgot to measure the length of the spring before he started hanging weights on it.

Use your graph to find the length of the spring.

d   Calculate the gradient of the graph.

e   Write the equation of the line in the form $L =$ _____ $F +$ _____

11 Isobel and Josh are doing an electricity experiment in their physics lesson.

They set up a circuit to measure the current, I, flowing through a resistor and the voltage, V, across it.

Their circuit is shown in the diagram.

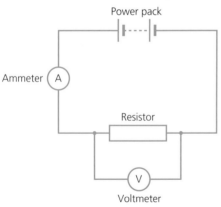

Power pack

Ammeter A

Resistor

V

Voltmeter

They set their power pack at 0 volts and record the readings shown on the voltmeter and the ammeter.

Isobel turns the control on the power pack to increase the voltage.

Josh records the new readings on both the voltmeter and the ammeter.

They repeat this several times.

Here are their results.

Voltage, V (volts)	Current, I (amps)	$V\mid I$
0.0	0.0	—
1.0	0.2	
2.0	0.4	
3.0	0.5	
4.0	0.8	
5.0	1.0	
6.0	1.2	

a Draw a graph of V against I, with I along the horizontal axis.

b Josh wrote an incorrect value for one of the results.

   i   Which result is it?

   ii What should you do about it?

c What is the current when the voltage is 4.5 V?

d What is the voltage when the current is 1.1 A?

e The resistance of the resistor is measured in ohms.

   The resistance equals the gradient of the line on the graph.

   Calculate the resistance.

12 On the graph below a point has been plotted and five lines drawn through it.

Draw a graph and plot a point of your choice.

Investigate the equations of lines which pass through your point.

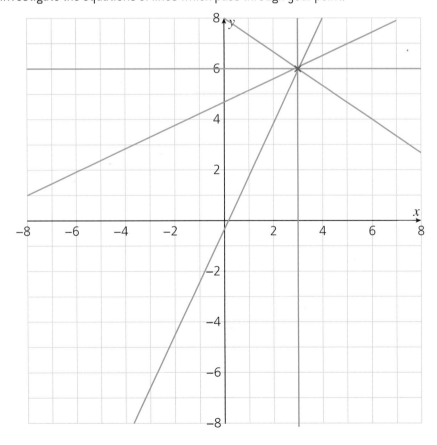

13 Avonford Autos are a car-hire company.

The basic charge is £20 plus a further 30p per mile.

a Show that $C = 0.3x + 20$, where C is the cost of driving x miles.

b Plot a graph of this equation for values of x from 0 to 200.

c Use your graph to find the cost of hiring a car and driving 80 miles.

d Use your graph to find how many miles are driven when the hire cost is £56.

14 Gas bills have a standing charge of £15 plus 10p per gas unit used.

The bill is £B.

a Show this is related to x, the number of gas units used, by the equation
$B = 15 + 0.1x$

b Plot a graph of this equation taking x values from 0 to 800.

c Use your graph to find Mr Smith's bill when he uses 275 units of gas.

d The Butterworths' bill is £89.

Use your graph to find how many units of gas they used.

15 A sequence has the position-to-term formula $5 - 2n$.

a Find the first 5 terms of the sequence.

b Plot a graph of the term on the vertical axis against n on the horizontal axis for the first 5 terms.

c Draw a line through the points.

Find the equation of this line.

8.3 Plotting quadratic graphs

✔ Skill checker

Ollie has some homework on substituting numbers into expressions.

He hasn't done very well when there's an x^2 term involved!

Find the mistakes in Ollie's working.

1. Substitute $x = 2$ into $3x^2 + 5x$	3. Substitute $x = -2$ into $x^2 - 4x$
$3x^2 + 5x$	$x^2 - 4x$
$= 3 \times 2^2 + 5 \times 2$	$= (-2)^2 - 4 \times -2$
$= 6^2 + 10$	$= 4 - 8$
$= 46$ ✗	$= -4$ ✗
2. Substitute $x = -3$ into $x^2 + 5x - 1$	4. Substitute $x = -5$ into $1 - x^2$
$x^2 + 5x - 1$	$1 - x^2$
$= (-3)^2 + 5(-3) - 1$	$= 1 - (-5)^2$
$= -9 - 15 - 1$	$= 1 + 25$
$= -25$ ✗	$= 26$ ✗

Introduction to quadratic graphs

An equation involving x^2 is not a **linear** function; instead, it produces a curve called a **quadratic** curve or a **parabola**.

> A linear function is a straight line on a graph. Its equation involves x and not x^2.

Worked example

a Construct a table of values, with values of x from -3 to 3.

Calculate the y values using the equation $y = x^2$

b Draw the graph of the curve $y = x^2$

Solution

a

x	-3	-2	-1	0	1	2	3
y	$(-3)^2 = 9$	4	1	0	1	4	9

b

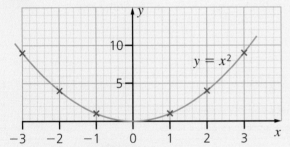

Note

Squaring a negative number gives a positive answer.

Worked example

a Make a table of values for $y = x^2 - 4x + 1$, taking values of x from -1 to 5.

b Draw the graph of $y = x^2 - 4x + 1$.

c Use your graph to solve the equation $x^2 - 4x + 1 = 0$.

Solution

a Work out the y values.

Use the x values from -1 to 5 in the equation of the curve. For example:

When $x = -1$:

$y = (-1)^2 - 4(-1) + 1$

$\quad = 6$

When $x = 0$:

$y = (0)^2 - 4(0) + 1$

$\quad = 1$

etc.

x	-1	0	1	2	3	4	5
$y^2 = x^2 - 4x + 1$	6	1	-2	-3	-2	1	6

b

Note

Join the points with a smooth curve.
Always draw curves freehand.

Note

Continue the curve to the edges of
the graph paper.

The curve crosses the line
$y = 0$ at approximately
$x = 0.3$ and $x = 3.7$.

c The solutions are $x = 0.3$ and $x = 3.7$

The solution to the equation $x^2 - 4x + 1 = 0$ is given by the x values at the points where the curve crosses the x axis
(the line $y = 0$).

Values taken from a graph are only approximate.

Solutions to an equation ... $= 0$ are sometimes called roots.

8.3 Now try these

Band 1 questions

1 **a** Copy and complete these calculations using the equation $y = x^2 - 2$.

When $x = -3, y = (-3)^2 - 2$

$\qquad = 9 - 2$

$\qquad = \rule{2cm}{0.15mm}$

When $x = -2, y = (\rule{1.5cm}{0.15mm})^2 - 2$

$\qquad = \rule{1.5cm}{0.15mm} - 2$

$\qquad = \rule{1.5cm}{0.15mm}$

b Using $y = x^2 - 2$, find the values of y when $x = 1, 2$ and 3.

c Copy and complete this table.

x	-3	-2	-1	0	1	2	3
$y = x^2 - 2$			-1	-2			

d What is the name of this type of equation?

e Draw axes with values of x from -3 to 3 and y from -3 to 8.

f Plot the points from your table and join them with a smooth curve.

2 a Copy and complete this table for $y = 10 - x^2$.

x	-4	-3	-2	-1	0	1	2	3	4
$y = 10 - x^2$	-6	1	6						

b Plot the points and join them with a smooth curve.

3 a Copy and complete this table for $y = 3x^2 + 7$.

x	-1	0	1	2	3
$y = 3x^2 + 7$	10	7			

b Draw the graph of $y = 3x^2 + 7$.

c Use your graph to estimate the value of x when $y = 15$.

4 a Copy and complete this table for $y = (x - 3)^2$.

x	-1	0	1	2	3	4	5	6	7
$y = (x - 3)^2$	16	9	4						

b Draw the graph of $y = (x - 3)^2$.

c What is the equation of the line of symmetry of the curve?

5 a Copy and complete this table of values.

x	-4	-3	-2	-1	0	1	2	3	4
$y = 3x^2 + 2$	50	29							

b Draw the graph of $y = 3x^2 + 2$.

c Use your graph to estimate the value of y when $x = 2.5$.

Band 2 questions

6 a Copy and complete this table of values for $y = 6x - x^2$.

x	-1	0	1	2	3	4	5	6	7
$y = 6x - x^2$	-7	0							

b Draw the points and join them with a smooth curve.

c Use your graph to solve the equation $6x - x^2 + 3 = 0$.

7 a Copy and complete this table of values.

x	-1	0	1	2	3	4	5	6	7
$y = 7x - x^2$	-8	0							

b Decide on suitable scales and draw x and y axes.

Plot the graph of $y = 7x - x^2$.

c What is the equation of the line of symmetry of this graph?

d What is the greatest value of y?

8 a Copy and complete this table.

x	-4	-3	-2	-1	0	1	2	3	4
$y = 20 - x^2$	4	11	16						

b Draw the graph of $y = 20 - x^2$.

c This graph has a line of symmetry.

What is the equation of this line?

d When would you expect to see a curve with this shape in real life?

9 **a** Copy and complete this table.

x	0	1	2	3	4
$y = x^2 - 4x + 4$			0		

b Draw a set of axes with values of x from 0 to 4 and values of y from -4 to 4.

Draw the graph of $y = x^2 - 4x + 4$.

c Use your graph to solve the equation $x^2 - 4x + 4 = 0$.

d Draw the reflection of the curve in the x-axis.

e What are the coordinates of the image of the points $(0, 4)$, $(2, 0)$ and $(4, 4)$?

f Do any of the points on the curve stay the same under the reflection?

Band 3 questions

10 Armal sits on a clifftop and throws a stone into the air.

The stone's height, y metres, above the clifftop after a time of x seconds is given by the equation $y = 18x - 5x^2$.

a Copy and complete this table of values.

x	0	1	2	3	4	5
$y = 18x - 5x^2$						

b Plot the points and join them with a smooth curve.

c Estimate the greatest height reached by the stone.

d When does this happen?

e Estimate for how long the stone is above Armal.

f What happens after that?

g The stone hits the beach after 5 seconds.

How high is the cliff?

h Estimate when the stone is 5 m above Armal.

i Estimate for how long the stone is more than 10 m above Armal.

11 **a** Copy and complete this table for $y = (x - 2)(x - 4)$.

x	0	1	2	3	4	5	6
$y = (x - 2)(x - 4)$	8	3					

b Draw the graph of $y = (x - 2)(x - 4)$.

c What is the equation of the line of symmetry of this graph?

d Label the points A$(0, 8)$, B$(2, 0)$ and C$(4, 0)$ on the curve.

Draw triangle ABC and find its area.

12 The flight of a football during a free kick is given by the equation

$$h = 4t - t^2$$

where h is the height of the ball, in metres, after t seconds.

a Plot a graph of this information for values of t from 0 to 4 seconds.

b What is the greatest height of the ball?

c The ball reaches the goal-line at time $t = 3.8$ seconds.

The goals are 2 metres high.

Could this free kick result in a goal?

13 The formula for the volume, V cm³, of a square-based pyramid is

$$V = \frac{1}{3}b^2 h$$

where b cm is the base length and h cm is the perpendicular height.

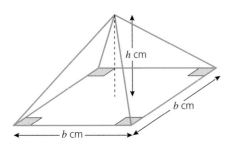

a A toy company produces wooden square-based pyramids with a perpendicular height of 6 cm.
Find a formula for V in terms of b.

b Plot the graph of V against b for values of b from 0 to 4 cm.

c Use your graph to estimate the value of b when $V = 20$.

d How could you find the answer to part **c** without drawing a graph?

14 A cargo ship travels at a speed of v kilometres per hour.

At this speed the cost, £C, of a 300-kilometre trip is $C = v^2 - 40v + 600$

a Copy and complete this table.

v	10	20	30	40	50
$C = v^2 - 40v + 600$	300	200			

b Draw a graph of C against v.

c Use your graph to estimate the cost of a journey at 35 km/h.

d State the speed at which the cost of the journey is lowest.

15 a i Draw the graphs of $y = x^2 + 2$ and $y = x^2 + 5$ for values of x from −3 to 3.

ii Use your graphs to explain the effect of c in the equation $y = x^2 + c$.

b i Draw the graphs of $y = 2x^2$ and $y = 3x^2$ for values of x from −3 to 3.

ii Use your graphs to explain the effect of a in the equation $y = ax^2$.

Key words

Here is a list of the key words you met in this chapter.

Curve　　　　　Gradient　　　　　Linear　　　　　Parabola
Quadratic　　　y-intercept

Use the glossary at the back of this book to check any you are unsure about.

Review exercise: graphs

1 Write down the coordinates of the y-intercept and the gradient of each of these lines.

    a $y = 2x + 5$ **b** $y = 3x + 2$ **c** $y = 4x - 5$

    d $y = 7 + 3x$ **e** $y = 10x$ **f** $y = -2x$

    g $y = \dfrac{2}{3} + \dfrac{1}{2}x$

2 Match the lines in this diagram with the correct equations.

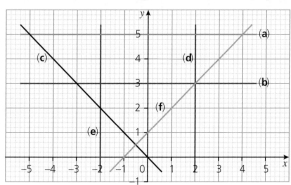

    i $x = 2$ **iii** $y = -x$ **v** $y = 5$

    ii $y = 3$ **iv** $y = x + 1$ **vi** $x = -2$

3 Here are the graphs of the lines $y = x - 2$ and $y = 2x$.

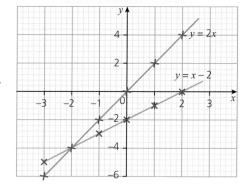

    a   Find the gradient of each line.

    b   Which is the steeper line?

    c   Find the y-intercept of each line.

    d   Write down the coordinates of the point where the two lines cross.

4 **a**   Draw x and y axes with values from −2 to 8 on each axis.

            Plot the line with gradient 2 and with a y-intercept of 1.

            Write down the equation of this line in the form $y = mx + c$.

    b   On the same axes, plot the line with gradient 3 and with a y-intercept of −2.

            Write down the equation of this line in the form $y = mx + c$.

    c   Extend your lines so that they cross.

            Write down the coordinates of the point where the lines cross.

5 Here are the equations of eight lines.

$y = 2x - 3$	$x + y = 5$	$3y = 6x + 10$	$y + 3x = 0$
$y = -3$	$y = 3 - x$	$y = 3x + 5$	$y = 4x - 7$

    Choose the equations of the lines which have

    a   a y-intercept at $(0, 0)$

    b   a gradient of 0

Key Stage 3 Mastering Mathematics: Book 3

Fluency   Reasoning   Fluency

c a negative gradient

d a gradient of 3

e a gradient of 2

f a gradient of −3

g the steepest slope

h a y-intercept at $(0, 5)$.

6 **a** Draw x and y axes.

Take values from −2 to 8 on each axis.

b Plot the line whose gradient is 1 and whose y-intercept is 2.

c Plot the line whose gradient is 2 and whose y-intercept is −2.

d Write down the coordinates of the point where these two lines meet.

e Plot the line whose gradient is $\frac{1}{2}$ and whose y-intercept is 4.

What do you notice about this line?

Band 3 questions

7 Liz and Danny do an experiment with an elastic string.

They measure the extension of the string each time they add a weight to it.

Here are their results.

Force, F (N)	0	2	4	6	8	10	12	14
Extension of string, E (mm)	0	19	39	56	75	95	115	133

a Plot the graph of force, F N, against extension, E mm, with force along the horizontal axis.

b Calculate the gradient of the line and use it to write down the equation of the line.

c What does your graph tell you about the relationship between E and F?

8 **a** Copy and complete this table of values.

x	−3	−2	−1	0	1	2	3
$y = 4x^2 + 9$	45	25					

b Draw axes, taking x from −3 to 3 and y from 0 to 50.

Plot the graph of $y = 4x^2 + 9$.

c What is the minimum value that y takes?

9 **a** Copy and complete this table of values.

x	−3	−2	−1	0	1	2	3
$y = x^2 - 2x - 3$	12	5					

b Plot the points and join them with a smooth curve.

c What is the minimum value that y takes?

10 **a** Draw the graph of $y = x^2 - 4x + 3$.

Take values of x from −1 to 5.

b What is the equation of the line of symmetry of the curve?

c What is the least possible value for $x^2 - 4x + 3$?

d Use your graph to solve the equation $x^2 - 4x + 3 = 0$.

175

⑪ A company makes rectangular metal strips to be used as machine components.

The length of each metal strip is 20 cm greater than its width x.

x

$x + 20$

a Show that the area A cm², of a strip is $A = x^2 + 20x$.

b Copy and complete this table:

x	2	4	6	8	10
$y = x^2 + 20x$					

c Plot a graph of A against x.

d Estimate the dimensions of a metal strip that has an area of 250 cm².

⑫ Here are the equations of eight lines.

$y = 6x + 3$	$y = 4x - 3$	$y = 7$	$y = 3 - 4x$	$y = 2 - x$

$y = 3x + 2$	$y = 5x + 2$	$y = 3x$	$y = 3x - 4$	$y = 8x - 5$

Choose the equation or equations that gives

a a line that passes through the origin

b a line that has a gradient of 5

c a line that has a gradient of -1

d a line that passes through the point $(0, 3)$

e a line that is parallel to $y = 4x$

f a line that passes through the point $(0, -4)$

g a line that is parallel to $y = 5 - 4x$

h a line that passes through the point $(1, 5)$

i a line with a zero gradient

j the steepest line.

Real-life graphs

 Coming up...

- ◆ Distance – time graphs (travel graphs)
- ◆ Reading from real-life graphs

Fractal triangles

The diagrams show a sequence of patterns made up of equilateral triangles.

To move from one pattern to the next, each triangle is divided into four smaller equilateral triangles.

The sides of the equilateral triangle in Pattern 1 are 1 metre in length.

In Pattern 2 there are four triangles each with sides $\frac{1}{2}$ metre in length.

In Pattern 3, there are 16 triangles each with sides of length $\frac{1}{4}$ metre.

Pattern 1	Pattern 2	Pattern 3

a Copy and complete this table for the **side length** of the small triangles in each pattern.

	Pattern 1	Pattern 2	Pattern 3	Pattern 4	Pattern 5
Length of side (m)	1	$\frac{1}{2}$	$\frac{1}{4}$		

b Copy and complete this table for the **number** of small triangles in each pattern.

	Pattern 1	Pattern 2	**Pattern 3**	Pattern 4	Pattern 5
Number	1	4	16		

c From one pattern to the next the **side length** of a small triangle halves.

This is known as **exponential decay**.

In which pattern would the small triangles have a side length of $\frac{1}{256}$ metres?

> When a quantity halves and then halves again in the same space of time, this is known as **exponential decay**.

> Quadruples means it is multiplied by 4.

d From one pattern to the next the **number** of small triangles quadruples.

This is known as **exponential growth**.

In which pattern would there be 256 small triangles?

> When a quantity doubles and then doubles again in the same space of time, this is known as **exponential growth**.

9.1 Distance–time graphs

✔ Skill checker

a For each of these travel graphs, work out the speed in kilometres per hour.

> **Remember**
>
> In Chapter 6 on Measure you learnt that speed = distance ÷ time.

i

ii

iii

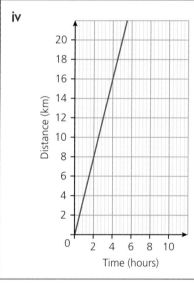

iv

b In which of the travel graphs is the speed greatest?

c Copy and complete these sentences:

The steepest graph shows the object travelling at the _____ speed.

The graph with the _____ gradient shows the object travelling at the lowest speed.

Reading distance–time graphs

Worked example

Look at this graph showing the height of a hot air balloon.

It is called a travel graph or a distance–time graph.

a How high does the balloon go?

b What is shown by the lines BC and DE?

c For how long is the balloon at a height of 300 m?

d How long does the balloon take to land?

e When is the balloon at a height of 500 m?

Solution

a The balloon reaches a maximum height of 700 m.

> The maximum height is the largest value of y that the graph reaches.

b The lines BC and DE represent times when the balloon remains at the same height.

> The lines BC and DE are horizontal lines.

c The balloon is at 300 m for 5 minutes.

> This is given by the length of line BC.

d It takes 15 minutes to come down.

> The line EF begins 25 minutes into the flight and finishes at 40 minutes.

e It is at a height of 500 m at $12\frac{1}{2}$ minutes on the way up and at 29 minutes on the way down.

> Draw a line horizontally from 500 m on the y axis and read off the x value of the point where it crosses the graph.

Drawing a distance–time graph

Worked example

Liam, Tilly and Raj leave Seatown and travel in the same direction.

- Liam sets off at 9:45 a.m. and travels 40 km by electric car.

  He drives at a constant speed and it takes him 1 hour.

- Tilly leaves at 9:15 a.m. She walks 3 km at a steady pace in one hour. Then she catches a bus which travels another 15 km at a constant speed. The bus journey takes 1 hour.

- Raj cycles, setting off at 9 a.m.

  He travels 20 km in 2 hours at a constant speed.

a Draw axes from 9 a.m. to 12 noon on the horizontal axis and from 0 km to 45 km on the vertical axis.

  Plot the travel graphs for all three people.

b At what time does Liam pass Tilly?

c At what time does Liam pass Raj?

d Does Raj pass Tilly? Explain your answer.

e At what speed is Raj cycling?

f At what speed is Liam driving?

> Sometimes when you read from a graph it is not always possible to get exact values. Here it is only possible to read an approximate time. There may be a range of answers that are acceptable.

Solution

a

b Liam's red line and Tilly's black line cross at about 9:50 a.m.
  This is the time at which Liam passes Tilly.

c Liam passes Raj at about 10 a.m.

d Raj's blue line and Tilly's black line do not meet, so Raj does not pass Tilly. Raj leaves Seatown earlier than Tilly and stays in front of her the whole time.

e Raj cycles 20 km in 2 hours.

$$\text{Speed} = \frac{\text{distance}}{\text{time}} = \frac{20}{2} = 10 \, \text{km/h}$$

f Liam drives 40 km in 1 hour.

$$\text{Speed} = \frac{\text{distance}}{\text{time}} = \frac{40}{1} = 40 \, \text{km/h}$$

Note

Sometimes when you read from a graph it is not always possible to get exact values. Here it is only possible to read an approximate time. There may be a range of answers that are acceptable.

Activity

Make a poster all about your journey to school.

① Include a map of your journey on your poster.

② Show a travel graph for your journey.

Remember to include every part of the journey (e.g. walking, cycling, bus and car).

You will need to research how far you travel for each part of the journey.

Try to be accurate about what time you begin and end each part.

③ Make up two questions for a friend to answer about your travel graph.
For example:

▶ How far have I travelled at 8:30 a.m?

▶ At what time have I cycled 1 kilometre?

▶ How fast do I travel in the car?

Remember

For the faster parts of your journey the graph will be steeper.

9.1 Now try these

Band 1 questions

❶ Suzie walks to her local shop to buy some eggs and then returns home.

Here is a distance–time graph for her journey.

a What does the shape of the graph tell you about Suzie's journey?

b How far is the shop from Suzie's home?

c How long does Suzie spend in the shop?

d How long does it take Suzie to walk home?

❷ A chef tosses a pancake. The graph shows the pancake's distance above the ground at different times, measured in seconds.

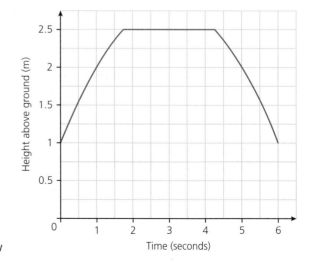

a How high is the pancake after one second?

b The chef tosses the pancake too high and it hits the ceiling.

How many seconds does the pancake take to hit the ceiling after being tossed?

c How high is the room?

d When the pancake hits the ceiling, it sticks there. How long is it stuck for?

3 A bear is climbing a very tall tree to find some honey in a bees' nest at the top. The graph below shows the height of the bear above the ground throughout its climb.

a How high is the tree?

b How long does it take the bear to climb the tree?

c How high is the bear after 6 minutes?

d How long does the bear spend eating the honey at the top of the tree?

e How long does it take the bear to climb down the tree?

4 Mr Wiggins has a busy day delivering fruit and vegetables. The graph below shows his distance from home at certain times through the day.

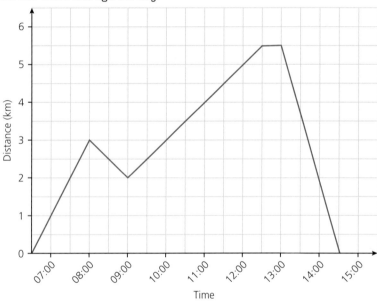

a Mr Wiggins' first delivery was 3 km away from his home. What time did he make this delivery?

b How far was Mr Wiggins from his home at 11:00 a.m.?

c Mr Wiggins made his third delivery of the day at 12:30 p.m.

This delivery was to a shop 5.5 km from his home.

How long did he stay at the shop?

Band 2 questions

5 Sketch a graph to represent the following situation:

From rest you start running until you reach flat-out speed.

Then you slow down gradually until you collapse from exhaustion. Your distance is plotted against time.

6 A cat jumps from ground level onto a fence.

The graph shows the height of the cat plotted against the time after it jumped.

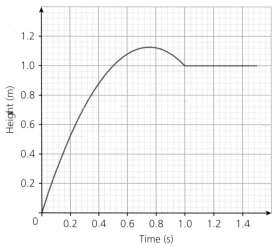

a Roughly what is the cat's greatest height?

b After roughly how many seconds does it reach this height?

c Give a reason for the shape of the graph:

  i at 0.8 seconds

  ii after 1 second.

7 Majella runs the Belfast Marathon. The graph shows her distance from the start line at certain times throughout the race.

a At what time does the marathon start?

b How far has Majella run by 11:00 a.m.?

c The marathon is 40 km long. At what time does Majella finish the race?

d Between which times does Majella run fastest?

Explain why she might run faster between these times.

e Majella's friend Paula is running in the same race. She runs at a steady speed of 10 km/h.

Copy the graph. Draw a line representing Paula's journey on the same diagram.

f At what times are the two women running together?

g When do they next meet?

h How long does it take Paula to complete the race?

8 Parthi travels to work.

He walks 0.4 km from his home to the bus stop in 5 minutes.

He then waits 3 minutes for the bus.

The bus travels 2.1 km in 10 minutes to a bus stop near his workplace.

Parthi walks the last 0.3 km to work in 4 minutes.

a Draw a horizontal axis from 0 minutes to 25 minutes.

Draw a vertical axis from 0 km to 3 km.

Plot a travel graph to represent Parthi's journey to work.

b What is the average speed of the bus in kilometres per hour?

9 Suresh walks to the bakery to buy some scones.

The bakery is 1800 m from his home.

It takes Suresh 10 minutes to get there.

Suresh spends 12 minutes in the bakery.

He sets off to return home.

He covers the first 1000 m in 10 minutes.

He then sits down to eat one of the scones for 5 minutes.

The final 800 m home takes him 5 minutes.

The graph shows the first stage of Suresh's journey.

Copy the diagram and draw lines to show the rest of his journey.

Band 3 questions

10 Sebastian cycles to school every day.

On some days he gets to school more quickly than on others.

The distance–time graph below shows his journeys each day this week.

a On Friday Sebastian took a different route, which was slightly longer.

Which number line shows Friday's journey?

b How far does Sebastian **usually** travel when he cycles to school?

c The red (number 1) and blue (number 2) graphs have roughly the same shape.

There is a steeper part of the graph, followed by a less steep part, followed by another steeper part.

Can you explain this?

d Sebastian arrived at school at the earliest time on Tuesday.

Which number line shows Tuesday's journey.

e On Thursday Sebastian stopped at the shop on the way to school.

Which number line shows Thursday's journey.

f On Wednesday Sebastian left his house a bit later than usual.

Which number line shows Wednesday's journey.

11 A bus is travelling at 10 metres per second towards a bus stop 50 metres away.

Here is a possible distance–time graph.

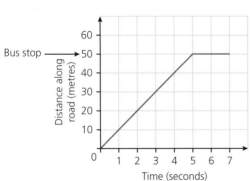

During the first 5 seconds, the bus is travelling at a constant speed of 10 m/s.

Then, on arrival at the bus stop, it suddenly stops dead in its tracks!

This is shown by the way in which the graph makes a sudden turn.

a What would happen if a real bus behaved in this manner?

b In the real world, a bus begins to slow down before it reaches the bus stop, and gradually comes to a halt.

This is represented using smooth curves.

Redraw the graph to show what that might look like.

c Use your graph to find:

i when the driver begins to brake

ii when the bus actually stops

iii for how long the bus decelerates (slows down).

12 For each of the situations below, sketch a distance–time graph which will represent the events shown.

a

b

c

d

e

9.2 Reading from real-life graphs

✓ Skill checker

In Chapter 8 you learnt how to plot a **quadratic** graph, for example for the curve $y = x^2 + 4x + 6$.

If y is the subject of the equation, you can use a table of values to plot any curve.

Jamie draws up a table of values for the quadratic equation above.

Here is his table of values.

x	−5	−4	−3	−2	−1	0	1
$y = x^2 + 4x + 6$	11	6	3	2	1	6	11

Jamie plots his points on a graph, shown here.

a One of the points looks wrong.
   Copy the table of values, correcting the mistake.

b Copy the graph, plotting all the points correctly.

c Join the points with a smooth curve.

Use your graph to answer these questions:

d Find the value of y when $x = 0.5$.

e Find the value of x when $y = 5$.
   There are two answers.

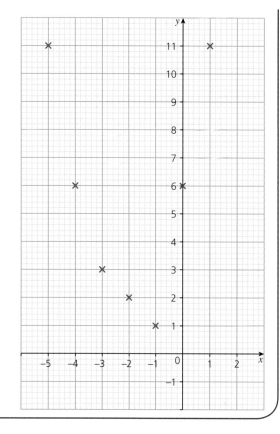

Reading information from a graph

Worked example

Paula has solar panels on the roof of her house to generate electricity.

The solar panels work best during the middle part of the day when the sun is higher in the sky. They also work less well when it is cloudy.

The graph shows the amount of electricity the solar panels generate throughout one day in April. Solar energy is measured in kilowatts (kW).

a The day was mainly sunny, but at one time it became partly cloudy.
   What time was this?

b How much electricity (in kW) were Paula's solar panels making at 11 a.m.?

c Is it possible to be completely accurate when making this reading from the graph?
   Fill in the blanks in this sentence:
   The true reading is between _____ and _____.

d Estimate at what time the solar panels were making the most electricity.

Roughly how much electricity (in kW) were the solar panels making at this time?

e At roughly what times were the solar panels making 1 kW of electricity? There is more than one answer.

Solution

Joining the points with a smooth curve allows you to answer this question more accurately.

a At 2 p.m. the reading is much lower than the curve. This must be the time at which it was cloudy.

b The black lines show that at 11 a.m. the solar panels were generating roughly 3.4 kW of electricity.

c It is not possible to be completely accurate.

The true reading is between 3.3 kW and 3.5 kW.

d The solar panels were making the most electricity at around 12:30 p.m.

They were making roughly 4 kW at this time.

e The blue lines show that the solar panels were generating 1 kW of electricity at roughly 8:30 a.m. and 4:30 p.m.

9.2 Now try these

Band 1 questions

1 It rains every day for the first part of September. Simon has a water butt in his garden, which fills up with rainwater.

He measures the level of the water in the water butt each day. These measurements are shown in the graph.

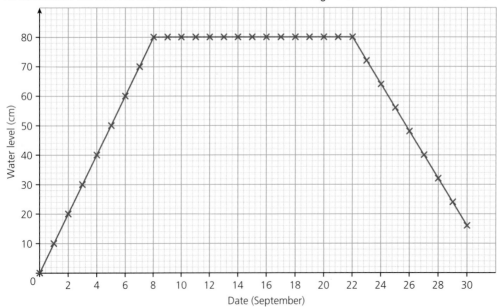

a On which day did it stop raining?

b After a while, Simon begins to use the water for his garden.

On which date did Simon begin using the water?

c Does Simon use up all the water by the end of September?

If not, how much is left?

2 The diagram shows the shape of an Olympic ski jump.

a How high above ground are the skiers at the start of the slope?

b How far from the start is the slope 20 metres high?

Hint

There is more than one answer.

3 Satwinder cycles from his house to the nearest post box.

Starting from rest he increases his speed steadily until he reaches a top speed of 10 m/s. This takes him 20 seconds.

He then stays at this speed for 70 seconds, when he is close to the post box.

He brakes and slows down steadily, coming to rest in 10 seconds.

a Using the information above, copy and complete this table of values.

Time (seconds)	0	20	30	50	70	90	100
Speed (m/s)	0		10				

b Draw axes with:

- time on the x-axis running from 0 to 100 seconds
- speed on the y-axis running from 0 to 10 m/s.
  Use different scales on the x- and y-axes to fit the graph on your page.

Note

This graph should be made up of three straight lines. It is called a piece-wise linear graph.

c Plot the points from your table on the graph.

Join the points using straight lines.

Use your graph to answer the following questions:

d What was Satwinder's speed 60 seconds after leaving home?

e At what times after leaving home was Satwinder travelling at 5 m/s ?

Problem solving

④ Sam throws a ball from an upstairs window of his house.

Later she plots a graph of the ball's height against its distance from the house, as shown.

The height of the ball can be calculated using this equation:

$$h = -\frac{1}{5}x^2 + 1.2x + 4$$

where h is the ball's height and x is its horizontal distance from the house.

a　How high above the ground is the window from which the ball was thrown?

b　Using the graph, estimate the maximum height the ball reaches.

c　Roughly how far from the house does the ball land?

Reasoning

⑤ Charlene is a mechanic in a garage in Brisbane, Australia.

For every car that comes in, she keeps a record of its age and an estimate of its value.

She plots a graph of the data she has collected this week.

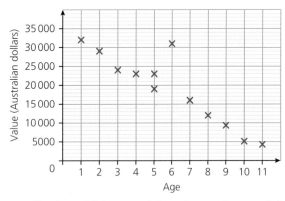

a　Charlene thinks one of the points on her graph looks wrong.

　　She knows she recorded the car's age correctly, so she thinks she has estimated its value wrongly.

　　What is the age of the car?

b　Estimate the value of this car more accurately for Charlene, based on the information in the graph.

c　Charlene wants to draw a straight line that passes as close as possible to all the points on her graph.

　　What should she do about the point that is wrong?

6 An offshore wind turbine is 120 metres tall. It casts a shadow across the sea.
The length of the shadow varies throughout the day, as shown in the graph.

a Use the graph to find the length of the shadow at 3 p.m.

b Use the graph to estimate the length of the shadow at 9:15 a.m.

c At roughly what times of the day is the shadow 200 metres long?

There are two answers.

7 If you climb a tall tower on a clear day you can see for miles.

The horizon is the imaginary line between the earth and the sky.
When you are higher up, the horizon appears to be further away.

The two diagrams show the distance to the horizon (the red curve) for two different towers.
From the taller blue tower, it is possible to see further.

The graph shows the distance to the horizon for different size towers.

The distance d can be calculated from the height h using the formula

$$d = 1.22\sqrt{h}$$

a How far can you see from a tower 50 feet
high?

b How high a tower would be needed to see
at least 10 miles?

Reasoning

8 A farmer needs a rectangular field with an area of 360 m² for his sheep.

There are many ways to do this. Some of them are shown in the table below.

Width (m)	5	10	15		20		36	72
Length (m)	72		24	20		15		

a Copy and complete the table.

b Can you think of any other ways to make an area of 360 m² ?

c Plot a graph of the length against the width, with the width on the x-axis.

Use values from 0 to 80 metres on both axes.

Use a scale of 1 cm for 10 metres.

Use your graph to answer these questions:

> **Note**
>
> The graph you have drawn is called a **reciprocal** curve.

d How long is the field if the width is 30 metres?

e Estimate the width of the field if its length is 25 metres.

Problem solving

9 Seema and Ross work in a university laboratory.

They are each studying a different colony of bacteria and they begin their experiments at the same time.

The graph shows the growth in the two populations of bacteria during the first 20 minutes of the experiments.

a What is the initial number of bacteria in Seema's colony? ⟵ Initial means at the start.

b Find approximately the number of bacteria in Seema's colony after four minutes.

Why do you think this is only an approximate figure?

c How long does it take for the number of bacteria in Seema's colony to reach 240?

d Which colony grows faster: Seema's or Ross's?

How can you tell from the graph?

e The number of bacteria in Seema's colony is initially lower than the number in Ross's colony. After how many minutes is Seema's colony larger?

f Roughly how long does it take for Seema's population of bacteria to double in size from its initial size?

Does the population double again in the same amount of time?

What is the name for this type of growth?

10 Mrs Jacobson is a busy teacher. She makes a cup of tea in the staff room. She then places it on a table and forgets about it.

The temperature of the tea every minute is shown in the graph.

a What was the temperature of the tea when it was first placed on the table?

b How long does it take for the tea to cool to 20 °C ?

c After a long time, the temperature of the tea becomes the same as the temperature of the room.

Using the graph, what is the temperature of the room?

d What is the difference between the tea's temperature and the room temperature at the start?

e How long does it take for this temperature difference to half?

f How long does it take for this temperature difference to half again?

g What is the name for this type of curve?

Review exercise: real-life graphs

❶ The Johnson family are going camping. They leave home in the morning and the graph below shows their distance from home during the journey.

a After they had been travelling some time, Mrs Johnson realises they have forgotten to bring the tent. They return home to pick it up.

At what time did Mrs Johnson realise this?

b Later, the Johnson family stopped to buy some drinks.

At what time did they do this?

c The Johnson family arrived at the campsite at 12:30 p.m.

How far from their home is the campsite?

❷ A walker climbs to the top of a mountain, then back down to ground level.
The graph below shows his height above ground level throughout the day.

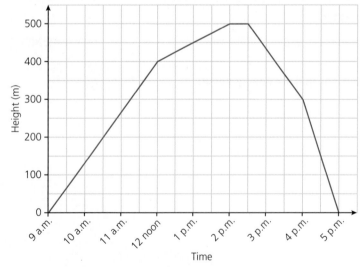

a At what time did the walker start climbing the mountain?

b When the walker reached the top, how long did he stop to look at the view?

c How high above ground level was the walker at 4 p.m.?

Band 2 questions

3 Leonard lives in London. He walks to a house called Howards End in the countryside outside London.

a When does Leonard leave London?

b How long does he spend at Howards End?

c On the way back Leonard stops for a rest.

How far is Leonard from London when he stops?

d How long does he stop for?

e Charles drives from London to Howards End.

He leaves at 1:15 p.m. and arrives at 1:45 p.m.

How far does he drive?

f Copy Leonard's graph onto graph paper.

Add a line to your graph representing Charles's journey.

g At what time does Charles pass Leonard?

What is Leonard doing at that time?

h How far is Charles from Howards End when he passes Leonard?

4 A scientist investigates the number of bees in a hive.

She finds that during the summer season their population N can be modelled by this exponential equation:

$$N = 640 + 4360 \times 1.3^{-t}$$

where t is the number of days into the summer season beginning on 1st June.

A graph of the number of bees is shown.

a Find the population of the bees at midnight on 1st June. ← This is time $t = 0$.

b Find the population of the bees at the beginning of 10th June.

c On which date does the population first fall below 1000?

d According to the equation, is it possible for the number of bees in the hive to fall to zero?

If not, what is the smallest possible number of bees?

⑤ A, B and C are three stops on a bus route.

The travel graph shows the journey of a bus from A to C via B.

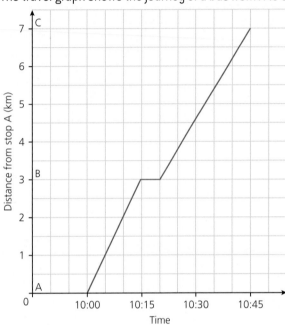

a **i** When does the bus leave stop A?

ii When does the bus arrive at stop B?

iii For how long does the bus stop at B?

iv What is the average speed of the bus between A and B?

v What is the distance between stops B and C?

b A second bus leaves C at 10:10.

It travels at a constant speed to B, arriving at 10:45.

i Copy the travel graph and show the second bus's journey on it.

ii When do the two buses pass each other?

iii Roughly how far apart are the buses at 10:40?

Band 3 questions

⑥ To film a scene for an action movie, a remote-controlled car is driven off a 50-metre-high cliff.

The height of the car can be calculated using this equation:

$$y = 50 - \frac{1}{5}x^2$$

where y is the car's height and x is its horizontal distance from the cliff.

x and y are both measured in metres.

Car

a   Copy and complete this table of values.

x (metres)	0	2.5	5	7.5	10	12.5	15
y (metres)	50				30		

b   Copy and complete this graph using the data in your table.

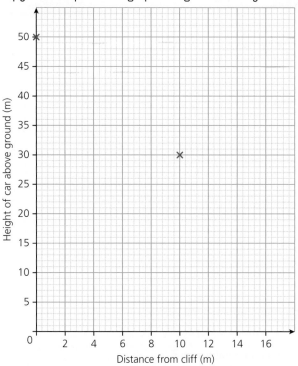

Join the points on your graph with a smooth curve.

Extend the curve so that it touches the x-axis.

Answer these questions using the graph:

c   How high above the ground is the car when it is 8 metres from the cliff?

d   How far from the cliff is the car when it is at a height of 10 metres?

Is your answer exact or an approximate reading from the graph?

e   Roughly how far from the cliff does the car land?

7   Seth was born on 14th May 2013.

His dad kept a record of his weight until he was 7 in the year 2020.

The graph shows Seth's weight and the average weight of a boy up to the age of 7.

a   When Seth was born, was he below the average weight for a boy, or above?

b   Roughly when did this change?

c   Roughly what was Seth's weight when he was 4 years old?

d   Roughly how old was Seth when his weight first went above 20 kg?

e   At the age of 7, was Seth below the average weight of a boy, or above?

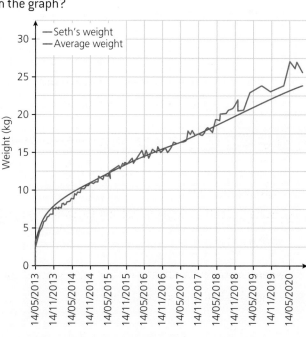

8 Richard studies the fish population in a large lake.

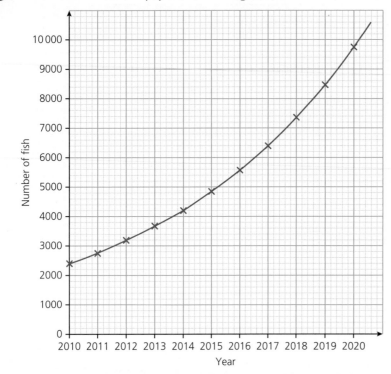

a How many fish are in the lake when Richard surveys the lake in 2010?

b When roughly is the fish population 5000?

c By roughly what percentage is the population increasing each year?

d Do you think this growth is exponential? Explain your answer.

e Do you think this type of growth could continue for the next 20 years? Explain your answer.

f If this growth continues for one more year, what figure would Richard expect for the fish population in 2021?

Transformations

▶ **Coming up...**

- ◆ Reflection and translation
- ◆ Rotation
- ◆ Enlargement

→ **Translation code words**

+	−	×	÷	/	:	space
)	T	U	V	W	X	Y
(	S	F	G	H	I	Z
?	R	E	start	A	J	1
.	Q	D	C	B	K	2
,	P	O	N	M	L	3
0	9	8	7	6	5	4

a Beginning at the start square, move using these vectors.

$$\begin{pmatrix} -2 \\ 1 \end{pmatrix}, \begin{pmatrix} 4 \\ -3 \end{pmatrix}, \begin{pmatrix} 0 \\ 3 \end{pmatrix}, \begin{pmatrix} -1 \\ -3 \end{pmatrix}, \begin{pmatrix} 0 \\ 0 \end{pmatrix}, \begin{pmatrix} -2 \\ 2 \end{pmatrix}, \begin{pmatrix} -1 \\ 0 \end{pmatrix}$$

What word do you spell?

b Decode this message.

$$\begin{pmatrix} 0 \\ 2 \end{pmatrix}, \begin{pmatrix} -1 \\ -2 \end{pmatrix}, \begin{pmatrix} 1 \\ -1 \end{pmatrix}, \begin{pmatrix} -2 \\ 3 \end{pmatrix}, \begin{pmatrix} 1 \\ -4 \end{pmatrix}, \begin{pmatrix} -1 \\ 2 \end{pmatrix}, \begin{pmatrix} 5 \\ 3 \end{pmatrix}, \begin{pmatrix} -3 \\ -4 \end{pmatrix}, \begin{pmatrix} -1 \\ -1 \end{pmatrix}, \begin{pmatrix} 0 \\ 1 \end{pmatrix}, \begin{pmatrix} 0 \\ 1 \end{pmatrix}$$

$$\begin{pmatrix} -1 \\ 1 \end{pmatrix}, \begin{pmatrix} 5 \\ 2 \end{pmatrix}, \begin{pmatrix} -2 \\ -3 \end{pmatrix}, \begin{pmatrix} -3 \\ 0 \end{pmatrix}, \begin{pmatrix} 1 \\ 0 \end{pmatrix}, \begin{pmatrix} 4 \\ 3 \end{pmatrix}, \begin{pmatrix} -4 \\ -3 \end{pmatrix}, \begin{pmatrix} 2 \\ 0 \end{pmatrix}, \begin{pmatrix} -3 \\ 1 \end{pmatrix}, \begin{pmatrix} 5 \\ 1 \end{pmatrix}, \begin{pmatrix} -6 \\ -3 \end{pmatrix}$$

10.1 Reflection and translation

✓ Skill checker

① **a** Copy the axes below and plot these straight lines, labelling each one.

   i $y = 2$

   ii $y = x$

b At which point do the two lines intersect?

② What are the equations of the two lines shown below?

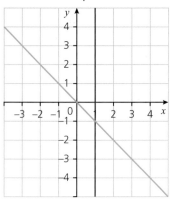

Recap: translations

A **transformation** moves an object according to a rule.

One type of transformation is a **translation**. You learnt about translations in Year 7.

In the diagram object PQR is translated to the image P'Q'R'.

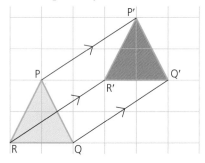

The object slides without turning.

The translation is described as 3 units right and 2 units up.

It can also be written as $\begin{pmatrix} 3 \\ 2 \end{pmatrix}$ ← This way of writing a translation is called a **vector**.

The vector representing the translation from A to B is sometimes written as $\overrightarrow{AB}$.

The image and the original object are congruent. This means they are the same shape and the same size.

Describing a translation

Worked example

Describe the translation that maps:

a A to C   **b** B to C   **c** C to A.

Solution

a The translation mapping A to C is 8 units right and 1 unit down. Using vector notation, this is: $\begin{pmatrix} 8 \\ -1 \end{pmatrix}$.

b The translation from B to C is 2 units right and 3 down, or $\begin{pmatrix} 2 \\ -3 \end{pmatrix}$.

c The translation from C to A is 8 units left and 1 up, so $\begin{pmatrix} -8 \\ 1 \end{pmatrix}$.

Worked example

Translating an object using a vector

a Draw and label an x axis from -5 to 7 and a y axis from 0 to 7.

Plot and label these points.

$(1, 0), (3, 1), (4, 3), (5, 1)$

Join the points in order to form a quadrilateral.

Label it A.

b Translate shape A by $\begin{pmatrix} 2 \\ 4 \end{pmatrix}$

Label the image B.

c Now translate shape B by $\begin{pmatrix} -7 \\ 0 \end{pmatrix}$

Label the image C.

d Describe the single transformation that maps A to C.

Solution

a–c To translate the shape A using the vector $\begin{pmatrix} 2 \\ 4 \end{pmatrix}$, translate each of the four corners.

The point $(1, 0)$ is moved 2 units to the right and 4 up.

The image point is $(3, 4)$.

Repeat this process with each of the four corners.

Join the four image points and label the shape B.

Then translate each of the corners of shape B 7 units to the left.

Join the four image points and label the shape C.

d The transformation A to C is a translation $\begin{pmatrix} -5 \\ 4 \end{pmatrix}$.

Summary: translations

- To translate a shape, translate each of the corners.
  All points on the object move according to the same instructions.
- To describe a translation, start by counting or measuring the units along and up through which a point moves.
- A translation of 4 units to the right and 5 up can be written as $\begin{pmatrix} 4 \\ 5 \end{pmatrix}$
  Using this notation, right is +, left − and up is +, down −.
  The image after a translation is always congruent to the original object. ← Congruent means the same shape and size.

Recap: reflections

In Year 7 you learnt that reflection is a type of transformation.

When an object is reflected in a line, its image is formed on the other side of the line.

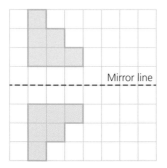

Mirror line

The line is called the **mirror line** or the **line of reflection**.

The image and the original object are **congruent**. This means they are the same shape and the same size.

The line of reflection does not have to be horizontal or vertical – it can be a diagonal line.

Lines that are commonly used for reflection are shown in the diagram below.

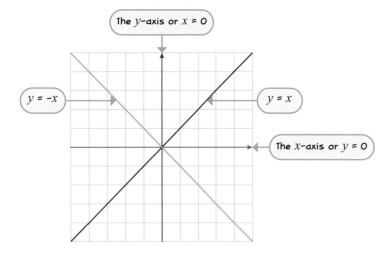

The y-axis or $x = 0$

$y = -x$

$y = x$

The x-axis or $y = 0$

Other commonly used lines of symmetry are vertical and horizontal lines e.g. $x = 3$ or $y = -3$.

It is often obvious where the image of a point should be, but if not, take these steps:

❶ Turn your page so that the mirror line is vertical.

❷ Draw a line from the point to the mirror line, **meeting the mirror line at right angles**.

❸ Continue the line the same distance on the opposite side of the mirror line, as shown below.

Worked example

Reflect the shape PQRSTU in the mirror line shown.

Solution

1 Turn the page to make the mirror line vertical.

2 Draw a line from one vertex of the shape to the mirror line, **meeting the mirror line at right angles**. This has been done for vertex Q.

3 Continue the line the same distance on the opposite side of the mirror line, as shown.

4 Repeat the reflection for each vertex.

5 Join all the vertices to form the **image** shape, labelled P′Q′R′S′T′U′ in the diagram.

Reflecting a shape on a coordinate grid

A point and its image are always the same distance from the mirror line.

Worked example

a Copy this diagram.

Draw the image of the triangle when it is reflected in the y-axis.

b Are the two triangles congruent?

How do you know?

Solution

a

b When an object is reflected, all the lines and angles on the object and its image are the same size.

So the object and image shapes are congruent.

Finding the line of reflection

Worked example

For each of these diagrams show the line of reflection and give its equation.

Solution

The line of reflection is $y = 2$

The line of reflection is $y = x$

The line of reflection is $y = -x$

To fully describe a reflection you must state the equation of the mirror line.

Activity

John is playing a computer game.

Shapes appear at the top of the screen.

The aim of the game is to get as many horizontal lines as possible completely filled by the shapes.

You can use any translation to move them to a final position at the bottom of the screen. Shapes must not overlap.

① This picture shows where the first shape appears (at the top of the screen) and where John places it.

Describe the translation of shape 1.

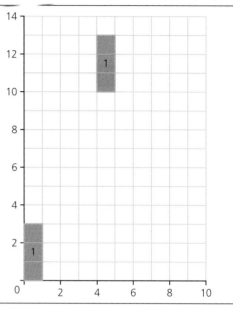

② This picture shows where the second shape appears (at the top of the screen) and where John places it.

Describe the translation of shape 2.

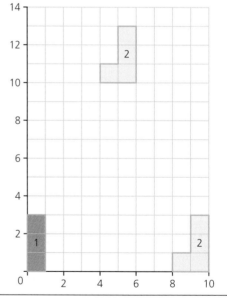

③ This is where the next two shapes appear.

John translates shape 3 by 5 to the right and 10 down.

Copy the diagram in part **2**.

Draw and label the final position of shape 3.

He translates shape 4 by 4 to the left and 10 down.

Draw and label the final position of shape 4 on your diagram.

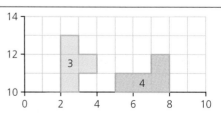

④ Here are the next three shapes.
Decide where to place each one.
  a Draw the final position of each shape on your diagram.
  b Describe the translation of each shape.

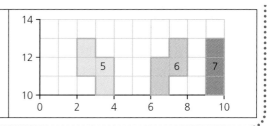

10.1 Now try these

Band 1 questions

❶ For each diagram write down how many units the blue shape has moved.
Write down if it moved left or right, up or down.

a

b

c

d

❷ Copy the diagram.

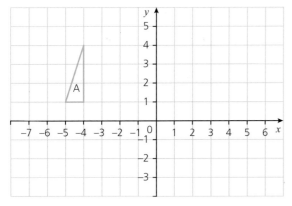

Draw shape A after:

a   a translation of 2 to the right and 1 up
b   a translation of 1 to the left and 1 up
c   a translation of 4 down
d   a translation of 6 to the right and 2 down.

3 Copy this diagram, extending the grid as necessary

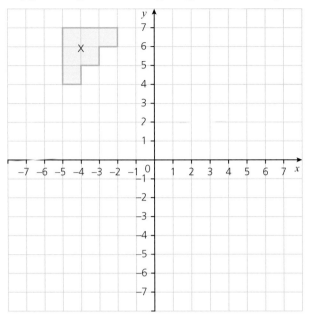

Draw the shapes given by the translations in the table.

Label each of the images.

Translation	Left/right	Up/down
X→Y	3 right	1 up
X→Z	2 right	6 down
X→P	2 left	5 down
Z→Q	4 left	4 down
Z→R	5 right	1 up
R→S	2 left	4 down

4 Look at these shapes.

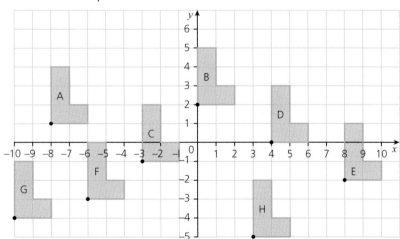

Copy this table and complete it to describe each translation.

Translation	Translation vector
A⟶B	$\begin{pmatrix} 8 \\ 1 \end{pmatrix}$
A⟶C	
A⟶H	
C⟶B	
C⟶G	
C⟶D	
E⟶D	
E⟶F	
G⟶D	
G⟶A	
G⟶H	

5 **a** Draw and label x and y axes from −6 to 8.

Plot the following points and join them to make a triangle.

(−6, 3), (−5, 7), (−1, 4)

Label this triangle P.

b Translate triangle P 5 to the right and 2 down.

Label the new triangle Q.

c What translation will map Q to P?

Band 2 questions

6

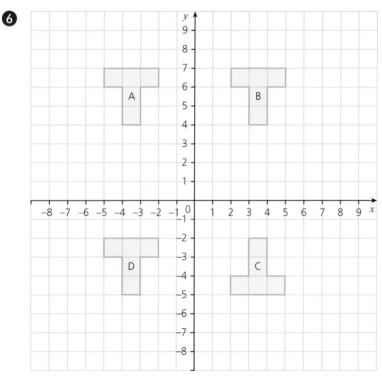

a Describe fully the transformation from shape A to shape B.

b Describe fully the transformation from shape A to shape D.

c Describe fully the transformation from shape B to shape C.

Fluency — Reasoning

7 Here is a part of a mosaic wall.

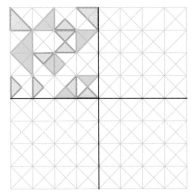

    a Copy the diagram.

        Reflect the coloured pattern in the y axis.

    b Now reflect the entire pattern in the x axis.

8 **a** Draw x and y axes from −8 to 8.

        Plot these points and join them to form a triangle.

        $(−7, −2), (−2, −3), (−5, −6)$

        Label the triangle A.

    b Reflect A in the x axis and label the image B.

    c Reflect B in the y axis and label the image C.

    d Reflect C in the x axis and label the new image D.

    e Reflect D in the y axis.

        What do you notice?

Band 3 questions

9 **a** Copy this diagram and reflect the shape in the y-axis.

        What can you say about the image?

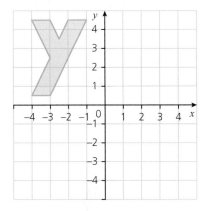

    b Copy this diagram and reflect the shape in the y-axis.

        What can you say about the image?

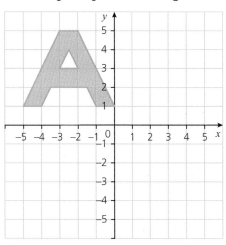

    c Why is the letter A the 'right way round' after the reflection, but not the letter y?

10 **a** Copy the diagram.

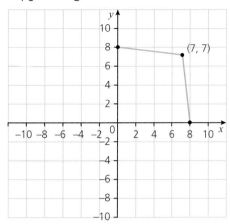

b Reflect the shape in the y-axis.

c Now reflect both shapes in the x-axis.

d Describe the shape you have drawn.

11 **a** Draw and label axes from −8 to 8.

b Plot the following points and join them to form a triangle.

(1, 2), (3, 7), (6, 1)

Label the triangle A.

c Reflect triangle A in the x-axis and label the image B.

d Write down the coordinates of the vertices of triangle B.

e Translate triangle B by $\begin{pmatrix} -5 \\ -1 \end{pmatrix}$

Label the image C.

f Reflect triangle C in the x-axis.

Label the image D.

g Describe the transformation that maps D on to A.

12 **a** Write down the translation vector where the object does not move.

b Write down a sequence of three different translations where the shape returns to its original position.

10.2 Rotation

✓ Skill checker

Fill in the blanks in these sentences, then find the words in the word search puzzle below.

The words can appear horizontally, vertically or diagonally. They can appear forwards or backwards.

There are 9 words to find. Good luck!

Clues

1 A 90° angle is a _ _ _ _ _ _ R of a _ _ L _ turn

2 180° is half a _ _ R _

3 270° is _ _ R _ _ quarters of a circle

4 360° is O _ _ full turn

5 There are several different types of transformation. For example, you can I _ _ _ _ _ _ _ _, reflect or R _ _ _ _ _ a shape.

6   You can use a _ _ _ _ _<u>R</u> to translate a shape

7   (1, 3) is an example of a _ _ _ _<u>T</u>

K	Q	F	Z	T	R	D	U	R
W	T	U	C	P	O	I	N	T
Y	C	L	A	N	T	E	O	F
J	E	L	S	R	A	O	N	E
N	L	I	B	A	T	H	R	G
R	F	T	H	R	E	E	U	P
U	E	V	E	C	T	O	R	L
T	R	A	N	S	L	A	T	E

Introduction to rotations

Another type of transformation is a rotation.

A rotation is performed by turning an object.

A full turn is 360°, so:

● a quarter turn is 90° (a right angle)
● a half turn is 180°
● a three-quarters turn is 270°.

In this diagram the orange triangle is the image of the green triangle when it is rotated through 90° clockwise about the origin.

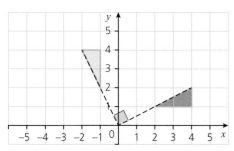

In this diagram the orange flag is the image of the green one when it is rotated through 180° about the point (1, 0).

A rotation of 180° can be clockwise or anticlockwise.

After any rotation, the image shape is always **congruent** to the original shape.

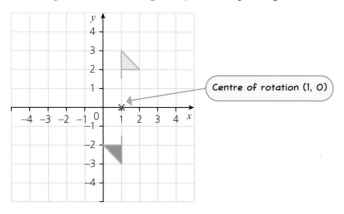

Centre of rotation (1, 0)

Rotating a shape about the origin

a   Rotate shape A by 90° in a clockwise direction, centre (0, 0).
Label the resulting image B.

b   Rotate shape A by 180°, centre the origin.

Label the resulting image C.

Why does the direction not matter for this rotation?

Solution

Using tracing paper is the easiest way to rotate a shape. Follow these steps.

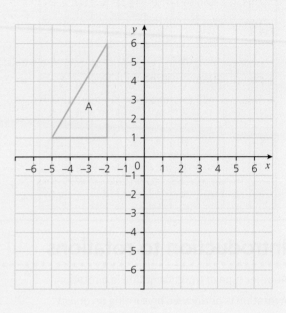

1   Trace the **original** shape AND some of the gridlines onto tracing paper.

2   Without moving the tracing paper, put the point of your pencil on the centre of rotation to fix that point.

3   Rotate the tracing paper. After a 90° or 180° rotation the gridlines on the tracing paper line up with those on the page.

4   Copy the shape back onto the page as the **image**.

a–b

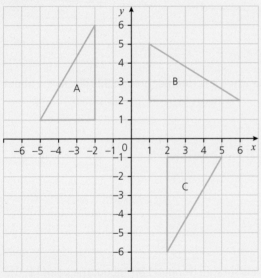

For part **b**, the direction does not matter because a turn of 180° is the same whichever direction you turn.

Describing a rotation

Look at this diagram showing three arrowheads.

a   Describe the transformation from shape A to shape B.

b   What are the coordinates of the four vertices of shape B?

c   Hannah says that shape B is congruent to shape A.

Gareth says that Hannah is wrong because the shape is upside down.

Say who is right and explain why.

d Describe the transformation from shape A to shape C.

Solution

> To describe a rotation you must give the angle, the direction and the centre of rotation.

a This is a rotation through 90° clockwise about (0, 0).

b The coordinates of the vertices of B are: (0, 2), (3, 3), (6, 2) and (3, 5).

c Hannah is right. Congruent shapes have the same size and shape. The **orientation** does not matter.

> Orientation means which way up the shape is.

d This is a rotation through 180° about (0, 0).

> To describe a rotation of 180° you don't need to give the direction. Both clockwise and anticlockwise are correct.

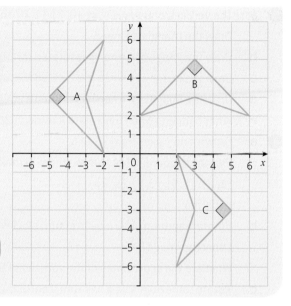

10.2 Now try these

Band 1 questions

1 Copy this diagram.

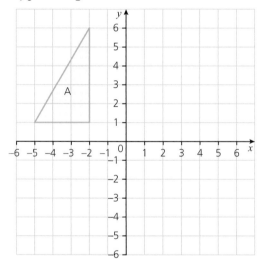

a The triangle A is rotated through a quarter turn in a clockwise direction.
Draw its image and label it B.

b The triangle A is rotated through a quarter turn in an anticlockwise direction.
Draw its image and label it C.

c Describe the rotation that maps triangle B on to triangle C.

2 a Draw x and y axes from −6 to 6.
Plot the points A(2, 1), B(2, 5) and C(4, 1).
Join them to form a triangle.

b Rotate the triangle through 90° clockwise about the origin.
Label the image A′B′C′ and write down its coordinates.

c Rotate A′B′C′ by a further 90° clockwise about the origin.
Label the image A″B″C″ and write down its coordinates.

> **Remember**
> You can use tracing paper in all questions on rotations.

3 **a** The vertices of triangle A are (0, 0), (1, 0) and (1, 4).

Draw the triangle on a grid.

b Draw the image of A when it is rotated through 90° in a clockwise direction, centre the origin.

c Draw the image of A when it is rotated through 180°, centre the origin.

d Draw the image of A when it is rotated through 270° in a clockwise direction, centre the origin.

e What happens when you rotate A through 360°, centre the origin?

4 **a** Draw x and y axes from −5 to 5.

Plot these coordinates and join them to make a trapezium.

(1, 2), (1, 5), (3, 5), (5, 2)

Label it A.

b Rotate trapezium A by a quarter turn clockwise, centre the origin.

Label the image B.

What are the coordinates of the vertices of B?

c Rotate trapezium A by a half turn, centre the origin.

Label the image C.

What are the coordinates of the vertices of C?

d What single transformation would map B on to C?

Band 2 questions

5

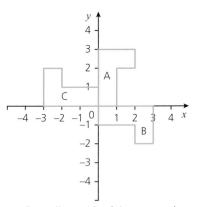

a Describe each of these rotations.

  i A to B   **ii** A to C   **iii** B to A

b Draw and label x- and y-axes from −5 to 5.

Copy shape A on to your diagram.

Now rotate A through 180° about the origin.

Label the image D.

c **i** Is shape D congruent to shape A?   **ii** Explain your answer.

6 Draw this arrow after each of these transformations.

Make it four squares long each time.

a A rotation 90° clockwise, centre the origin.

b A rotation 270° anticlockwise, centre the origin.

c A rotation 180° clockwise, centre the origin.

d A rotation 180° anticlockwise, centre the origin.

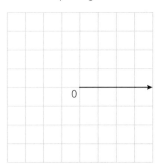

7 This clock has three hands.

Through what angle does each of the hands turn in:

a 1 minute **b** 30 seconds **c** 15 seconds?

Band 3 questions

8 Draw a pair of axes from −6 to 6.

a Plot these points and join them to form a letter L.

$(0, 0), (−5, 0), (−5, 6), (−3, 6), (−3, 2), (0, 2)$

Label this object A.

b Rotate A by a right angle clockwise, centre the origin.

Label the image B.

c Rotate B by a right angle clockwise, centre the origin.

Label the image C.

d What single transformation maps A to C?

9 The diagram shows a plan of a children's roundabout.

O and T show the starting positions of Olga and Tilly.

a Make a copy of the diagram.

On your diagram show the positions of Olga and Tilly after each of these transformations from their starting positions.

i A clockwise rotation of $90°$ about C.

Label them O_1 and T_1.

ii A clockwise rotation of $270°$ about C.

Label them O_2 and T_2.

b Describe two transformations for each of these mappings.

i O_1 to O_2 **ii** T_1 to T_2

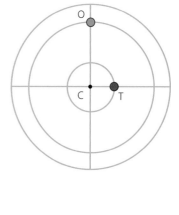

10 Look at shapes A, B, C and D in the diagram.

All four shapes are congruent.

a Describe fully the transformation C to D.

b Describe fully the reflection that maps A to B.

Describe fully the translation that maps A to B.

c Describe fully the reflection that maps A to C.

Describe fully the rotation that maps A to C.

Is there a translation mapping A to C?

d Can you explain why there is a difference in the types of transformation mapping A to B compared with A to C?

e Describe fully a transformation mapping A to D.

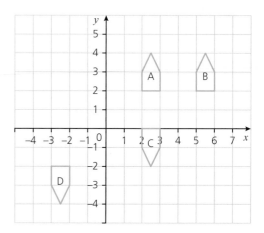

⑪ Describe fully these transformations.

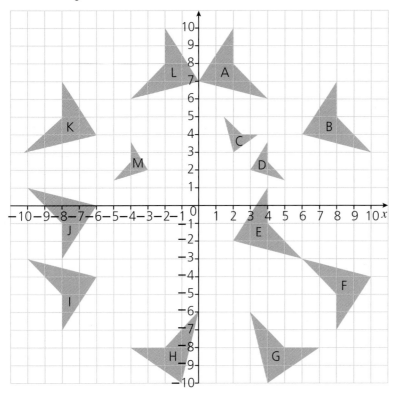

a	K to L	b	A to B	c	K to B	d	I to B	e	K to I
f	C to M	g	F to E	h	F to I	i	A to L	j	H to G
k	C to D	l	J to I	m	F to J				

⑫ Look at the picture of a spanner turning a bolt.

The bolt head is a regular hexagon.

Point C is the centre of rotation.

a The spanner is rotated 60° clockwise about C.

What can you say about the appearance of the bolt before and after the rotation?

b Write down three other clockwise rotations which do not change the appearance of the bolt.

c Write down two anticlockwise rotations which do not change the appearance of the bolt.

d What is the rotational symmetry of the bolt? ← You learnt about rotational symmetry in Year 7.

⑬ A car drives round a racetrack. A to B is a translation of 1 km due East.

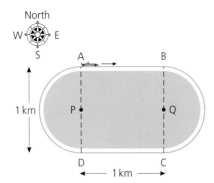

a Describe the transformation C to D.

b B to C is a rotation of 180° about Q.

Describe the transformation D to A.

c Use a combination of transformations to describe the movement of the car from:

   i A to C

   ii B to D.

10.3 Enlargement

✓ Skill checker

True or false?

Are these statements true or false? Explain your answers.

① If a picture measures 6 cm by 4 cm, it could be enlarged so it would fit in a frame measuring 15 cm by 10 cm.

② The Big Ben clock tower is 96 metres high and has a 15-metre square base. A scale model 64 cm high has a square base measuring 10 cm by 10 cm.

③ A scale drawing of a classroom has side lengths that are one tenth of the actual sizes. The area of the scale drawing is also one tenth of the size of the real classroom.

④ A passport photo must be 35 mm wide by 45 mm high. Ben has a photo of himself measuring 7 cm by 8 cm. If he reduces this photo in size, he could use it as a passport photo.

⑤ A running track has two straight edges and two semicircular ends. The overall length could be doubled if the two straight edges are doubled in length.

⑥ The bark of a cork tree is used to make bottle corks. A cork tree doubles in height in 5 years. In this time the thickness of the trunk also doubles. Twice as many bottle corks can be made from the bark now.

⑦ A scale model of a boat is made for the bath. The model's width is $\frac{1}{100}$ of the actual width. The length of the model should be $\frac{1}{100}$ of the actual boat's length.

⑧ A road is being expanded to take more traffic. The width of the road is doubled, going up from 2 lanes to 4 lanes. The length of the road will also double.

Introduction to enlargements

Enlargement is a transformation that changes the size of an object.

One shape is an enlargement of another if all the angles in the shape are the same and the lengths of the sides have all been increased by the same scale factor. ← ⟨ A shape and its enlargement are called **similar** shapes. ⟩

In this diagram the pentagon ABCDE is enlarged by a scale factor of 3 to A′B′C′D′E′.

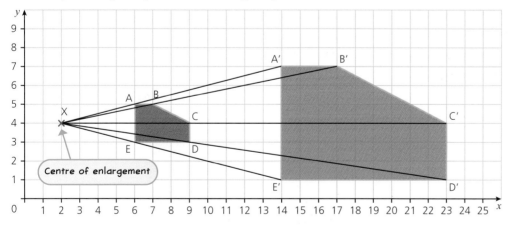

The position of the image depends on the centre of enlargement X.

Because the scale factor of enlargement is 3:

● side A′B′ is three times as long as AB
● side E′D′ is three times as long as ED, etc.
● the distance XB′ is three times the distance XB
● the distance XD′ is three times the distance XD, etc.

The term enlargement is also used in situations where the shape is made smaller.

In these cases, the scale factor is a fraction, like $\frac{1}{2}$ or $\frac{1}{3}$.

In the diagram the scale factor for the enlargement of A'B'C'D'E' to ABCDE is $\frac{1}{3}$.

Finding the scale factor of an enlargement

Worked example

The diagram shows an enlargement from centre P.

The small rectangle is the original shape; the larger rectangle is the image.

a What is the scale factor of the enlargement?

b What happens if you change the centre of enlargement?

Solution

a The scale factor is 3 because all the sides of the second shape are three times as long as those of the first shape.

b The image would be in a different place.

Enlarging a shape

Follow these steps to draw an enlargement.

❶ Choose one of the vertices of the original shape.

❷ Draw a 'ray' from the centre of enlargement to this vertex.

❸ Multiply the length of this ray by the scale factor.

❹ Draw the new ray from the centre of enlargement to the image vertex. ◀

> Note: If an enlargement has a fractional scale factor, then it results in a reduction in size.

Worked example

Plot the points A(2, 4), B(4, 4), C(4, 6) and D(2, 6).

Join the points to form a square.

Enlarge ABCD using (0, 5) as the centre of enlargement and a scale factor of 2.

Label the image A'B'C'D'

a What are the coordinates of the points A', B', C' and D'?

b What shape is A'B'C'D'?

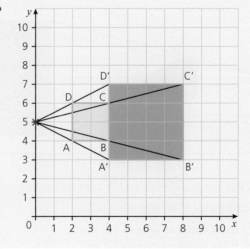

Solution

a A'(4, 3), B'(8, 3), C'(8, 7), D'(4, 7)

b A square

Describing an enlargement

Worked example

Emma draws the rectangle ABCD.

She then transforms it as shown to A′B′C′D′.

a Describe fully the transformation from ABCD to A′B′C′D′.

b What can you say about the distances AB and A′B′?

Solution

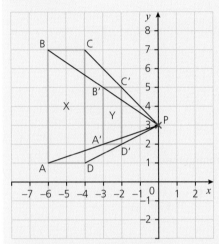

a Join point A with its image A′, B with B′, etc. Extending these lines, they meet at point P(0, 3). This is the centre of enlargement.

The length A′B′ is half of AB, etc. The scale factor is half.

This transformation is an enlargement, with a scale factor of $\frac{1}{2}$ and a centre of enlargement (0, 3).

b Since the scale factor is $\frac{1}{2}$, the distance A′B′ is half of the distance AB.

10.3 Now try these

Band 1 questions

1 A shape is enlarged. The scale factor is 2.

What happens to:

a the lengths   **b** the angles?

2 Draw and label a pair of axes, with x from −7 to 10 and y from −4 to 10.

Draw a rectangle with vertices at (−2, 3), (3, 3), (3, −1), (−2, −1).

Using the origin as centre, enlarge the rectangle with a scale factor of

a 2   **b** 3.

3 Copy each of these shapes onto a grid and enlarge it by a scale factor of 3.

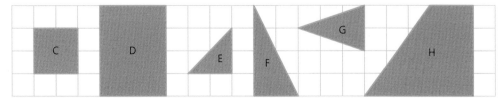

Reasoning

Fluency

4 Copy this diagram.

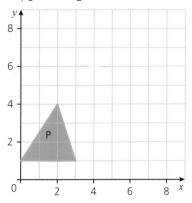

a Enlarge shape P with scale factor 2 and centre of enlargement (0, 2).
Label the image Q.

b Enlarge Q with scale factor $\frac{1}{2}$ and centre of enlargement (8, 2).
Label the image R.

c Describe the transformation that maps P to R.

5 Copy each of these diagrams.
Enlarge each shape by a scale factor of $\frac{1}{2}$ using the origin as the centre of enlargement.

a

b

c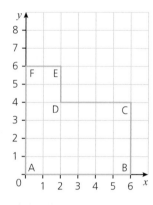

Band 2 questions

6 You will need a protractor for this question.

a Draw and label an x-axis from 0 to 10 and a y-axis from 0 to 8.
Plot these points and join them to form triangle T.
(6, 8), (6, 4), (10, 6)

b Measure the angles of triangle T.

c Enlarge triangle T by scale factor $\frac{1}{2}$ using (1, 8) as the centre of enlargement.

d Measure the angles of the image.
What do you notice?

7 Draw an x-axis from 0 to 16 and a y-axis from 0 to 8.

a Draw the trapezium whose vertices are P(2, 8), Q(8, 8), R(5, 2) and S(2, 2).

b Using (14, 5) as the centre of enlargement:

i enlarge PQRS by scale factor $\frac{1}{3}$ and label the image P'Q'R'S'

ii enlarge PQRS by scale factor $\frac{2}{3}$ and label the image P''Q''R''S''.

c P'Q'R'S' is an enlargement of P''Q''R''S''.

    i What are the coordinates of the centre of enlargement?

    ii What is the scale factor?

Band 3 questions

8 The enlargement reading on a photocopier is 100% when the copy is to be the same size as the original.

When the reading is 120% then each length is increased by 20%.

  a What enlargement reading do you use if you want:

    i each length decreased by 10%

    ii a 5 cm line increased to 7 cm

    iii a 6 cm line reduced to 4.5 cm?

  b On the original a rectangle is 20 cm by 12 cm. The enlargement is set to 125%.

    i What is the area of the rectangle on the original?

    ii What is the area of the enlarged rectangle?

    iii What is the percentage increase of the area in the enlargement?

9 Russian dolls are wooden toys in the shape of dolls that fit inside each other.

  a There are five Russian dolls in a set. The smallest has a width of 1 cm and a height of 2 cm.

The second doll is twice the size of the first.

The third doll is three times the size of the first, and so on.

Find the width and height of each doll in the set.

Start with the smallest and end with the biggest.

Write your answers in a copy of this table.

Width	Height
1 cm	2 cm

  b What is the scale factor of the enlargement from the largest to the smallest?

10 In the diagram there are six different shapes and their enlargements.

One shape does not pair up with any other.

  a Match the shapes to their enlargements.

  b Name the shapes.

  c Work out the scale factor of enlargement for each pair of shapes.

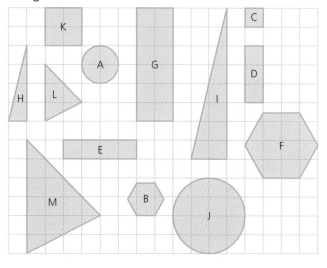

11 **a** Copy this diagram.

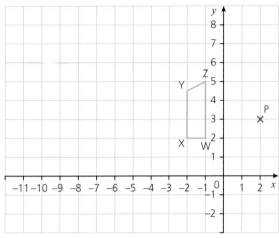

b Draw an enlargement of WXYZ, scale factor 2, centre P.

Label the image W'X'Y'Z'.

c Draw an enlargement of WXYZ, scale factor 3, centre P.

Label the image W"X"Y"Z".

d What transformation maps W'X'Y'Z' to W"X"Y"Z"?

12 Maddie draws shape PQRS.

She transforms it to the image XYZW.

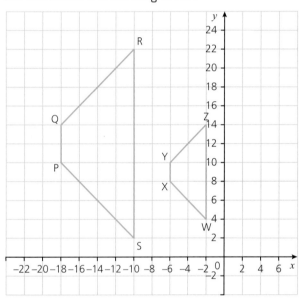

Describe fully the transformation which maps shape PQRS to shape XYZW.

13 P is the centre of enlargement for each of these pairs of shapes.

Find the scale factor of the enlargement from the larger shape to the smaller in each case.

a

b

c

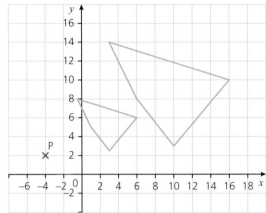

Key words

Here is a list of the key words you met in this chapter.

Congruent	Enlargement	Reflection	Rotation
Transformation	Translation	Vector	

Use the glossary at the back of this book to check any you are unsure about.

Review exercise: transformations

Reasoning

1

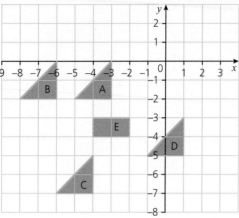

a Describe each of these translations.

    i A to B   **ii** A to C   **iii** A to D   **iv** B to C   **v** B to D   **vi** C to D

b Why is A to E impossible?

Fluency

2 Draw x- and y-axes from -3 to 8.

On the same grid draw these images.

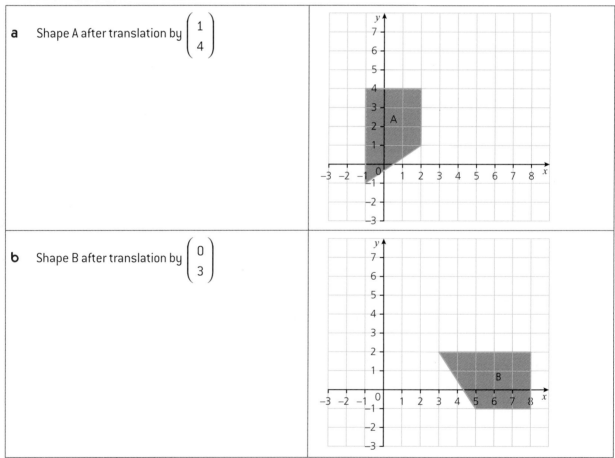

a Shape A after translation by $\begin{pmatrix} 1 \\ 4 \end{pmatrix}$

b Shape B after translation by $\begin{pmatrix} 0 \\ 3 \end{pmatrix}$

Key Stage 3 Mastering Mathematics: Book 3

c Shape C after translation by $\begin{pmatrix} -6 \\ 0 \end{pmatrix}$

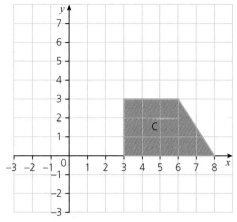

d Shape D after translation by $\begin{pmatrix} -3 \\ -6 \end{pmatrix}$

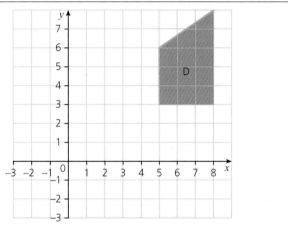

3 The diagram shows **the same word** written in both lower case letters and capital letters.

b	i	?		
B	l	?		

The last letter is missing from the word in both cases.

The short red line is a vertical mirror line.

The longer red line is a horizontal mirror line.

When the word is written in lower case it has vertical symmetry. When it is reflected in the vertical mirror line, it appears the same.

When the word is written in capital letters it has horizontal symmetry. When it is reflected in the horizontal mirror line, it appears the same.

What is the missing letter of the word?

4 **a** You only need one piece of information to describe a translation.

What is it?

b You need three pieces of information to describe a rotation fully.

What are they?

c Look at the diagram.

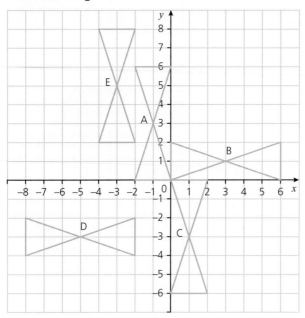

What translation could be used for each of these transformations?

i A to E   **ii** A to C   **iii** E to C   **iv** B to D

d What rotation could be used for each of these transformations?

i A to B   **ii** A to C   **iii** B to D   **iv** C to E

Band 2 Questions

⑤ Copy this flag.

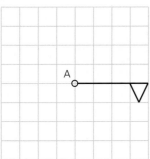

Rotate the flag about point A through:

a a quarter turn anticlockwise   **b** a half turn clockwise   **c** a three-quarter turn clockwise.

⑥ The triangle A in the diagram is rotated through 90° anticlockwise with centre of rotation D($-2, 2$).

Its image is B.

The triangle B is rotated through 90° clockwise with centre of rotation E($1, 1$).

Its image is C.

Find the single transformation that maps A onto C.

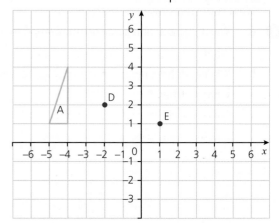

7 P is the centre of enlargement for this pair of shapes.

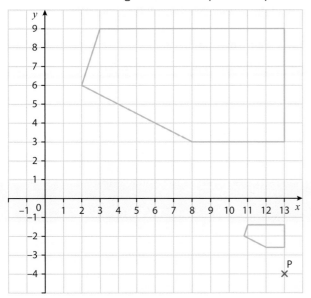

a Find the scale factor of the enlargement from the smaller shape to the larger shape.

b Find the scale factor of the enlargement from the larger shape to the smaller shape.

Band 3 questions

Reasoning

8 Look at the word ZERO, written in capital letters.

It has been reflected in the horizontal line shown.

a The letters E and O look the same as the originals. What property of these letters allows them to look the same after the reflection?

b Write all the numbers from ONE to TEN in capital letters.

Reflecting them in a horizontal line, would any of these words look exactly the same after the reflection?

c The letter T remains unchanged after a reflection in a vertical line. What property must a letter have for this to happen?

d Can you think of any words that would look the same after a reflection in a vertical line?

Problem solving

9 Draw an x-axis from -8 to 14 and a y-axis from 0 to 14.

a Draw these three parallelograms.

i A$(-4, 11)$, B$(-2, 13)$, C$(0, 12)$, D$(-2, 10)$

Enlarge this parallelogram using scale factor 2 and centre of enlargement $(-8, 12)$.

ii E$(-4, 3)$, F$(-4, 6)$, G$(-2, 5)$, H$(-2, 2)$

Enlarge this parallelogram using scale factor 2 and centre of enlargement $(-8, 2)$.

iii J$(9, 5)$, K$(9, 8)$, L$(11, 10)$, M$(11, 7)$

Enlarge this parallelogram using scale factor 2 and centre of enlargement $(14, 8)$.

b What 3-D shape have you drawn?

10 a Draw coordinate axes with both the x-axis and y-axis running from -3 to 8.

b Plot these points: A$(-3, 1)$, B$(-3, 3)$, C$(-1, 1)$ and D$(-1, 3)$.

c Join these pairs of points with straight lines.

i A and B

ii B and C

iii C and D.

d What letter have you drawn?

e Translate the entire shape using the vector $\begin{pmatrix} 4 \\ 0 \end{pmatrix}$. Label the image of shape ABCD as A'B'C'D'.

f Rotate the lines A'B' and C'D' by 90° clockwise, using a centre of rotation (4, 0).

Label the image of point A' as A''. Label the images of the other three points B'', C'' and D''.

g Reflect the diagonal line B'C' in the mirror line $x = 4$.

h Enlarge the shape A''B''C''D'' using a scale factor of 2 and a centre of enlargement (7, −2).

What letter have you drawn?

11 Copy and complete this table. It shows the scale factor for the enlargement of the shape in the first row to the shape in the first column.

		From shape			
		A	B	C	D
To shape	A	1	2	3	4
	B	$\frac{1}{2}$	1	1.5	
	C		$\frac{2}{3}$		
	D				

Chapters 8–10

4

Fluency

Band 1 questions

1. Write down the gradient and the coordinates of the y-intercept for each of these lines.

   a $y = 5x + 3$ b $y = 7x + 6$ c $y = 5 - 10x$

   d $y = 7x$ e $y = -x$ f $y = 2x - 1$

   g $y = 4 + 8x$ h $y = 5 - 3x$ i $y = 8 + 3x$

2. A line has a gradient of $\dfrac{2}{3}$ and y-intercept of -2.
   What is its equation?

3. A ship is sailing past a lighthouse.

   The graph below shows the distance between the ship and the lighthouse at certain times through the day.

Distance between ship and lighthouse

   a How far is the ship from the lighthouse at 10:30 a.m.?

   b There are two times during the day that the ship is 20 km from the lighthouse. What are these times?

   c At what time is the ship closest to the lighthouse?

4. Work out the gradient of the line joining each of these pairs of points.

   a $(5, -3)$ and $(3, 1)$

   b $(-4, -7)$ and $(2, 2)$

   c $(-8, -1)$ and $(7, -6)$

   d $(-4, -2)$ and $(-9, 4)$

5 Lucy goes to school on Monday.

After school, she goes to her friend Sarah's house, where they spend some time doing their homework together.

The graph below shows Lucy's distance from home at different times of the day.

Lucy's distance from home

a How long does it take Lucy to travel to school?

b How far from Lucy's home is her school?

c What time does Lucy arrive at Sarah's house?

d How far from home is Lucy at 4 p.m.?

e How long did Lucy spend doing her homework?

f On Tuesday Lucy went straight home after school finished at 15:00.

Her journeys to school and home again both took the same time as her journey to school on Monday.

Draw her travel graph for Tuesday.

Band 2 questions

6 Look at the diagram.

a Describe fully two different transformations that take shape A to shape B.

b Translate shape A using the vector $\begin{pmatrix} 2 \\ -4 \end{pmatrix}$.

Label the image shape C.

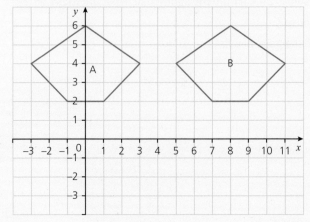

7 Some birds fly a long way to be somewhere warmer for the winter.

The graph below shows the distance some birds have flown on their journey from Norway to Scotland.

Distance from Norway

a   How far had the birds travelled after 3 days?

b   On their way to Scotland, the birds stopped at the Shetland Islands.

How many days did it take them to reach the Shetland Islands?

c   How long did the birds rest in the Shetland Islands?

d   The birds took 8 days to complete the journey. How far was the entire journey from Norway to Scotland?

8 Look at these equations of straight lines.

A $y = -3x - 4$ B $y = 4 - 3x$ C $y = 3x - 4$

D $y = 4 + 3x$ E $y = 4x + 3$ F $y = 4x - 3$

a   Which lines are parallel? There is more than one pair of parallel lines.

b   Which pairs of lines have the same y-intercept?

9 a   Draw x and y axes.

Use the same scale on each axis and take values from −4 to 4.

b   Plot the points A(−4, −1), B(−1, 3), C(2, 2) and D(2, −3).

c   Work out the gradient of the lines BC and AD.

d   What type of quadrilateral is ABCD?

10 Ed the electrician charges a £15 callout fee.

For every 30 minutes he works he charges an additional £10.

a   Copy and complete this table:

Number of hours worked n	1	2	3	4	5
Charge C		£55			

b   Draw horizontal and vertical axes.

Use values from 0 to 5 on the horizontal axis for the number of hours worked.

Use values from 0 to 120 on the vertical axis for the charge.

Plot the points from your table and join them with a straight line.

c   What is the equation of the straight line you have drawn?

Use the letters C for the charge and n for the number of hours worked.

Use your graph to answer the following questions:

d   How much does Ed charge for $3\frac{1}{2}$ hours' work?

e   How long does Ed work if he charges £65?

11 **a** Copy and complete this table.

x	0	1	2	3	4	5	6
$y = x^2 - 6x + 6$			-2				

b Draw axes with values of x from 0 to 6 and values of y from −4 to 7.

Draw the graph of $x^2 - 6x + 6$.

c Use your graph to solve the equation $x^2 - 6x + 6 = 0$.

d Draw the reflection of the curve in the x-axis.

e What are the coordinates of the image of the points $(0, 6)$ and $(2, -2)$?

f Do any of the points on the curve stay the same under the reflection?

12 Pinocchio's nose grows when he lies.

If he stops talking, his nose stays the same length.

It shrinks again when he tells the truth.

This is a graph of the length of his nose after he started talking on Monday morning.

Length of Pinocchio's nose

a How long is Pinocchio's nose normally?

b For how long was he telling lies altogether?

c Find the length of Pinocchio's nose after 14 minutes.

d At what times was Pinocchio's nose 8 cm long?

There is more than one answer.

e For how long was he telling the truth to make his nose shrink back to its normal size?

f What is the name given to a graph of this type, made up of two or more straight line segments?

13 While studying a disease in cattle, scientists found that the number of toxic cells in one cow's bloodstream increased over time, according to this equation:

$N = 14 \times (1.15)^t$

where N is the number of the toxic cells in the bloodstream per litre and t is the time in hours.

A graph of the number of toxic cells against time is shown:

Number of toxic cells

Answer the following questions using the graph.

a Find the initial number of toxic cells in this cow's bloodstream.

b Find the number of toxic cells in the bloodstream after 5 hours.

c Find the time it takes for the number of toxic cells in the bloodstream to first exceed 70 per litre.

14 A designer begins by plotting the four points $(0, 0)$, $(6, 3)$, $(4, 4)$ and $(3, 6)$. She joins these points to make a quadrilateral as shown in the first diagram.

She then performs three transformations to make the logo shown in the second diagram: an enlargement, a reflection and a rotation.

Can you describe the three transformations completely?

There is more than one way to answer this

CHAPTER 11

Prisms and cylinders

▶ Coming up…

- ◆ Finding the volume of a prism
- ◆ Finding the volume of a cylinder
- ◆ Finding the surface area of prisms and cylinders

➡ Water pouring puzzles

Solve these water pouring puzzles.

You are by a river and you have these two jugs.

5 litres   3 litres

How can you use the jugs to measure out exactly 4 litres?

You are by a river and you have these two jugs.

9 litres   4 litres

How can you use the jugs to measure out exactly 6 litres?

You have these three jugs (you have left the river!) The 8-litre jug is filled with water.

8 litres   5 litres   3 litres

How can you use the jugs to measure out exactly 4 litres?

11.1 Volume of a prism

✔ Skill checker

① **a** Match these shapes with the appropriate area formula.

| Triangle | Rectangle | Parallelogram | Square | Trapezium |

lw $\frac{1}{2}(a+b)h$ $\frac{1}{2}bh$ s^2 bh

b Draw a diagram of each shape and mark on your diagram the sides used in the formula.

c Which two formulas could be used for more one than shape?

② Work out the area of each of these shapes.

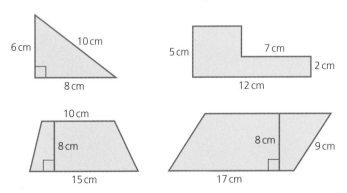

Volume of cubes and cuboids

Remember how to find the volume of a cube and a cuboid

length, l

Volume of a cube = side length^3
Volume of cube = l^3

height, h

width, w

length, l

Volume of a cuboid = length × width × height
Volume of a cuboid = lwh

Worked example

The volume of the cube is the same as the volume of this cuboid.

Work out the height of the cuboid.

h cm

5 cm

12 cm

6 cm

Solution

Volume of cuboid = $12 \times 5 \times h = 60\,h$ cm^3

Volume of cube = $6^3 = 216$ cm^3

Volume of cuboid = Volume of cube

$$60h = 216$$

$$h = \frac{216}{60}$$

$$= 3.6$$

So the height of the cuboid is 3.6 cm.

Volume of a prism

Cuboid

Triangular prism

Hexagonal prism

Octagonal prism

Remember

A prism is a three-dimensional shape with the same cross-section all along its length.

The volume of a prism is measured in cubic units such as cubic centimetres (cm^3) or cubic metres (m^3).

Volume = area of cross-section × length

Or height.

Worked example

Work out the volume of each of these prisms.

a

Area = 25 cm²

0.11 m

b

5 cm

6 cm

20 cm

Solution

a Area of cross-section = 25 cm²

Length = 0.11 m = 11 cm ◄———— Take care! Make sure you don't mix your units!

Volume = area of cross-section × length

$= 25 \times 11$

Volume = 275 cm³ (Don't forget your units.)

b Area of cross-section = $\frac{1}{2} \times 6 \times 5 = 15$ cm² ◄———— Area of triangle = $\frac{1}{2}$ x base x height

Volume = area of cross-section × length

$= 15 \times 20$

Volume = 300 cm³

11.1 Now try these

Band 1 questions

1 Work out the volume of each of these prisms.

Each cube is 1 cm³.

a

b

c

d

e

f

g

2 Calculate the volume of each of these cuboids.

a

2 cm
8 cm
2 cm

b

4 cm
7 cm
3 cm

c

1.8 m
2.5 m
0.6 m

3 Calculate the volume of these cubes.

a

5 cm
5 cm
5 cm

b

2.5 m
2.5 m
2.5 m

c

30 mm
30 mm
30 mm

4 Match each of these objects with a suitable volume shown below.

a A shoe box

b A classroom

c A matchbox

d A large swimming pool

| 2500 m³ | 1500 mm³ | 9000 cm³ | 50 m³ |

Band 2 questions

5 Work out the volume of these prisms.

Watch out! Check the units carefully.

a

Area = 16 cm²
6.2 cm

b

Area = 3.7 m²
160 cm

c

4 cm
Area = 650 mm²

Fluency

Reasoning

Fluency

6 Work out the volume of each of these triangular prisms.

a

3 m
4 m
6 m

b

2 cm
8 cm
2 cm

c

3 mm
4 mm
5 mm

7 For each of these prisms:

i state the name of the shape of the end-face

ii find its volume.

a

2 cm
5 cm
7 cm

b

1 cm
3 cm
3 cm
8 cm

8 Calculate the volume of this prism.

4.6 cm
5.1 cm
11.4 cm
10.5 cm
12.2 cm

Give your answer correct to the nearest cubic centimetre.

9 The volume of a cube is 343 cm³.

What is the length of one side of the cube?

10 The volume of this cuboid is 240 m³.

h m
6 m
5 m

Work out the height of the cuboid.

Problem solving

Band 3 questions

11 The volume of this triangular prism is 96 cm³.
The area of the cross-section is 12 cm².
Calculate the value of x and of y.

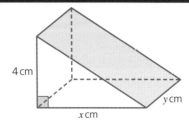

4 cm

y cm

x cm

12 A carton of orange juice is in the shape of a cuboid.
The orange juice is 3 cm below the top of the carton.
Ted lies the carton flat on the side that says 'ORANGE'.
What is the depth of the orange juice now?

ORANGE

20 cm

6 cm

8 cm

13 A silver bar is in the shape of a prism with a trapezium as its cross-section.
The bar is melted down and used to make a triangular prism of the same volume.
Calculate the height of the triangular prism.

6 cm

8 cm

15 cm

10 cm

20 cm

8 cm

14 Calculate the volume of this triangular prism.

4 cm

6 cm

6 cm

3 cm

3 cm

Hint

You'll need to use Pythagoras' theorem.

11.2 Volume of a cylinder

Give your answers correct to 3 significant figures.

① Write down the formula for the area of a circle.

② Work out the area of each of these circles.

a

4 cm

b

1.2 m

c

9.8 cm

③ Calculate the radius of this circle.

Area = 100 cm²

Find the volume of a cylinder

A cylinder is like a prism with a circular base.

The area of its cross-section is πr^2.

So its volume is $\pi r^2 \times h$.

r

h

Volume of cylinder $= \pi r^2 h$

Worked example

Work out the volume of this cylinder.

Solution

Method 1: Using the formula, $V = \pi r^2 h$

Volume of cylinder $= \pi r^2 h$

$$= \pi \times 5^2 \times 10$$

$$= 785.398...$$

The volume of the cylinder is $785\,\text{cm}^3$ (to 3 significant figures).

Method 2: Using the formula, volume of prism = area of cross-section × height

Area of circle $= \pi r^2$

$$= \pi \times 5^2$$

$$= 78.539...$$

> Store this number in your calculator – don't round it!

Volume of cylinder $=$ area of cross-section × height

$$= 78.539... \times 10$$

$$= 785.398...$$

The volume of the cylinder is $785\,\text{cm}^3$ (to 3 significant figures).

> Can you see that these two methods are really the same?

Sometimes you'll be given the volume and you'll need to work back to find the length or height of the cylinder.

Worked example

A cylinder has a diameter of 16 cm and a volume of $1000\,\text{cm}^3$.

Work out the length of the cylinder.

Solution

Diameter $= 16\,\text{cm}$ so radius $= 8\,\text{cm}$ ← You must use the radius.

Method 1: Using a reverse number machine

Start by working out the area of the circular cross-section:

Area of circle $= \pi \times r^2$

$$= \pi \times 8^2$$

$$= 201.06...$$

To find the volume of the cylinder you can input the length into this number machine.

You can reverse the number machine to find the length given the volume.

Input volume $= 1000$ and area of circle $= 201.06...$

So the length $= 4.97\,\text{cm}$ (to 3 s.f.).

Method 2: Solving an equation

$\pi r^2 \times l = $ volume of cylinder

$\pi \times 8^2 \times l = 1000$

$\qquad 201.06 \times l = 1000$

$\div 201.06...$ $\div 201.06...$

$\qquad\qquad l = 4.973$

So the length $= 4.97$ cm (to 3 s.f.).

You also may need to work back from the volume of a cylinder to find the radius.

Worked example

A cylinder has a height of 12 cm and a volume of 600 cm³.

Work out the radius of the cylinder.

Solution

Method 1: Using a reverse number machine

Here is a number machine to work out the volume of a cylinder.

| Radius | → | Square | → | Multiply by π | → | Multiply by height | → | Volume |

Here is the reverse number machine.

Input volume $= 600$ and height $= 12$.

| Radius | ← 3.989... | Square root | ← 15.9... | Divide by π | ← 50 | Divide by height | ← 600 | Volume |

So the radius $= 3.99$ cm (to 3 s.f.).

Method 2: Solving an equation

$\pi r^2 \times h = $ volume of cylinder

$\pi \times r^2 \times 12 = 600$

$\qquad 12\pi \times r^2 = 600$

$\div 12\pi$ $\div 12\pi$

$\qquad\qquad r^2 = 15.9...$

square root square root

$\qquad\qquad r = 3.989...$

So the radius $= 3.99$ cm (to 3 s.f.).

11.2 Now try these

Give your answers correct to 3 significant figures.

Band 1 questions

1 Look at this number machine.

Use the number machine to work out the volume when:

a   radius = 5 cm and height = 8 cm

b   radius = 7 cm and height = 15 cm

c   radius = 2 m and height = 3 m

d   radius = 10 mm and height = 18 mm.

2 Work out the value of πr^2 when:

a $r=6$ b $r=8$ c $r=10$.

3 Work out the value of these.

a $\pi \times 4^2 \times 10$ b $\pi \times 12^2 \times 15$ c $\pi \times 3^2 \times 4$

4 Work out the value of $\pi r^2 h$ when

a $r=3$ and $h=5$ b $r=6$ and $h=6$ c $r=7$ and $h=4$.

5 Work out the volume of each of these cylinders.

a

b

c

Band 2 questions

6 **a** Work out the area of each of these circles.

i

ii

iii

b Use your answers to part **a** to help you work out the volume of each of these cylinders.

i

ii

iii

7 Onick is buying topsoil to fill a flower bed in his garden.

He is going to fill a rectangular flower bed of area 50 m² to a depth of 0.15 m.

What volume of topsoil does he need?

8 Work out the volume of each of these cylinders.

a

2 cm

6 cm

b

←—7 cm—→

6 cm

9 A circular lawn has a path round it.

←— 5 m —→

1 m

a Find the area of:

    i the lawn   **ii** the lawn and path   **iii** the path.

The path is covered in gravel 5 cm thick.

b Find the volume of the gravel.

10 A cylinder has base area 16 cm² and volume 80 cm³.

What is its height?

Band 3 questions

11 A large jug is in the shape of a cylinder.

It is filled with lemonade to a depth of 33 cm.

How many of these cylindrical glasses can it fill?

33 cm

6 cm

11 cm

6 cm

12 Work out the missing length on each of these cylinders.

a

3.6 cm

Volume = 400 cm³

x cm

b

r cm

4 cm

Volume = 700 cm³

c

d cm

Volume = 325 cm³

11.5 cm

13 A cylinder is cut in half along its length.

Work out the volume of this shape.

8 cm

4 cm

14 A cylindrical candle has diameter 6 cm and length 15 cm.

Carlos packs it into a cuboid box in which it just fits.

Find the volume of air in the box.

15 Ann is a scientist.

She pours 50 ml of acid into a measuring cylinder of diameter 3 cm.

Find the depth of the acid in the cylinder.

11.3 Surface area

✔ Skill checker

Give your answers correct to 3 significant figures.

① Write down the formula for the circumference of a circle.

② Work out the circumference of each of these circles.

a

4 cm

b

1.2 m

c

9.8 cm

③ For each prism in parts a–b write down:

i how many faces each prism has

ii what shape the faces are.

a cube

b triangular prism

c hexagonal prism

Finding the surface area of a prism

The **surface area** of a prism is the total area of all the faces.

Worked example

Calculate the surface area of this cuboid

5 cm

4 cm

12 cm

Solution

A cuboid has 6 faces

Front and back:

5 cm

12 cm

Total area = 2 × 12 × 5
= 120 cm²

Top and bottom:

4 cm

12 cm

Total area = 2 × 12 × 4
= 96 cm²

2 sides:

5 cm

4 cm

Total area = 2 × 4 × 5
= 40 cm²

Surface area = 120 cm² + 96 cm² + 40 cm²
= 256 cm²

Worked example

Calculate the surface area of this prism.

Solution

Work out the area of each face individually.

> There are 5 faces altogether.

Area of one triangular face = $\frac{1}{2}$ × base × height

$= \frac{1}{2} \times 6 \times 8$

$= 24\,cm^2$

> The two triangular faces are both the same.

8 cm

10 cm

15 cm

6 cm

Area of other triangular face = 24 cm²

Area of rectangular base: 6 × 15 = 90 cm²

Area of rectangular side face: 8 × 15 = 120 cm²

Area of sloping rectangular face: 10 × 15 = 150 cm²

Total surface area = 24 cm² + 24 cm² + 90 cm² + 120 cm² + 150 cm²
= 408 cm²

Finding the surface area of a cylinder

 Activity

Take a piece of paper.

Roll your paper up to make a hollow cylinder like this:

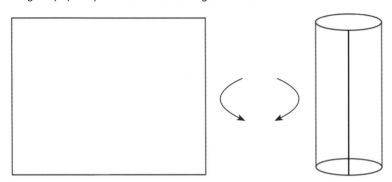

a   What do the width and length of your paper tell you about the cylinder?

How can you work out the area of the curved surface of a cylinder?

b   Seb has a piece of paper that is 20 cm by 15 cm.

He rolls it up to make a cylinder.

i   What is the area of the curved surface of Seb's cylinder?

ii   What is the diameter of the cylinder that he makes?

Find two different answers.

c   Malika makes a hollow cylinder by rolling up a piece of paper.

Her cylinder has a radius of 6 cm and a height of 25 cm

i   What size is her piece of paper?

ii   What is the area of the curved surface of Malika's cylinder?

In the activity you found that the curved surface of a cylinder can be unrolled to make a rectangle.

Area of the curved surface = circumference of the cylinder × height

Worked example

Work out the surface area of this cylinder.

Solution

Area of top circle $= \pi r^2$

$= \pi \times 5^2$

$= 78.53\ldots$ cm² ← *Don't round yet!*

Area of bottom circle: $78.53\ldots$ cm²

Diameter $= 2 \times 5$ cm $= 10$ cm

Circumference $= \pi d$

$= \pi \times 10$

$= 31.41\ldots$ cm

5 cm

10 cm

Area of curved surface = circumference × height

$$= 31.415... \times 10$$

$$= 314.15... \text{ cm}^2$$

Total surface area = curved surface + top circle + bottom circle

$$= 314.15... \text{ cm}^2 + 78.53... \text{ cm}^2 + 78.53... \text{ cm}^2$$

$$= 471.2... \text{ cm}^2$$

$$= 471 \text{ cm}^2 \text{ (to 3 s.f.)}$$

11.3 Now try these

Give your answers correct to 3 significant figures.

Band 1 questions

① Look at this cube.

   a   How many faces does the cube have?

   b   Work out the area of one face.

   c   Work out the surface area of the cube.

② Work out the surface area of these cubes.

   a

   b

   c

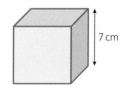

③ Look at this cuboid.

   a   How many faces does the cuboid have?

   b   Work out the area of the face marked:

      i   A   **ii**   B   **iii**   C

   c   Work out the total surface area of the cuboid.

Key Stage 3 Mastering Mathematics: Book 3

Fluency

4 Here is the net of a cuboid.

Each rectangle makes a face of the cuboid.

a What is the area of the bottom face?

b What is the area of the top face?

c What does the area of the net tell you?

Peter folds up the net to make a cuboid.

d What is the volume of the cuboid?

Band 2 questions

5 Find the surface area of each of these cuboids.

a

b

6 Find the volume and surface area of each of these cuboids.

Give your answers in suitable units.

a

b

c

7 The diagram shows Natasha's water tank.

It is full of water.

a Work out the volume of water in the tank.

b Given that 1000 cm³ = 1 litre, write down the volume in litres.

The tank is made of metal. It has no top.

c Work out the area of metal used to make the tank.

8

5 km

10 km

3 km

4 km

a How many faces does this triangular prism have?

b Work out the total area of the two triangular end faces.

c Calculate the surface area of the prism.

9 Calculate the surface area of these triangular prisms.

a

2.4 m 2.6 m

3.5 m

1 m

b

17 cm

8 cm 20 cm

15 cm

10 Calculate the surface area of each of these wooden letters.

a

1 cm

2 cm

5 cm

2 cm

1 cm

1 cm 1 cm

b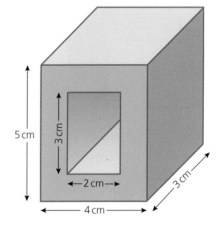

5 cm

3 cm

2 cm

4 cm

3 cm

11 A cube has a surface area of 486 cm².

Calculate the volume of the cube.

Band 3 questions

12 A cube has a surface area of x cm² and a volume of x cm³

Work out the value of x.

13 The surface area of this cuboid is 258 cm².

h cm

5 cm

9 cm

Calculate the height of the prism.

Problem solving

⑭ Look at this triangular prism.

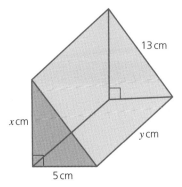

13 cm

x cm

y cm

5 cm

Hint

Use Pythagoras' theorem.

 a Calculate the value of x.

 b The surface area of the prism is 360 cm². Calculate the value of y.

Fluency

⑮ Find the surface area of each of these cylinders.

 a 3 cm, 5 cm

 b 6 cm, 4 cm

 c 1.4 mm, 4.8 mm

 d 15 m, 20 m

Problem solving

⑯ Jim is painting the outside of a ship's funnel.

The funnel is a cylinder of diameter 4 m and height 20 m.

A tin of paint covers 8 m².

How many tins of paint does Jim need?

⑰ Adam draws a net of a cylinder on paper.

The sheet of paper measures 20 cm by 15 cm.

He cuts out the net and makes a cylinder.

Its radius is 2 cm and its height is 10 cm.

Show that the net will fit on the paper.

(ABC) Key words

Here is a list of the key words you met in this chapter.

Area	Circle	Circumference	Cube
Cuboid	Cylinder	Diameter	Prism
Radius (radii)	Surface area	Volume	

Use the glossary at the back of this book to check any you are unsure about.

Review exercise: prisms and cylinders

Give your answers correct to 3 significant figures.

Band 1 questions

Fluency

1 Work out the volume of each of these cuboids.

a

5 cm
4 cm
10 cm

b

3 cm
8 cm
4 cm

c

4 cm
9 cm
2 cm

2 Work out the surface area of each of these cuboids.

a

4 cm
8 cm
2 cm

b

1.9 m
1.7 m
0.8 m

c

165 mm
216 mm
113 mm

Problem solving

3 Look at Lilia's new chicken shed.

6 m
3 m
1.5 m

a   What is its volume?

Each chicken needs 0.5 m³ of space in the shed.

b   How many chickens can Lilia have?

Lilia paints the outside of the shed (but not the roof) brown.

One tin of paint covers 10 m².

c   How many tins of paint does she buy?

Band 2 questions

Problem solving

4 A new outdoor swimming pool is planned.

This is one of the designs.

a What is the volume of the paddling section?

b What is the volume of the swimming section?

c How many litres of water does the pool hold altogether?

1 litre = 1000 cm³

The bottom and inside walls of the entire pool are to be covered with tiles.

d Find the area to be covered with tiles.

Fluency

5 Look at this triangular prism.

The end face is an isosceles triangle.

Work out the volume and the surface area of the prism.

Lengths are in mm

Reasoning

6 A cuboid has length *l* cm, width *w* cm and height *h* cm.

Using *l*, *w* and *h*, write down the formula for:

a its volume

b its surface area.

State the unit for each formula.

Problem solving

7 Find the volume and surface area of each of these solids.

All lengths are in centimetres.

Remember to give the units for each of your answers.

a

b

c

8 A cube of side 5 cm is removed from a cuboid shaped block.

Calculate the volume and surface area of the remaining shape.

9 Calculate:

i the volume

ii the surface area of each of these cylinders.

a

40 cm

28 cm

b

18 cm

10.5 cm

10 **a** Calculate the volume of this triangular prism.

b Calculate the surface area of the prism.

9 cm

12 cm

7 cm

11 The surface area of this cuboid is 446 cm². Calculate the length of the cuboid.

6 cm

8 cm

x cm

12 The volume of this cylinder is 396 cm³.

a Calculate the radius of the cylinder.

b Calculate the surface area of the cylinder.

14 cm

13 A fence consists of 25 cylindrical posts each with a diameter of 6 cm and a height of 92 cm.

a Find the volume of wood used to make this fence.

b The curved surface and the top of each post are painted. Find the area of the fence that is painted.

14 Lisa is making a wedding cake with three cylindrical layers.

The radii are 6 cm, 10 cm and 20 cm.

The heights of the layers are 5 cm, 6 cm and 8 cm, respectively.

a Find the total volume of cake she needs to make.

She covers the top and sides of each layer with icing 3 mm thick.

b Find the volume of icing she needs to make.

CHAPTER 12

Constructions

▶ Coming up...

- ◆ Finding the perpendicular bisector of a line
- ◆ Constructing a perpendicular to a line through a point

- ◆ Bisecting an angle
- ◆ Solving problems involving constructions
- ◆ Understanding congruent triangles

→ The Penrose Triangle

This diagram is called 'The Penrose triangle'.

Follow these steps to draw your own Penrose triangle.

Make sure you keep your pencil lines light as you need to do some rubbing out!

Step 1 Draw an inverted equilateral triangle like this one.

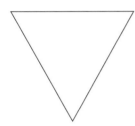

Step 2 Extend one side and draw 2 parallel lines about 1 cm away from one edge of your triangle.

Step 3 Repeat **Step 2** for the other 2 sides of your triangle.

Step 4 Rub out some of the 'short' lines so your diagram looks like this.

Step 5 Draw 3 short lines to make the triangle look more 3D.

Step 6 Rub out the three 'corners'.

Step 7 Add some shading to make it look 3D.

12.1 Constructions

✔ Skill checker

① Make accurate drawings of these angles and label them.

a

b

c

d

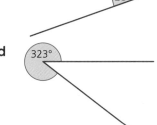

② Draw these circles on the same diagram.

Use the same point as the centre of them all.

The circles form a pattern.

You can easily see if one of them is wrong.

a	Radius 8 cm	b	Radius 7 cm
c	Radius 6 cm	d	Radius 5 cm
e	Diameter 8 cm	f	Diameter 6 cm

Using a ruler and protractor

Follow the steps in the next activity to find out how to accurately construct (draw) triangles using a ruler and protractor.

✎ Activity

Constructing triangles using a ruler and protractor

① Constructing a triangle when two sides and the included angle are given

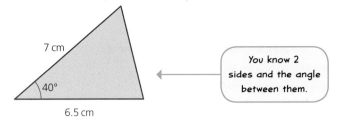

You know 2 sides and the angle between them.

Step 1 Use a ruler to draw one side of 6.5 cm.

Step 2 Use a protractor to draw an angle of 40° at one end of the side.

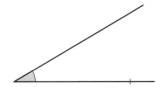

Step 3   Use a ruler to mark a length of 7 cm on the second side.

Step 4   Draw the third side to form the triangle.

②   Constructing a triangle when two angles and the included side are given

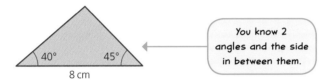

You know 2 angles and the side in between them.

Step 1   Use a ruler to draw one side of length 8 cm.

Step 2   Use a protractor to draw the correct angle at each end of the side

The lines cross at the vertex of the triangle.

Using compasses

You already know how to use a pair of compasses to construct (or draw) a circle. The next activity will show you how to use compasses to construct a triangle.

Activity

Constructing a triangle when you know the lengths of all 3 sides

Follow these steps to make an accurate drawing of this triangle.

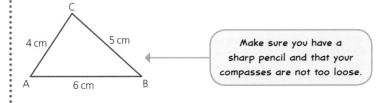

Make sure you have a sharp pencil and that your compasses are not too loose.

Step 1   Draw a line 6 cm long.

Step 2   Draw an arc of radius 4 cm and centre A.
The point C is somewhere on this arc.

> **Remember**
>
> An arc is part of a circle.

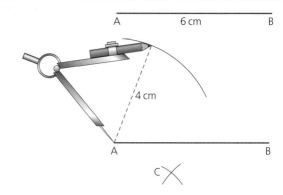

Step 3   Now draw an arc of radius 5 cm and centre B.
The two arcs meet at C.

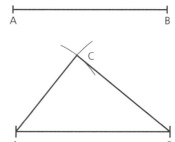

Step 4   Join AC and BC to form the triangle.

When you construct a triangle, make sure you follow these rules.

- Choose one line to be the base line of the triangle.
- Measure the angles and other lines from this starting point.
- Measure the lines and angles as accurately as you can.
- Use a sharp HB pencil.
- Make sure your compasses are not too loose.
- Don't rub out your construction marks.

> **Note**
>
> The arcs at C are called **construction marks**. You must not rub them out as they show your teacher or an examiner that you have followed the right steps.

12.1 Now try these

Band 1 questions

① Use a ruler and protractor to make accurate drawings of these triangles. In each case, measure the remaining sides and angles.

a

b

> **Hint**
>
> Look at the activity on page 257.

2 Use a ruler and protractor to make accurate drawings of these triangles.
In each case, measure the remaining sides and angles.

a

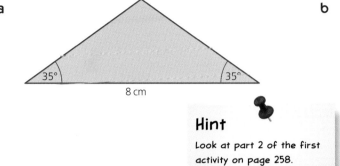

35°   35°
8 cm

Hint
Look at part 2 of the first
activity on page 258.

b

40°   100°
3.5 cm

3 Use a ruler and protractor to make accurate drawings of these triangles. In each case, measure the remaining sides
and angles.

a

4 cm
40° 110°

b

5.7 cm
28°
6 cm

c

4 cm
70° 5.8 cm

d

40°
8 cm
65°

4 a Use a ruler and protractor to construct this triangle.
b Measure the lengths of the other two sides.
Why are these equal?

45°   45°
6 cm

Band 2 questions

5 Construct these triangles.
Measure the angles of each triangle.

a

5 cm   8 cm

7 cm

Hint
Look at the last
activity on page 258.

b

9 cm
4 cm
6 cm

6 Construct a triangle with sides 6.5 cm, 6 cm and 5 cm.

Measure its angles.

7 **a** Construct triangles with sides of these lengths.

Describe each triangle.

i 6 cm, 6 cm and 6 cm

ii 6 cm, 8 cm and 8 cm

b What happens if the sides are 6 cm, 5 cm and 12 cm?

Hint

Split each parallelogram into two triangles.

8 Construct these parallelograms.

a

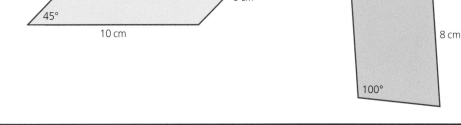

45°

6 cm

45°

10 cm

b

5 cm

100°

8 cm

100°

Band 3 questions

9 Kim's dad is designing a slide for the garden.

This is his sketch of the slide.

a Use a scale of 1 cm to represent 1 m.

Make an accurate scale drawing of the side of the slide.

b How long must Kim's dad make the ladder?

c What is the angle between the slide and the ladder?

7 m

40°

6 m

10 Barton is 6 km due north of Avonford.

Carville is 8 km due east of Avonford.

a Use a scale of 1 cm to 1 km to make a scale drawing.

b Use your diagram to find how far it is from Barton to Carville.

c Use Pythagoras' theorem to check your answer to part **b**.

Barton

N

6 km

Avonford   8 km   Carville

11 Josh is making a hanging basket support from a metal strip for his design and technology project.

He has made this sketch.

He is going to use a ready-formed hook.

a Make an accurate scale drawing of the frame.

b Use the diagram to find the length of metal strip that Josh needs.

Metal Strip

40 cm

60°   50 cm

12 Construct these triangles.

In each case, say what is special about the triangle.

a   AB = 8 cm, BC = 8 cm, angle ABC = 60°

b   Angle PQR = 70°, angle QRP = 40°, QR = 8 cm

c   LM = 8 cm, MN = 4 cm, angle LMN = 60°

d   XY = 9.9 cm, YZ = 14 cm, angle XYZ = 45°

12.2 Further constructions

✔ Skill checker

Which of these diagrams are impossible? Give a reason for your answers.

①

②

③

④

⑤

⑥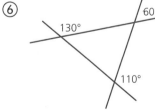

Using compasses for other constructions

Bisect means to cut exactly in half.

You can use your compasses to bisect a line. ⟵   Cut the line exactly in half.

Bisecting a line

Follow these steps to bisect the line AB.

Step 1   Draw the line AB on your paper.

Step 2   Open your compasses.

             Put the point on A.

             Draw arcs above and below the line.

Step 3   Do not adjust the compasses.

             Put the point on B.

             Draw two more arcs to cut the first two.

Step 4   The arcs meet at X and Y.

             Draw the line XY. ◀ —— *XY is called the bisector of AB.*

             Mark a point on the line XY.

             Measure the distance from your point to A and to B.

             What do you notice? Is that always true?

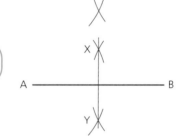

When two lines are at right-angles you say they are perpendicular to each other. In the last activity, XY and AB are at right-angles to each other. So XY is also called the **perpendicular bisector** of AB. You have constructed the perpendicular to AB that goes through the middle of AB.

Every point on the line XY is the **same distance** from A as it is from B. You say that every point on XY is **equidistant** from A and B. You can also construct the perpendicular from another point on AB.

 Activity

Constructing a perpendicular from a point on a line

Follow these steps to construct a perpendicular to this line at point T.

Step 1   Draw a line and mark a point T on the line.

Step 2   Put the point of your compasses at T and open them so you can make an arc on either side of T. ◀ —— *Don't change the setting of your compasses.*

Step 3 Open your compasses wider.

With the point on A draw an arc below the line.

Or above if you prefer!

Step 4 Do not adjust the compasses.

With the point on B draw another arc so
that it intersects the first arc.

Step 5 Draw a line through T and the intersection X.

Line TX is a perpendicular to AB from point T.

You can also construct a perpendicular to a line from a point that is not on the line.

Activity

Constructing a perpendicular from a point to a line

Follow these steps to construct the perpendicular from the point R to the line.

Step 1 Draw a line and mark a point R near the line.

Step 2 Put the point of the compasses on R.
Draw an arc.
It intersects the line at A and B.

Step 3 With the point on A, draw an arc on
the opposite side of the line from R.

Step 4   Do not adjust the compasses.
             With the point on B, draw another arc.
             The arcs intersect at X.

Step 5   Draw a line through R and X.   ← The line RX is perpendicular to the line AB.
             RM is the shortest distance
             between R and the line AB.

You can also use your compasses to cut an angle exactly in half. This is called bisecting an angle.

 Activity

Bisecting an angle

Follow these steps to bisect this angle.

Step 1   Draw an angle.

Step 2   Put the point of the compasses on V.
             Draw an arc cutting both lines.

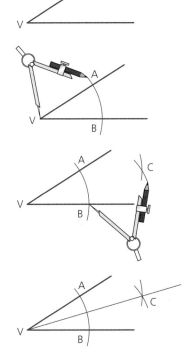

Step 3   Put the point of the compasses on A.
             Draw an arc.
             Do not adjust the compasses.
             Put the point of the compasses at B.
             Draw an arc.   ← Your two arcs meet at C.

Step 4   Join V to C.   ← The line VC is called **the angle bisector**. Any point on VC is the same distance from VA as it is from VB. Every point on VC is **equidistant** from VA and VB.

12.2 Now try these

Band 1 questions

1 Draw lines of these lengths. *Look at the first activity on page 262.*

Then construct the perpendicular bisector of each line.

a 8 cm   **b** 10 cm   **c** 12 cm

2 Copy each of these lines. *Look at the last activity on page 262.*

Then construct the perpendicular to each line through the point A.

a

b

3 Copy each of these lines. *Look at the last activity on page 263.*

Then construct the perpendicular to each line from the point P.

a

P×

b

P×

4 Copy each of these angles. *Look at the last activity on page 264.*

Use a ruler and compasses to bisect each angle.

a 30°

b 90°

c 135°

Band 2 questions

5 **a** Construct a square with side 8 cm.

    b Construct the angle bisector of angle ABC.

       What angle have you made?

6 **a** Construct this rhombus.

    b Draw in the diagonal AC.

       Construct the perpendicular bisector of AC.

       What do you notice?

7 ABCD is a kite.

AB = 5 cm, BC = 5 cm, CD = 8 cm and DA = 8 cm.

Angle ABC = 40°.

   a   Construct the kite ABCD.

   b   Construct the perpendicular bisector of AC.

       What do you notice?

8 **a**   Open your compasses to about 5 cm and draw a circle.

   b   Without adjusting the compasses, use them to make marks around the circumference.

       Draw the first mark on the circumference as a starting point.

       To make the second mark put the point of the compasses on the first mark, draw a mark, and so on.

   c   Join the marks with straight lines as shown to draw a six-pointed star.

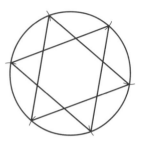

9 Construct this diagram accurately, using a ruler and a pair of compasses only.

10 Construct a regular hexagon in a circle.

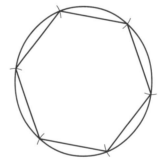

11 **a**   Construct an angle of 60°.

   b   Bisect your angle to construct an angle of 30°.

   c   Use your diagram to construct an angle of 15°.

Hint

The angles in an equilateral triangle are 60°.

Band 3 questions

12 Look at this diagram.

Martyn is leaving the cave in a rowing boat.

He is keeping as far from the rocks as he can.

   a   Copy the diagram.

   b   Bisect the angle to show his path to the sea.

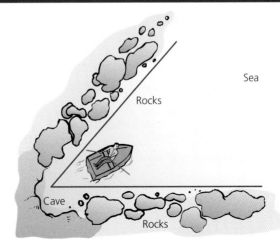

13 The diagram shows a garden and the position of two bird feeders A and B.

Alan wants to plant a tree in the garden.

The tree must be equidistant from the two bird feeders.

Alan wants the tree to be nearer the southern wall of the garden.

Make a copy of the garden and construct a line to show the possible positions of the birdfeeder.

14 **a** Make an accurate drawing of this triangle.

b What type of triangle is it?

c Bisect angle A.

The angle bisector meets BC at D.

Mark point D on your triangle.

d Measure BD and DC.

e What do you notice?

15 **a** Draw a circle of radius 6 cm with centre O.

b Draw a diameter AB and bisect it.

Label the points where the bisector meets the circle C and D (see diagram).

c What name is given to the quadrilateral ACBD?

d Bisect angle AOC.

Label the point where the bisector meets the circle E.

Extend the bisector to meet the circle again at F.

e Bisect angle COB.

The bisector meets the circle at G.

Extend it to meet the circle again at H.

f What shape is the polygon AECGBFDH?

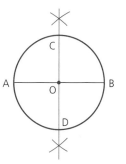

16 **a** Draw a line AB.

Construct the perpendicular bisector of AB.

b Join A to X, X to B, B to Y and Y to A.

c What is the special name given to the quadrilateral AXBY?

17 Use a ruler and compasses to construct each of these angles.

a 120°

b 45°

c 75°

d 315°

e 345°

12.3 Congruent triangles

✔ Skill checker

Match together the congruent L shapes.

Which shape is the odd one out?

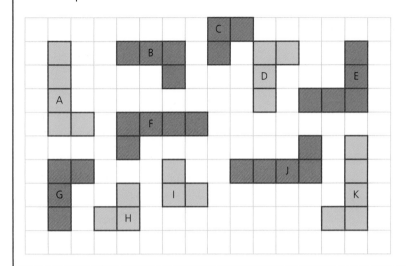

> **Remember**
>
> Congruent shapes are exactly the same shape and size.

How you know if two triangles are congruent

✎ Activity

Draw each of these triangles.

Triangle R has 3 sides of 4 cm, 5 cm and 6 cm

Triangle S has 3 angles of 50°, 60° and 70°

Triangle T has sides	**Triangle U has sides**	**Triangle V has sides**	**Triangle W has sides**
AB, BC and AC	AB, BC and AC	AB, BC and AC	AB, BC and AC
Angle A = 50°	Angle B = 90°	Angle A = 40°	Angle A = 50°
Angle B = 60°	Side BC = 6 cm	Side AB = 8 cm	Angle AB = 8 cm
Side AB = 6 cm	Side AC = 10 cm	Side BC = 6 cm	Side AC = 5 cm

For some of these triangles you can draw two triangles that **are not** congruent.

Which ones?

In the activity you should have found that when you draw three sides of a triangle then there is only one way to draw that triangle.

Here is triangle R from the activity. There is only one way you can draw it .

These triangles are both congruent to R so they don't count as a different way of drawing R.

R is reflected to make this triangle.

R is rotated to make this triangle.

You say that all triangles with the same side lengths are **congruent**.

However, there are many different triangles with the same three angles.

All three of these triangles have the same angles, but they are different sizes.
They are called **similar triangles** – you'll learn more about similar triangles in chapter 13.

Two triangles are congruent if all the sides are the same AND all their angles are the same. However, you don't actually need to know all the sides and angles to check if two triangles are congruent. You can use one of these four special conditions for congruence in triangles.

❶ 3 equal sides: **Side-Side-Side** or **SSS** congruence.

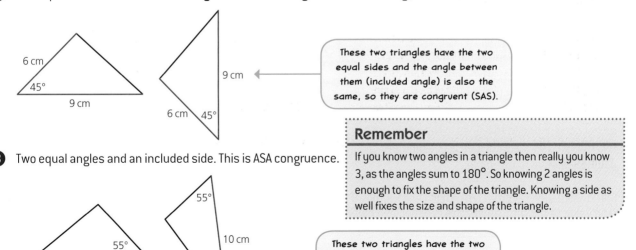

These two triangles have the same length sides, so they are congruent (SSS).

❷ Two equal sides and an **included angle**. This is **Side-Angle-Side** or **SAS** congruence.

These two triangles have the two equal sides and the angle between them (included angle) is also the same, so they are congruent (SAS).

Remember
If you know two angles in a triangle then really you know 3, as the angles sum to $180°$. So knowing 2 angles is enough to fix the shape of the triangle. Knowing a side as well fixes the size and shape of the triangle.

❸ Two equal angles and an included side. This is ASA congruence.

These two triangles have the two equal angles and the side between them is also the same length, so they are congruent (ASA).

4 The triangle is right-angled and you know the hypotenuse (longest side) and one of the other sides. This called right-angle-hypotenuse-side or RHS.

Worked example

Two of these triangles are congruent.

Decide which ones are congruent. Explain your answer fully.

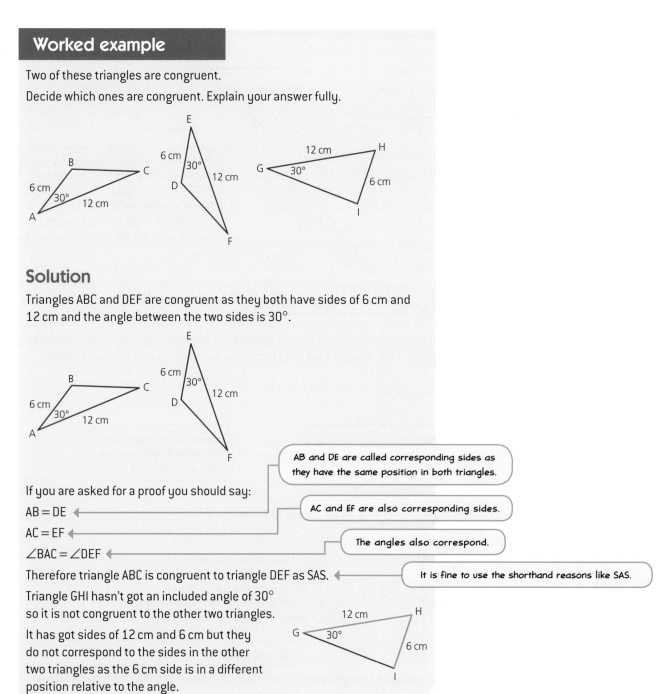

Solution

Triangles ABC and DEF are congruent as they both have sides of 6 cm and 12 cm and the angle between the two sides is 30°.

If you are asked for a proof you should say:

AB = DE ← AB and DE are called corresponding sides as they have the same position in both triangles.

AC = EF ← AC and EF are also corresponding sides.

∠BAC = ∠DEF ← The angles also correspond.

Therefore triangle ABC is congruent to triangle DEF as SAS. ← It is fine to use the shorthand reasons like SAS.

Triangle GHI hasn't got an included angle of 30° so it is not congruent to the other two triangles.

It has got sides of 12 cm and 6 cm but they do not correspond to the sides in the other two triangles as the 6 cm side is in a different position relative to the angle.

Remember if you are given two angles in a triangle it is a good idea to write in the value of the third angle. This is especially helpful if you are looking for ASA congruence.

Watch out! The triangles won't necessarily be drawn to scale so you can't just trace them to check for congruence.

12.3 Now try these

Band 1 questions

1 Match together the congruent triangles.

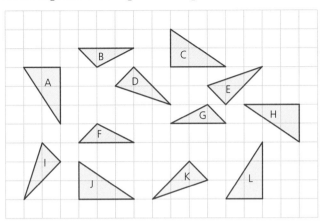

2 Ten people are told to draw these triangles.

   a Do they all draw them exactly the same?

   b Is the answer the same for this triangle?

3 **a** Triangle ABC has sides AB = 5 cm, BC = 7 cm and AC = 10 cm.

     Construct a triangle which is congruent to triangle ABC.

   b What condition for congruence have you used?

4 **a** Decide whether each these pairs of right-angled triangles are congruent.

   i

   ii

   iii

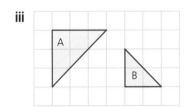

   b What condition for congruence have you used?

Reasoning

5 Which **two** these of triangles show SSS congruence?

Give a reason for your answer.

6 Which **two** these of triangles show SAS congruence?

Give a reason for your answer.

Fluency

7 Which **two** these of triangles show ASA congruence?

Give a reason for your answer.

Reasoning

8 Construct this parallelogram.

Can you split your parallelogram into two congruent triangles?

Give a reason for your answer.

9 Each of these pairs of triangles is congruent.

Match each pair of triangles with the correct condition for congruence.

ASA	RHS	SSS	SAS

a

b

c

d

Key Stage 3 Mastering Mathematics: Book 3

10 Decide whether each of these pairs of triangles are congruent.

Give a reason for your answer.

a

b

c

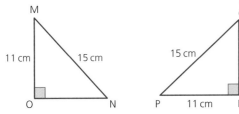

11 Kim says these two triangles are not congruent because they have different angles.

Is Kim correct? Explain your reasoning fully.

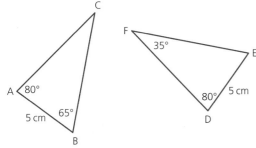

12 Ellie and Dan each draw a triangle with one side of 5 cm, one side of 8 cm and one angle of 60°.

Ellie says their triangles are congruent.

Is Ellie correct?　　Explain your answer fully.

13 Triangle ABC is an equilateral triangle.

D is the midpoint of BC.

a Draw a diagram to show this information.

b Prove that triangle ABD and triangle ADC are congruent.

14 In the diagram AB and ED are parallel and AB = ED.

Prove that triangle ABC is congruent to triangle CDE.

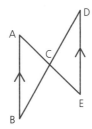

Key words

Here is a list of the key words you met in this chapter.

Angle	Angle bisector	Arc	Bisect
Congruent	Construct	Hypotenuse	Intersect
Perpendicular	Perpendicular bisector	Protractor	Prove
Vertex			

Use the glossary at the back of this book to check any you are unsure about.

Review exercise: constructions

Band 1 questions

Fluency

1 Use a ruler and protractor to make accurate drawings of these triangles.

In each case, measure the remaining sides and angles.

a

b

Reasoning

2 **a** Draw a triangle with angles of 60°, 60° and 60°.

    b Measure its sides.

    c What do you notice?

    d What sort of triangle have you drawn?

Fluency

3 Which two of these triangles are congruent?

What condition for congruency have you used?

Band 2 questions

Problem solving

4 Look at this plan of a house.

A garden wall is built from M.

It is perpendicular to the house.

Copy the diagram and construct the line of the wall.

5 **a** Construct this triangle.

Measure the length of AB.

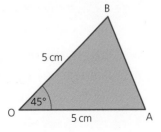

b Now add seven more triangles to make a regular octagon.

Measure the angles

i COF   **ii** CDE   **iii** DOF.

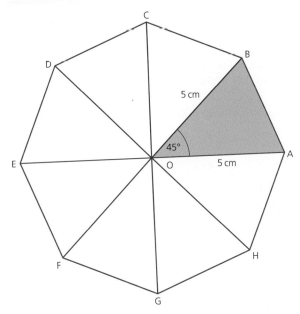

c What is the perimeter of the octagon?

6 a Make an accurate drawing of this triangle.

b Construct the perpendicular bisector of AC.

c What do you notice?

7 Construct this flower.

8 Draw a rectangle.

Can you split your rectangle into two congruent triangles?

Give a reason for your answer.

9 Make an accurate drawing of this triangle.

Construct the bisector of each angle.

What do you notice about where these bisectors intersect?

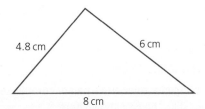

Band 3 questions

10 a Draw a triangle with sides 10 cm, 10 cm and 10 cm.

b Bisect its angles.

c What angles have you now made?

d Now construct angles of 15° and 7.5° on your diagram.

11 **a** Draw a triangle. Label it ABC.

Construct the perpendicular bisectors of the three sides.

They should meet at a point. Label the point M.

b Draw a circle with centre M, going through the point A.

What do you notice?

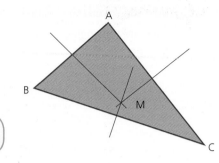

This circle is called the circumcircle of the triangle.

12 A mobile phone mast is to be built in a field. The diagram shows the position of the mast, M, relative to a road.

By making an accurate construction, find the minimum distance between the mast and the road.

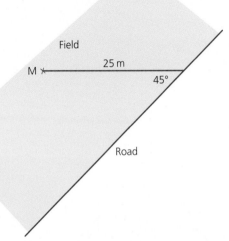

Field

25 m

M ⚹

45°

Road

13 Which **two** of these triangles are congruent to triangle A?

Give a reason for your answer.

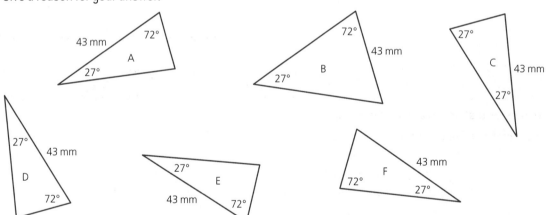

43 mm   72°

A

27°

72°

43 mm

B

27°

27°

C   43 mm

27°

27°

43 mm

D

72°

27°

E

43 mm   72°

43 mm

F

72°   27°

14 Draw a horizontal line 12 cm long.

Now, using only your ruler and a pair of compasses, construct a spider's web like the one shown here.

CHAPTER 13

Trigonometry

▶ Coming up...

- ◆ Recognising similar shapes
- ◆ Solving problems with similar triangles
- ◆ Labelling the sides in right-angled triangles

- ◆ Using trigonometry to find:
  - the length of an unknown side
  - the size of an unknown angle in a right-angled triangle
- ◆ Using trigonometry to solve problems

➜ Enlargements

Draw a shape on squared paper.

Enlarge your shape using a scale factor of 2.

How many times does your original shape fit inside the enlarged shape?

Investigate further using different starting shapes and different scale factors.

Here are two shapes to get you started.

Try some of your own shapes.

Is it always possible to fit your original shape inside the enlarged shape without cutting it up?

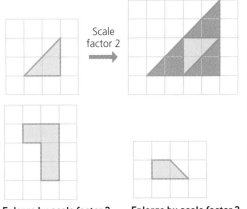

Enlarge by scale factor 2   Enlarge by scale factor 3

✔ Skill checker

Match the rectangles that are enlargements of each other.

Which rectangle is the odd one out?

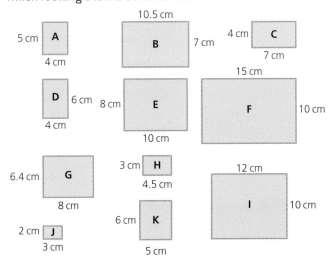

13.1 Similarity

When one shape is an enlargement of another shape the two shapes are said to be **similar**.

Similar shapes have the **same** angles but are different sizes.

Worked example

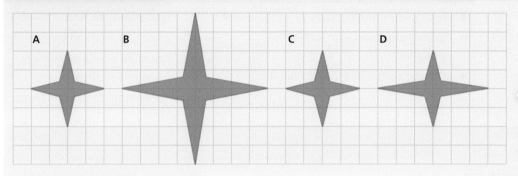

Notice that D is a different shape.

Jessica has drawn stars on this grid.

a   Which stars are congruent to A?

b   Which stars are similar to A?

Solution

a   Congruent shapes are the same shape and size.

   Only A and C are congruent.

b   Similar shapes are the same shape but they are usually different sizes.

   A, B and C are all similar.

Watch out! All congruent shapes are similar but similar shapes are rarely congruent.

Look at these parallelograms.

8 cm × 1.5 = 12 cm and
6 cm × 1.5 = 9 cm

All the lengths in B are 1.5 times longer than those in A but the corresponding angles remain the same.
Parallelograms A and B are similar.

They are same shape but different sizes.

The lengths of the sides in similar shapes are all in the same **ratio**. For example:

Parallelogram A   base : slant height $= 8 : 6$

$\qquad\qquad\qquad\qquad\quad = 4 : 3$

Parallelogram B   base : slant height $= 12 : 9$

$\qquad\qquad\qquad\qquad\quad = 4 : 3$

When two shapes are similar you can use the scale factor of enlargement and the ratios of their sides to work out missing lengths.

Worked example

These triangles are similar.

What is the value of x?

Solution

Method 1 – using the scale factor of enlargement

First work out the scale factor of enlargement: $15\,\text{cm} \div 5\,\text{cm} = 3$

> The sides are 3 times longer in the larger triangle.

So $x = 6 \div 3$

$\phantom{\text{So } x} = 2$

> So the base of the small triangle is 2 cm long.

Method 2 – using the ratios of corresponding sides

The ratio of the vertical sides, small : large is $5 : 15 = 1 : 3$.

So the ratio of the bases is also $1 : 3$.

> So the sides of the large triangle are three times those of the small triangle.

For the bases: $3x = 6$

$\phantom{\text{For the bases: }} x = 2$

Method 3 – using the ratios of sides

In the large triangle the ratio of the sides, base : height is $6 : 15 = 1 : 2.5$.

For the small triangle: $2.5x = 5$

$\phantom{\text{For the small triangle: }} x = 2$

> So the height of each triangle is 2.5 times the base.

You need to be able to recognise when two triangles are similar. When two triangles have the **same angles** they are similar and corresponding sides will be in the same ratio.

> Watch out! This is only true for triangles. Other shapes may have the same angles but not be enlargements of each other. For example:
>
> [ ] and [   ] have the same angles but they are not similar.

Worked example

Look at this diagram.

CD is parallel to BE.

a   Show that triangles ABE and ACD are similar.

b   Work out the length of

   i   BE

   ii   BC.

Solution

a

As CD and BE are parallel, the angles at B and C are corresponding angles so they are equal.

The angles at D and E are also corresponding angles so they are equal.

The angle at A is common to both triangles.

Since triangles ABE and ACD have the same angles the triangles are similar.

b i It often helps to redraw the two triangles separately.

AD = 8 cm + 4 cm = 12 cm and AE = 8 cm

The scale factor is $12 \div 8 = 1.5$ ◄────

> So triangle ACD is 1.5 times larger than triangle ABE.

$1.5 \times BE = CD$

So BE = 9 cm ÷ 1.5 = 6 cm

ii You can't find BC directly, but you can work out AC.

$1.5 \times AB = AC$

$AC = 1.5 \times 7 = 10.5$

$BC = 10.5 \text{ cm} - 7 \text{ cm} = 3.5 \text{ cm}$

13.1 Now try these

Band 1 questions

1 Choose the correct words from the box to complete the sentences below.

sides	angles	similar	congruent	rotations	enlargements	ratio	reflections

_____ shapes have all _____ the same and all sides in the same _____.

They are _____ of each other.

2 Sam writes down two statements about similar shapes.

   A   All squares are similar.

   B   All rectangles are similar.

Are Sam's statements correct? Explain your answers fully.

Reasoning

3 a Which rectangles are similar to rectangle A?

b What is the scale factor for an enlargement mapping A on to each of those rectangles?

Band 2 questions

Fluency

4 The triangles in each of these pairs are similar.

Find the sides marked x.

a

b

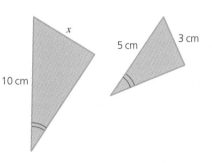

Problem solving

5 Triangle ABC is enlarged to give triangle XYZ.

The scale factor is 4.

a Find the length

i XY

ii YZ

iii AB.

b What is the ratio of the perimeter of ABC to the perimeter of XYZ?

6 A photograph is 10 cm by 15 cm.

a The diagrams show some possible enlargements.

Find the missing measurements.

| 15 cm |
| 10 cm |

| E | 30 cm |
| ? | |

| F | 60 cm |
| ? | |

| G | ? |
| 15 cm | |

b What is the ratio, the width of E : the width of F?

c Calculate the areas of the photographs E, F and G.

7

a   Show that these two triangles are similar.

b   Find the value of p and the value of q.

8   You need two sheets of A4 paper, a ruler and a pair of scissors.

Copy this table and complete it with your results.

Size of paper	Longer side (mm)	Shorter side (mm)	Longer ÷ shorter
A4			
A5			
A6			

Measure the sides of a sheet of A4 paper.

Work out the ratio of longer side ÷ shorter side.

Cut the second sheet of A4 paper in half as shown in the diagram.

Each half is now an A5 sheet.

Measure the sides and work out the ratio longer side ÷ shorter side for an A5 sheet.

Cut one of the A5 sheets in half (see diagram) to get two A6 sheets.

Measure the sides and work out the ratio longer side ÷ shorter side for an A6 sheet.

What do you notice about the three ratios that you have worked out?

Band 3 questions

9   These rectangles are similar.

a   Find the lengths marked x and y.

The rectangles represent gardens.

b   i   Find their perimeters.

   ii   Find the ratio of their perimeters.

c   i   Find the areas of the gardens.

   ii   Find the ratio of the areas.

d   Fauzia does scale drawings of all three gardens with a scale of 1 : 2000.

   What are the measurements of her scale drawings?

10   The diagram shows triangle ABC and triangle DEC.

a   Show that triangles ABC and DEC are similar.

b   Find the length of:

   i   DE   ii   BE.

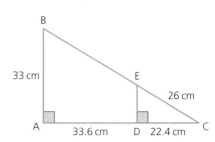

⑪ The diagram shows triangle ABC and triangle ADE.

BC and DE are parallel.

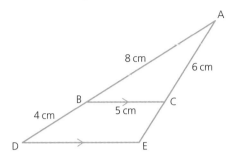

a   Show that triangles ABC and ADE are similar.

b   Find the length of:

   i   DE   **ii**   EC.

⑫ The diagram shows triangle ABC and triangle CDE.

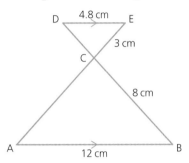

a   Show that triangles ABC and DEC are similar.

b   Find the length of:

   i   DC   **ii**   AE.

13.2 Finding a missing side

✔ Skill checker

a   Draw these two triangles accurately.

b   Measure the other two angles. What do you notice about the angles?

c   Measure the other side. What do you notice about the sides?

d   Work out

   i $\dfrac{\text{base}}{\text{height}}$ **ii** $\dfrac{\text{base}}{\text{hypotenuse}}$ **iii** $\dfrac{\text{height}}{\text{hypotenuse}}$

   for each triangle.

   What do you notice?

Labelling right-angled triangles

The Greek letter theta, θ, is often used to show an unknown angle. The three sides in a right-angled triangle have special names:

- The longest side is the hypotenuse.

The hypotenuse is fixed – it is the longest side and it is opposite the right-angle.

Watch out! The opposite and adjacent swap around depending on which of the acute (small) angles is θ.

The adjacent side has the right-angle at one end of it and θ at the other.

- The side next to the angle θ is the adjacent.
- The side opposite the angle θ is the opposite.

Adjacent means 'next to'.

 Activity

Label the hypotenuse, opposite and adjacent sides in these right-angled triangles.

①

②

③

④

⑤

⑥

You might find it helps to turn the triangle round before you label it.

Trigonometry

Trigonometry is the study of right-angled triangles and their side lengths and angles. In the next activity you'll be investigating similar right-angled triangles.

 Activity

① Accurately draw a right-angled triangle with an angle of 30°.

Accurately measure the lengths of the opposite and the hypotenuse.

Work out the ratio $\dfrac{\text{opposite}}{\text{hypotenuse}}$

Repeat with at least two other right-angled triangles with an angle of 30°.

What do you notice?

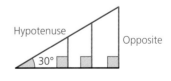

② Work out the sides and angle marked with letters.

Hint

All these triangles are similar to the triangles you drew in part 1.

The sine ratio

In the activity you found that when a right-angled triangle has one angle of 30°, the ratio $\dfrac{\text{opposite}}{\text{hypotenuse}}$ was always equal to $\dfrac{1}{2}$. This is because all right-angled triangles.

with one angle of 30° are **similar**.

If you repeated the activity using a right-angled triangle with an angle of 40°, you would find that the ratio $\dfrac{\text{opposite}}{\text{hypotenuse}}$ is approximately 0.64.

In fact, the ratio $\dfrac{\text{opposite}}{\text{hypotenuse}}$ always has the same value for a given angle θ.

The ratio $\dfrac{\text{opposite}}{\text{hypotenuse}}$ is called the **sine of the angle θ.**

You write $\sin\theta = \dfrac{\text{opposite}}{\text{hypotenuse}}$ ← Say 'sine theta equals opposite over hypotenuse'.

So $\sin 30° = \dfrac{1}{2}$ and $\sin 40° = 0.64\ldots$

Hint

Check you get an answer of 0.5: if you don't then you need to make sure that your calculator is in degrees mode. **Watch out!** Your calculator may automatically open a bracket when you press sin, so you need to close it!

Using your calculator

You can use the [sin] button to find the value of $\sin\theta$ for any angle θ.

To use your calculator to find $\sin 30°$ press [sin][3][0][=].

You can use the sine ratio to find the length of either the opposite or the hypotenuse in a right-angled triangle.

If you know the opposite and θ.

If you know the hypotenuse and θ.

Use your calculator to find the value of
a $\sin 90°$ **b** $\sin 60°$
c $\sin 20°$.

Worked example

Work out the value of x.

Solution

The two sides are the opposite, x, and the hypotenuse, 12 cm.

You know that $\theta = 50°$.

Use $\sin\theta = \dfrac{\text{opposite}}{\text{hypotenuse}}$

Substituting gives: $\sin 50° = \dfrac{x}{12}$

Rearrange: $12\sin 50° = x$ ← You don't need to write the x symbol.

Use your calculator: $x = 12\sin 50°$

$\qquad\qquad = 9.192\ldots$

So the missing side is 9.19 cm (to 3 s.f.).

Activity

You can use this formula triangle to help you rearrange the formula.

Use $\sin\theta = \dfrac{\text{opposite}}{\text{hypotenuse}}$ to work out the value of x and of y.

a

b

The cosine ratio

The ratio $\dfrac{\text{adjacent}}{\text{hypotenuse}}$ is called the **cosine** of the angle θ.

You write it as $\cos\theta = \dfrac{\text{adjacent}}{\text{hypotenuse}}$

You can use the cos button on your calculator to find the value of $\cos\theta$ for any angle θ.

For example, $\cos 60° = \dfrac{1}{2}$ ◄ *Use your calculator to check that you get the same answer.*

Worked example

Work out the value of x.

Solution

Label the sides of the triangle.

Using $\cos\theta = \dfrac{\text{adj}}{\text{hyp}}$ gives:

$\cos 40° = \dfrac{x}{15}$

$\quad x = 15\cos 40°$

$\quad\quad = 11.49...$

$\quad\quad = 11.5$ (to 3 s.f.)

So the missing side is 11.5 cm (to 3 s.f.).

You can use this formula triangle to help you to rearrange the formula.

The tangent ratio

The ratio $\dfrac{\text{opposite}}{\text{adjacent}}$ is called the **tangent** of the angle θ.

You write it as $\tan\theta = \dfrac{\text{opposite}}{\text{adjacent}}$

You can use the [tan] button on your calculator to find the value of $\tan\theta$ for any angle θ.

For example, $\tan 50° = 1.191\ldots$ ◄———

Use your calculator to check
that you get the same answer.

Opposite

θ

Adjacent

Worked example

Work out the value of x.

11.6 cm

35°

x cm

Solution

Label the sides of the triangle.

Using $\tan\theta = \dfrac{\text{opp}}{\text{adj}}$ gives:

$\tan 35° = \dfrac{11.6}{x}$

$x = \dfrac{11.6}{\tan 35°}$

$\quad = 16.56\ldots$

So the missing side is 16.6 cm
(to 3 s.f.).

11.6 cm
Opposite

35°

x cm
Adjacent

opp

$\tan\theta$ | adj

You can use this formula triangle to
help you to rearrange the formula.

Choosing the right ratio

$\sin\theta$, $\cos\theta$ and $\tan\theta$ are trigonometric ratios.

You can use this acronym to remember the trigonometric definitions and the formula triangles.

$s{}^o h \sim c{}^a h \sim t{}^o a$

$\sin\theta = \dfrac{\text{opp}}{\text{hyp}}$

$\cos\theta = \dfrac{\text{adj}}{\text{hyp}}$

$\tan\theta = \dfrac{\text{opp}}{\text{adj}}$

o

s | h

a

c | h

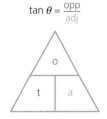

o

t | a

You usually need to decide which ratio is the correct one to use.

● Label the side you are given and the side you want.
● Choose the ratio that connects these two sides

Worked example

Work out the value of *x*.

Solution

Label the sides:

$$\cos 37° = \frac{14.2}{x}$$

$$x = \frac{14.2}{\cos 37°}$$

$$= 17.78...$$

So the missing side is 17.8 cm (to 3 s.f.).

13.2 Now try these

Give your answers correct to 3 significant figures where appropriate.

Band 1 questions

1 Label the **opposite**, **adjacent** and **hypotenuse** in each of these triangles.

a   b   c

2 Complete the trigonometric ratios.

a $\boxed{} = \dfrac{\text{adjacent}}{\text{hypotenuse}}$ b $\boxed{} = \dfrac{\text{opposite}}{\text{adjacent}}$ c $\boxed{} = \dfrac{\text{opposite}}{\text{hypotenuse}}$

3 Use your calculator to work out these.

    a cos 45°   **b** sin 45°   **c** tan 45°   **d** sin 75°   **e** cos 15°   **f** tan 60°   **g** tan 30°   **h** cos 60°

4 Use your calculator to work out these.

    a $2 \times \cos 25°$ **b** $5.4 \times \sin 30°$ **c** $2\tan 45°$ **d** $7\sin 32°$ **e** $8 \div \cos 60°$ **f** $12 \div \tan 50°$

    g $\dfrac{12}{\sin 30°}$ **h** $\dfrac{11.7}{\tan 80°}$

Band 2 questions

5 Use the ratio for sin θ to find the value of x and of y.

a

10 cm, x cm, 30°

b

5.4 cm, y cm, 48°

6 Use the ratio for cos θ to find the value of x and of y.

a

x cm, 60°, 3.2 cm

b

7.5 m, 25°, y m

7 Use the ratio for tan θ to find the value of x and of y.

a

8.4 m, x m, 35°

b

8.4 cm, y cm, 42°

8 Look at these right-angled triangles.

a

12 m, x, 30°

b

x, 7 cm, 50°

c

4 mm, x, 60°

For each triangle:

i   make a sketch and label the sides O, A and H

ii   write down (using O, A or H) which side you know and which side you want to find

iii   write down the trigonometric ratio that involves these two sides

iv   use the correct trigonometric ratio and your calculator to find the side length that you want.

Fluency

9 Find the length of each side marked with a letter.

a

38°
8.7 cm
a

b

36°
b
11 m

c

32 mm
50°
c

d

d
18.7
20°

Problem solving

10 Find the area of triangle *ABC*.

A
10 cm
C 70° B

11 The diagram shows a rectangular field ABCD.

A   B
50° 25 m
D   C

AC = 25 m and angle CAD = 50°.

A farmer wants to build a fence around the field.

He needs to put a 2.5 metre gate on each of sides AD and BC.

Fencing costs £45 per 2 metres.

Gates cost £225 each.

How much does it cost the farmer to fence and gate the field?

12 Work out the length of AD.

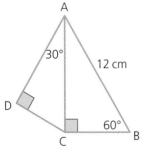

A
30°
12 cm
D
C 60° B

Key Stage 3 Mastering Mathematics: Book 3

① Label the **opposite**, **adjacent** and **hypotenuse** in the triangle.

② Triangles ABC and PQR are similar.

   a Work out the value of x and of y.

   b Write down the value of:

      i $\cos\theta$

      ii $\tan\theta$.

Diagrams **NOT** accurately drawn

Using trigonometry to find an angle

Look at this triangle.

You can see that

$$\sin\theta = \frac{\text{opp}}{\text{hyp}}$$

$$= \frac{8}{10}$$

$$= 0.8$$

Your calculator uses the **inverse trigonometric functions**

$\cos^{-1}$, $\sin^{-1}$ and $\tan^{-1}$ to 'undo' cos, sin and tan.

Your calculator can work out what angle has a sine of 0.8.

$\sin\theta = 0.8$

$\theta = \sin^{-1} 0.8$

$= 53.1°$ (to 1d.p.)

> Sometimes these are written as arccos, arcsin and arctan.

> Say inverse sin for $\sin^{-1}$.

> You need to use the shift or 2nd F button on your calculator for $\sin^{-1}\theta$, so you need these keys:
>

① Use Pythagoras' theorem to work out the adjacent side.

② Copy and complete the following:

   a $\cos\theta = \dfrac{\text{adj}}{\text{hyp}}$

      $= \dfrac{\square}{\square}$

      $= \square$

     So $\theta = \cos^{-1}\square$

      $= \square$ (to 1 d.p.)

     What do you notice?

   b $\tan\theta = \dfrac{\text{opp}}{\text{adj}}$

      $= \dfrac{\square}{\square}$

     So $\theta = \tan^{-1}\dfrac{\square}{\square}$

      $= \square$ (to 1 d.p.)

Worked example

a Look at the diagram. Which ratio would you use to find θ?

b Find θ.

6 cm

θ

11 cm

Solution

a You know the adjacent and the hypotenuse so use $\cos\theta = \dfrac{\text{adj}}{\text{hyp}}$

6 cm

θ

11 cm

> The adjacent side is 6 cm.
> The hypotenuse is 11 cm.

b $\cos\theta = \dfrac{6}{11}$

So $\theta = \cos^{-1}\left(\dfrac{6}{11}\right)$

> Use your calculator to work this out.

$= 56.9°$ (to 1 d.p.)

Angles are usually given correct to 1 decimal place and side lengths to 3 significant figures.

Make sure you know how to use your calculator correctly. If you get the wrong answer, make sure your calculator is in 'degrees' mode.

13.3 Now try these

Unless exact, give all angles correct to 1 decimal place.

Band 1 questions

1 ABC is a right-angled triangle with a right-angle at B.

The angle BAC is θ.

Find the value of θ when:

   a $\cos\theta = 0.5$ b $\sin\theta = 0.5$ c $\cos\theta = 1$.

2 Use your calculator to find the angles for which:

   a $\sin x = 0.2$ b $\cos y = 0.45$ c $\tan z = 0.8$.

3 Here is a right-angled triangle.

Write down the value of:

   a $\cos\theta$ b $\sin\theta$ c $\tan\theta$.

21 cm   29 cm θ 20 cm

Band 2 questions

4 Use the ratio for $\sin\theta$ to find the angle θ in each triangle.

   a

4 cm   12 cm θ

   b

θ 13.1 cm   7.2 cm

Fluency

5 Use the ratio for cos θ to find the angle θ in each triangle.

a

2.8 cm   3.2 cm

b

10.3 m
7.4 m

6 Use the ratio for tan θ to find the angle θ in each triangle.

a

7.2 cm   6.6 cm

b

8.2 m
4.6 m

Band 3 questions

Fluency

7 Find angle θ in each of these triangles.

a

9 cm   15 cm

b

5 m
2 m

c

12 mm
7 mm

8 Find angle θ in each of these triangles.

a

3.2 cm   4.6 cm

b

7.6 m   11.8 m

c

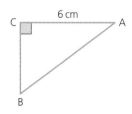

6.3 mm
5.9 mm

Problem solving

9 In triangle PQR:

PQ = 8 mm, PR = 1.2 cm, $\angle$PQR = 90° and $\angle$QPR = x°.

Work out the value of x.

10 The area of triangle ABC is 24 cm².

Calculate the angle ABC.

C   6 cm   A

B

Reasoning

11 Evie writes down some statements about a right-angled triangle.

Decide whether each of Evie's statements is 'always true', 'sometimes true' or 'never true'.

Give a reason for each of your answers.

   A   cos θ is less than 1

   B   sin θ could be greater than 1

   C   tan θ could be greater than 1

   D   tan θ could equal 1

① Write down Pythagoras' theorem.

② LMN is a right-angled triangle.

∠LNM = 90°, ∠NLM = 40° and LN = 7.2 cm

   a Sketch triangle LMN.

   b Calculate the length of LM.

   c Use Pythagoras' theorem to calculate the length of MN.

③ PQR is a right-angled triangle.

∠ PQR = 90°, PR = 4.5 cm, and PQ = 3.6 cm

   a Sketch triangle PQR.

   b Use Pythagoras' theorem to calculate the length of QR.

   c Calculate the angle RPQ.

Using trigonometry to solve problems

Use these tips to help you use trigonometry and Pythagoras' theorem to solve problems.

- Draw a diagram.
- Look for 'hidden' right-angled triangles.

Note

- Make a plan. Sometimes you have to find a different length or angle **before** you can find the one you want.
- Remember to use Pythagoras' theorem to find the 3rd side of a right-angled triangle when you know the other 2 sides.

Angles of elevation and depression

When you look up at an object the angle of elevation is the angle between the horizontal and your line of sight.

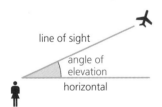

When you look down at an object the angle of depression is the angle between the horizontal and your line of sight.

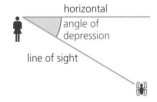

Worked example

A surveyor wants to work out the height of a tree.

She stands 30 m away from the base of the tree on level horizontal ground.

She measures the angle of elevation from her instrument to the top of a tree.

The angle of elevation is 25°.

Her instrument is 1.6 m above the ground.

Calculate the height of the tree.

Solution

Draw a diagram to help you.

You know the adjacent and you want the opposite so use tan.

$$\tan 25° = \frac{x}{30}$$

$$x = 30\tan 25°$$

$$= 13.98...$$

$$= 14.0 \text{ (to 3 s.f.)}$$

So the height of the tree is 14.0 m + 1.6 m = 15.6 m (to 3 s.f.).

13.4 Now try these

Unless the answers are exact, round any lengths to 3 significant figures and any angles to 1 decimal place.

Band 1 questions

1 A bird is flying above a rabbit in a field.

The bird looks down at the rabbit.

The diagram shows the position of the bird at B and the rabbit at R.

a The angle of elevation is angle ☐

b The angle of depression is angle ☐

c The angle of elevation is the same as angle ☐

d RB is called the line of ☐

2 Calculate the value of x and of y.

a

2.4 m
4.3 m
$x°$

b

$y°$
8 km
3200 m

3 Calculate the lengths of the sides marked with a letter.

a

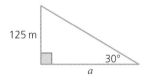
125 m
30°
a

b

35°
b
24 m

c

25°
3.2 miles
c

d

57°
0.95 km
d

4 John is a window cleaner. His ladder is 6 m long.

The angle between the ladder and ground is 70°.

Find the height that his ladder reaches up the wall.

5 A rectangular field is 160 m long and 120 m wide.

A straight path along one diagonal cuts across it.

a Find the angle the path makes with the longer side.

b Work out the length of the path.

Band 2 questions

6 A girl flies a kite at the end of a 25 m long string.

The angle of elevation from the girl's hand to the kite is 75°.

Calculate the height of the kite above the girl's hand.

7 Greta is in a small boat.

It is 1500 m away from the bottom of a cliff.

The height of the cliff is 230 m.

Find the angle of elevation of the top of the cliff from the boat.

8 A mouse is 5 m away from a 6 m high wall.

The mouse looks up at the wall and sees a cat sitting on the wall.

a Calculate the angle of elevation from the mouse to the cat.

b Write down the angle of depression from the cat to the mouse.

Band 3 questions

9 A ship is 8 km from port on a bearing of 036°.

How far north and how far east is the ship from the port?

N
8 km
036°
Port

10 An owl sits on a branch at O, part way up a tall tree.

There is a mouse on the ground at point M, 35 m away from the foot of the tree.

The angle of depression from the owl to the mouse is 25°.

The angle of elevation from the mouse to the top of the tree is 40°.

Work out the distance between the owl and the top of the tree.

11 Danielle cycles from Abbotville to Bradbury along a straight road.

Bradbury is 4 km north and 3 km east of Abbotville.

a Find the bearing of her journey.

b How far does she cycle?

c What is the return bearing?

12 Look at this diagram.

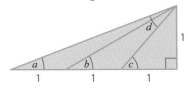

a Use trigonometry to find the value of $a + b + c$.

b Use your answer to part **a** to prove that $b = d$.

13 The diagram shows a form of spiral.

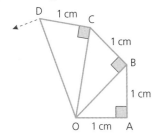

It continues with more triangles.

a Work out the lengths of:

   i OB   **ii** OC   **iii** OD.

Use square root signs in your answers when you need to.

b How many triangles are needed to complete:

   i 180° of the spiral   **ii** 360° of the spiral?

Key words

Here is a list of the key words you met in this chapter.

Adjacent	Angle of depression	Angle of elevation	Congruent
Corresponding	Cosine (cos)	Hypotenuse	Pythagoras' theorem
Ratio	Sine (sin)	Similar	Tangent (tan)
Trigonometry			

Use the glossary at the back of this book to check any you are unsure about.

Review exercise: trigonometry

Unless the answers are exact, round any lengths to 3 significant figures and any angles to 1 decimal place.

Band 1 questions

Fluency

1 Which **two** of the following are correct?

    A opposite × sin θ = hypotenuse   **B** cos × θ hypotenuse = adjacent

    C $\tan \theta = \dfrac{\text{adjacent}}{\text{opposite}}$ **D** hypotenuse $= \dfrac{\text{opposite}}{\sin \theta}$ **E** opposite × tan θ = adjacent

Reasoning

2 **a** Construct a triangle with sides of lengths 6 cm, 12 cm and 7.5 cm.

    b Construct a triangle with sides of lengths 4 cm, 8 cm and 5 cm.

    c Measure the angles in each triangle.

       What do you notice? Why is this?

3 Group these triangles into sets of similar triangles.

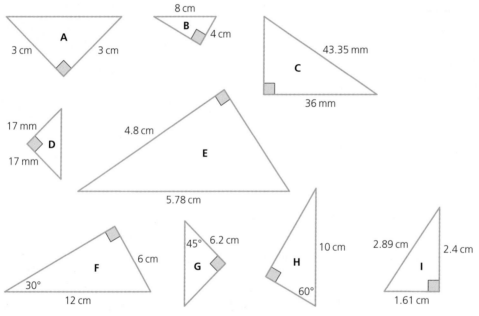

Fluency

4 Look at the triangle LMN.

Angle LNM is a right angle.

    a Find the length of the side LN without using trigonometry.

    b Write tan θ, sin θ and cos θ as fractions.

    c Now use your calculator to find θ three times, using the three trigonometric ratios.

       Check that you get the same answer each time.

Band 2 questions

5 Triangle ABC is similar to triangle PQR.

Angle ACB = Angle QPR.

Find the length of

a QR

b BC.

6 The triangles in each of these pairs are similar.

Find the sides marked x.

a

b

7 For each of these triangles, find the side labelled x.

a

b

c

8 Find the angle labelled with a letter in each of these triangles.

a

b

c

d

e

f

9 Triangle ABC is isosceles.

Angle BAC is 130°

BC = 12 cm

Work out:

a the height of triangle ABC

b the area of triangle ABC.

10 A 3 metre long ladder leans against a vertical wall.

The ladder is on level horizontal ground and the foot of the ladder is 90 cm away from the wall.

a Calculate the angle between the top of the ladder and the wall.

A window on the wall is 2.8 metres above the ground.

b **i** Does the top of the ladder reach the window?

Show all your working clearly.

ii Show how you can use a different method to answer this question.

Band 3 questions

11 Say whether each of these statements is true or false.

a The green triangle on the right shows you that $\sin 60° $ can be $\frac{5}{5} = 1$.

b $\sin 90° = 1$

c $\tan 0° = 0$

d Whatever the value of θ, $\sin\theta$ cannot be greater than 1.

e Different triangles give different values for $\tan\theta$.

12 A ship is 1.2 km north-east of a lighthouse when the captain radios for help.

A lifeboat is 3.7 km south-east of the lighthouse.

a How far is the lifeboat away from the ship?

b What is the bearing of the ship from the lifeboat?

Give your answer correct to the nearest degree.

13 The diagram shows a trapezium.

The trapezium has 1 line of symmetry.

Calculate the area of the trapezium.

14 PB is a vertical flagpole.

It is tethered by ropes AP and CP.

A, B and C are on level horizontal ground.

AP = 6.3 m, CP = 4.8 m and ∠PAB = 40°

Calculate:

a the height of the flagpole

b the angle BPC.

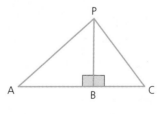

15 The diagram shows the quadrilateral ABCD.

∠BCA = 47°, ∠CAD = 25°, ∠ABC = ∠ACD = 90° and BC = 5.2 m

Calculate the perimeter of ABCD.

Give your answer correct to the nearest centimetre.

Chapters 11–13

Unless the answers are exact, round any lengths to 3 significant figures and any angles to 1 decimal place.

Band 1 questions

Fluency

① Calculate the surface area of each of these cuboids.

a

3 cm
2 cm
6 cm

b

4 cm
3 cm
10 cm

c

5 cm
5 cm
5 cm

d

15 cm
1 cm
5 cm

Reasoning

② Would you expect these two boxes to weigh the same?

Explain your answer fully.

5 cm
3 cm 4 cm
TEA

6 cm
5 cm
2 cm
SUGAR

Problem solving

③ This is the swimming pool at Avonford Leisure Centre.

   a   What shape is the swimming pool?

   b   What is the volume of the swimming pool?

   c   How many litres of water does the swimming pool hold?

   d   The bottom and sides of the inside of the pool are lined with tiles. What area is tiled?

10 m
20 m
2 m

1m³ = 1000 litres

Fluency

④   a   Draw a triangle PQR where PQ = 10 cm, PR = 10 cm and QR = 12 cm.

   b   Construct a line from P at right angles to QR. It crosses at S.

   c   Measure the lengths QS and PS.

P
10 cm   10 cm
S
Q   12 cm   R

301

5 Calculate the volume and surface area of this prism

4 cm

8 cm

6 cm

6 Find the volume and surface area of each of these solids.

Give your answers in suitable units.

a The lengths are in centimetres

3

3

5

8

6

b The lengths are in millimetres.

4

10

6

8

4

7 Ella is an artist.

She makes sculptures from marble.

i

25 cm

50 cm

20 cm

25 cm

50 cm

100 cm

ii

20 cm

10 cm

20 cm

10 cm

10 cm

20 cm

20 cm

iii

150 cm

50 cm

30 cm

50 cm

10 cm

a Work out the volume of each of these sculptures.

b How much marble is there in all the sculptures together?

c Marble has a density of 2.7 g/cm³.

How much does each sculpture weigh? Give your answer in kilograms.

8 a Construct these triangles accurately.

i

7.2 cm

9.6 cm

ii

31°

8 cm

iii

7.5 cm

6 cm

iv

v

vi

b Measure the lengths of the unknown sides to the nearest 0.1 cm.

Sort the triangles into two groups of similar triangles.

Are any of these triangles congruent?

9 a Use a ruler and protractor to make an accurate drawing of ABDC.

b Measure:

i the angle ABC   **ii** the length BC   **iii** the length CD.

10 Look at this regular hexagon.

The hexagon has been drawn inside a circle.

a Draw a circle with a radius of 4 cm.

Use a ruler and compasses to construct the hexagon inside it.

b Bisect each of the angles at the centre of the hexagon.

Use the bisectors to make a 12-sided regular polygon.

11 This right-angled triangular prism has height h, width w and length l.

a Write an expression for the volume.

b Write an expression for the surface area.

12 Rosie stands on the edge of the river opposite a tall tree at R.

She measures the angle of elevation of the top of the tree, T, as 50°.

Alan is 25 m behind Rosie at A.

He measures the angle of elevation of the top of the tree, T, as 23°.

a Make an accurate scale drawing of triangle ART.

b Extend the line AR.

Construct the perpendicular from T to this line.

c By taking appropriate measurements from your scale drawing find:

i the height of the tree

ii the width of the river.

⑬ Draw this design yourself. You will need to measure some of the lengths with a ruler. As well as the ruler, use only a pair of compasses.

Band 3 questions

⑭ Fatima measures rainfall for a geography project.

The rain is collected from a cylindrical tray which has radius 25 cm.

It then flows into a measuring cylinder underneath, which has diameter 10 cm.

What is the depth of water in the measuring cylinder after 0.4 cm of rain has fallen into the tray?

⑮ The diagram shows a rectangular field. There two trees at A and B.

The field has a footpath which is equidistant from the two trees.

Make a copy of the diagram and construct the footpath on your diagram.

⑯ Tom is a film star. He sends out souvenir models of his Oscar.

16 cm

24 cm

Photograph C

8 cm

height

Photograph D

The souvenirs are packed in boxes.

There are two sizes, large and small.

The boxes are similar.

On the front of each box is a photograph of Tom.

Photograph C is an enlargement of photograph D.

a What is the ratio, width : height, for photograph C?

b What is the height of photograph D?

The small box is 10 cm by 8 cm, and 12 cm high.

The ratio of the heights of the two boxes is 2 : 1.

12 cm

10 cm

8 cm

c What are the dimensions of the larger box?

d What is the surface area of:

   i the larger box

   ii the smaller box?

e **i** What is the ratio of the surface areas (large : small) in its simplest form?

   ii What is the connection between this and the ratio of the heights?

f Calculate the volume of each box and write down the ratio of their volumes in its simplest form.

g Find a connection between this ratio and the ratio of the heights.

17 Look at this prism. The end face is an isosceles triangle.

Calculate:

a the volume

b the surface area of the prism.

18 The diagram shows the quadrilateral WXYZ.

$\angle WYZ = 50°$, $\angle XYW = 30°$, $\angle XWY = \angle WZY = 90°$ and WX = 12.6 cm.

4 cm   8 cm

6 cm

X

12.6 cm

W   30°

50°   Y

Z

Calculate the area of WXYZ.

Give your answer correct to the nearest square centimetre.

19 This glass display case is of length 60 cm and external diameter 24 cm.

The glass is 1 cm thick.

The case stands on a wooden base 1 cm thick.

a Find the volume of the wooden base.

b Find the volume of glass required to make the case.

20 The diagram shows a regular pentagon inscribed inside a circle of radius 10 cm.

Work out the area of the shaded region.

21 **a** Draw x and y axes using the same scale for each.

b Using values of x from 0 to 4, draw the line $y = 2x + 3$.

c Calculate the angle that the line $y = 2x + 3$ makes with the x axis.

Working with data

▶ Coming up...

- Calculating mean, median, mode and range from a frequency table
- Grouping data
- Estimating the mean from a grouped frequency table
- Identifying the modal group and the group containing the median from a grouped frequency table
- Displaying grouped data using a frequency diagram
- Displaying bivariate data using a scatter diagram
- Interpreting a scatter diagram

➔ Roll the dice!

Here are some graphs. They show the scores for 20 rolls of a dice. Two of them are not correct.

A

B

C

D

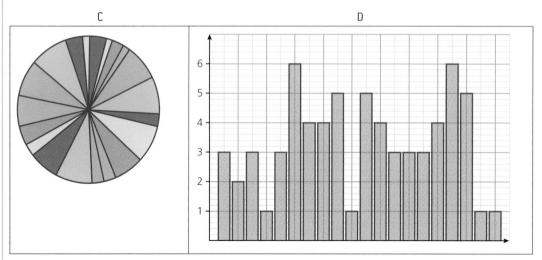

a   Which of the graphs are not correct?

b   Here are some sets of data. Match them with the graphs.

1	2	3	4
3, 1, 2, 1, 6, 6, 2, 6	3, 2, 3, 1, 3, 6, 4, 4	4, 3, 4, 6, 2, 3, 4, 4,	3, 5, 3, 2, 3, 5, 2, 4
5, 2, 2, 6, 5, 2, 3, 5	5, 1, 5, 4, 3, 3, 3, 4	1, 2, 3, 3, 2, 5, 1, 4	6, 6, 5, 2, 6, 2, 2, 1
6, 6, 3, 1	6, 5, 1, 1	5, 1, 2, 6	1, 6, 5, 6

c   Explain why the two graphs are incorrect.

d   Explain why the two incorrect graphs are poor representations of the data.

e   Explain why the two correct graphs are better representations of the data.

14.1 Grouped frequency tables

✔ Skill checker

① Decide whether each statement is true or false.

a $4 > 17$

b $3 \leqslant 3$

c $2 < 2$

d $7 \geqslant 6.5$

② Janice plays cricket for an under-12 team. These are her scores in eight games.

2, 4, 10, 9, 20, 5, 30, 2

a   Say whether each statement is true or false for this data set and explain how you know.

   i   The mode is 2.   ii   The median is 7.5.   iii   The range is 16.

③ Dawn and James both choose five cabbage plants.

They count the numbers of caterpillars on them. Their results are in this table.

Dawn	2, 0, 5, 14, 10
James	7, 2, 5, 3, 1

a   Work out the range for each set of data.

b   Work out the mean for each set of data.

④ Trishna asks everyone in her class how much pocket money they get each week.

Here are her results.

Amount	Frequency
£2	9
£2.25	6
£2.50	5
£3	8
£3.50	2

Work out the mean amount of pocket money for the class.

Grouped frequency tables

 Activity

Look at the frequency tables.

What is the same and what is different?

Score	Frequency
10	3
20	8
30	5
40	4

Score	Frequency
$10 \leqslant s < 20$	3
$20 \leqslant s < 30$	8
$30 \leqslant s < 40$	5
$40 \leqslant s < 50$	4

The second frequency table contains grouped data. It is a **grouped frequency table**. The data set is sorted into groups defined so that there is exactly one group for each item of data.

The original data was:

10, 12, 14, 20, 22, 24, 24, 25, 26, 27, 28, 30, 31, 34, 36, 38, 42, 46, 48, 49

The groups have been chosen with a width of 10. ◀———

> It is easy to assign each item to its group and to draw a graph of it.

There are four groups. ◀———

> Between 4 and 10 is not too many and not too few.

The groups are described using inequality notation.

$$10 \leqslant s < 20$$

> 10 is in this group

> 20 is not in this group but is in the next one.

This ensures that each value belongs to exactly one group.

 Activity

Use the frequency tables in the previous activity.

a   Work out the mean for the first frequency table.

b   The scores for the first frequency table are changed to 20, 30, 40 and 50. Work out the mean.

c   The scores for the first frequency table are changed to 15, 25 35 and 45. Work out the mean.

d   Which of the answers for **b**, **c** and **d** do you think is closest to the mean of the data in the second frequency table?

Remember

To work out the mean from a frequency table:

- multiply each score by its frequency
- add the results
- divide by the sum of the frequencies (20).

The first frequency table in the activity above retains all the detail of the data so the mean can be calculated. The second frequency table does not have that detail so the mean cannot be calculated.

However, the mean can be estimated.

The midpoint of each group is the most representative value in that group. It is used to estimate the mean.

Worked example

The maximum temperature, in °C, is recorded in Buenos Aires for each day in June one year.

16.4	12.8	17.6	19.1	16.6	15.5
11.2	18.7	19.5	16.1	15.3	14.2
15.8	15.7	14.9	14.4	13.4	12.1
13.9	11.9	13.1	12.6	10.9	13.5
14.2	15.4	16.6	15.9	15.6	14.3

June

a Present this data in a grouped frequency table.

Temperature, $T°C$	Frequency, f	$m \times f$
$10 \leqslant T < 12$		
$12 \leqslant T < 14$		
$14 \leqslant T < 16$		
$16 \leqslant T < 18$		
$18 \leqslant T < 20$		

b Calculate an estimate for the mean temperature.

The data ranges from 10.9 to 19.5 so groups of width 2 are chosen.

Solution

It is more efficient to be systematic and use tallies to count the number of values in each group.

a

Temperature, $T°C$	Tally	Frequency
$10 \leqslant T < 12$	III	3
$12 \leqslant T < 14$	IIII II	7
$14 \leqslant T < 16$	IIII IIII II	12
$16 \leqslant T < 18$	IIII	5
$18 \leqslant T < 20$	III	3

The midpoint of each group is calculated.

The calculation is the same as for ungrouped frequency tables.

b

Temperature, $T°C$	Midpoint, m	Frequency	$m \times f$
$10 \leqslant T < 12$	11	3	33
$12 \leqslant T < 14$	13	7	91
$14 \leqslant T < 16$	15	12	180
$16 \leqslant T < 18$	17	5	85
$18 \leqslant T < 20$	19	3	57
	Totals	30	446

The calculation is an estimate because the midpoints are used instead of the original data.

In this example the estimate could be compared with the mean calculated from the original data.

Mean = 446 ÷ 30 = 14.866 = 14.9 °C (1 d.p.)

This is an estimate of the mean of the data.

Usually the original data is not available.

14.1 Now try these

1. The Little Dons football team has played eight games this season.

   The chart below shows the number of people who have attended their games, to the nearest thousand.

   Attendance of Little Dons' football games this season

   a   Which game had the highest attendance?

   b   What is the range of the attendance figures?

   c   What is the median number of people attending a game?

   d   The club makes a profit if the attendance is over 2500.

        In what fraction of their matches so far has the club made a profit?

2. Samir has counted the lengths of the first 50 words in his reading book.

   Here are his results.

Number of letters	Frequency
1	5
2	7
3	10
4	17
5	5
More than 5	6

   a   Find the mode.

   b   Draw a vertical line chart to show Samir's results.

3. Three athletes enter the long jump trial for their club.

Athlete	Length of jump (metres)									
John Wells	3.45	4.12	3.56	3.75	2.96	2.77	3.98	3.25	3.78	3.44
Dipesh Raj	2.91	3.46	3.75	2.88	3.24	3.51	3.63	2.99	3.33	3.22
Zak Trent	4.02	3.55	4.06	4.03	3.70	3.84	3.99	4.03	3.24	3.53

   a   How many jumps does each athlete complete?

   b   Find the median length of jump for each athlete.

   c   Find the range for each athlete.

   d   Which athlete has the longest jump?

   e   Which athlete would you choose to represent the club?

        Give a reason for your choice.

4 A jogger runs an average of 7 km each day for 16 days.

She runs an average of 13 km each day for the next 8 days.

Find the average distance each day over the 24 days.

5 A survey was taken for the number of pets in 20 households.

The results were:

1, 2, 1, 3, 2, 3, 4, 3, 3, 22

5, 4, 3, 2, 0, 1, 0, 3, 4, 4

   a Copy and complete the frequency table.

Number of pets						
Frequency						

   b Which of the numbers is an outlier?

   Give one reason for including it.

   Give one reason for removing it.

Work out the answers to parts **c** and **d** both with the outlier and without it.

   c **i** What is the mean number of pets?

   ii What is the mode?

   iii What is the median?

   d What is the range of this data?

   e Comment on the effect of the outlier on the answers to parts **c** and **d**.

6 Seema goes 10-pin bowling.

The table shows how many pins she knocks down.

Number of pins	0	1	2	3	4	5	6	7	8	9	10
Number of turns	5	0	2	2	1	4	6	5	3	2	0

   a How many turns does Seema have?

   b Work out the total number of pins Seema knocks down.

   c Work out Seema's mean score.

Band 2 questions

7 The list below contains the total time, in minutes, spent at a gym by 30 people during a period of 3 weeks.

30	360	380	320	360	310	260	360	80	510
520	410	270	370	440	440	520	270	40	160
210	280	200	320	450	450	470	170	40	100

   a Complete a copy of this tally chart and frequency table.

Time, t (minutes)	Tally	Frequency
$0 \leqslant t < 99$		
$100 \leqslant t < 199$		
$200 \leqslant t < 299$		
$300 \leqslant t < 399$		
$400 \leqslant t < 499$		
$500 \leqslant t < 599$		

   b Explain why the groups are a good choice for this data.

   c Which is the modal group?

8 Amy's telephone bill shows the length of her last 20 calls to the nearest minute.

10 min	2 min	5 min	8 min
7 min	6 min	12 min	2 min
15 min	12 min	3 min	4 min
8 min	14 min	2 min	14 min
12 min	10 min	13 min	9 min

a What is the range of the data?

b Copy and complete this tally chart and frequency table.

Length of call, t (minutes)	Tally	Frequency
$2 \leqslant t < 4$		
$4 \leqslant t < 6$		
$6 \leqslant t < 8$		
$8 \leqslant t < 10$		
$10 \leqslant t < 12$		
$12 \leqslant t < 14$		
$14 \leqslant t < 16$		

c How many calls lasted:

i at least 10 minutes but less than 16 minutes

ii 8 minutes at the most?

d What is the modal group?

9 A newsagent records the number of magazines she sells on each of 15 days.

a Copy and complete this grouped frequency table.

Number of magazines sold, n	Midpoint, m	Frequency, f	$m \times f$
$10 \leqslant n < 20$		3	
$20 \leqslant n < 30$		7	
$30 \leqslant n < 40$		5	
Totals			

b In which group does the median value lie? Estimate its value.

c Use the table to estimate the mean number of magazines sold.

10 A speed camera recorded the speed, v mph, of 60 cars on a busy road.

Speed, v (mph)	Midpoint, m	Frequency, f	$m \times f$
$0 \leqslant v < 10$		1	
$10 \leqslant v < 20$		3	
$20 \leqslant v < 30$		12	
$30 \leqslant v < 40$		38	
$40 \leqslant v < 50$		6	
Totals		60	

a State the modal class.

b What do you think the speed limit was on this road?

Give a reason for your answer.

c Estimate the mean car speed on this road.

11 The grouped frequency table shows information about the waiting times (in minutes) for a bus.

Waiting time, b (minutes)	Number of people
$0 \leqslant b < 10$	3
$10 \leqslant b < 20$	6
$20 \leqslant b < 30$	10
$30 \leqslant b < 40$	4
$40 \leqslant b < 50$	2

a The time spent waiting by one person for a bus is 20 minutes.

In which class interval is this recorded?

b One person arrived at the bus stop at the same time as the bus.

In which class interval is their waiting time recorded?

c Write down the modal class interval.

d What can you say about the range of the waiting times?

e Estimate the mean time spent waiting for a bus.

12 Two researchers Halley and Malini recorded the lengths, in seconds, of birds' songs.

Halley's data	
$10 \leqslant x < 14$	5
$14 \leqslant x < 18$	8
$18 \leqslant x < 22$	4
$22 \leqslant x < 26$	3

Malini's data	
$12 \leqslant x < 18$	3
$18 \leqslant x < 24$	4
$24 \leqslant x < 30$	2
$30 \leqslant x < 36$	1

a For each set of data:

   i estimate the mean

   ii state the modal class.

b Do you think they were recording the same birds? Explain your answer.

Band 3 questions

13 Hassan is collecting data on the heights of adult men for a clothing company.

He measures the height, in centimetres, of 50 adult men.

Height, h (cm)	Frequency
$155 \leqslant h < 160$	2
$160 \leqslant h < 165$	6
$165 \leqslant h < 170$	8
$170 \leqslant h < 175$	10
$175 \leqslant h < 180$	11
$180 \leqslant h < 185$	7
$185 \leqslant h < 190$	4
$190 \leqslant h < 195$	2

a What is the modal class?

b Extend your table and calculate an estimate for the mean.

c Why do you think Hassan collected this information?

14 A safari park keeps a record of the number of cars visiting each day during the month of June.

Number of cars, n	Frequency
$100 \leqslant n < 150$	1
$150 \leqslant n < 200$	1
$200 \leqslant n < 250$	2
$250 \leqslant n < 300$	4
$300 \leqslant n < 350$	6
$350 \leqslant n < 400$	8
$400 \leqslant n < 450$	3
$450 \leqslant n < 500$	4
$500 \leqslant n < 550$	1

   a   Use your table to calculate an estimate for the mean.

   b   What is the maximum possible value for the range?

   c   What is the minimum possible value for the range?

15 The table shows the time, in minutes, that 30 customers had to wait to get a new car tyre.

Time, t (minutes)	Frequency
$0 \leqslant t < 8$	4
$8 \leqslant t < 16$	16
$16 \leqslant t < 24$	6
$24 \leqslant t < 32$	4

   a   Calculate an estimate for the mean waiting time.

   b   Work out the range.

   c   At another garage, the mean waiting time is 18 minutes with a range of 5 minutes.

       Compare the waiting times of the two garages.

16 A consumer organisation wants to compare two different seed composts, A and B.

150 seeds are sown in each compost and the heights of the seedlings that have germinated are measured after three weeks.

This table shows the heights, h mm, of each set of seedlings.

	A	B
$0 \leqslant h \leqslant 10$	6	18
$10 \leqslant h \leqslant 20$	23	16
$20 \leqslant h \leqslant 30$	45	20
$30 \leqslant h \leqslant 40$	36	48
$40 \leqslant h \leqslant 50$	11	31

   a   Estimate the mean height for each set of seedlings.

   b   Which compost do you think is better and why?

17 In a survey a group of Year 9 students were asked how long they had spent on their science homework the previous night.

Time, t (minutes)	Frequency
$0 \leqslant t < 10$	2
$10 \leqslant t < 20$	6
$20 \leqslant t < 30$	7
$30 \leqslant t < 40$	8
$40 \leqslant t < 50$	5
$50 \leqslant t < 60$	3
$60 \leqslant t < 70$	4

The results, in minutes, are shown.

a How many students were surveyed?

b Use the table to estimate the mean time spent on Science homework.

c i Using 20-minute intervals, draw and complete another grouped frequency table for the data.

   ii Calculate an estimate for the mean using this table.

d Compare the two means you have calculated. Which estimate is more accurate?

18 A fish breeder is testing two new types of food.

Two hatchings of baby fish are fed the different foods.

After two months the weights of the baby fish are measured to the nearest 0.1 gram.

Weight of baby fish, w (grams)	Batch A frequency	Batch B frequency
$0 \leqslant w < 0.5$	0	2
$0.5 \leqslant w < 1.0$	3	2
$1.0 \leqslant w < 1.5$	7	5
$1.5 \leqslant w < 2.0$	7	5
$2.0 \leqslant w < 2.5$	4	4
$2.5 \leqslant w < 3.0$	2	2
$3.0 \leqslant w < 3.5$	0	1
$3.5 \leqslant w < 4.0$	0	2

a Estimate the mean, the median and the range for Batch A.

b Estimate the mean, the median and the range for Batch B.

c Which fish food do you think is more effective?

   Give a reason for your answer.

14.2 Displaying grouped data

✔ Skill checker

① Write down the values indicated by the arrows.

② Lisa has drawn a bar chart to show how the people in her class travel to school.

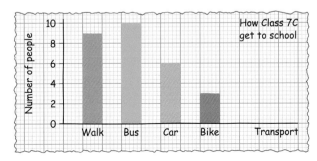

a What is the most popular way to get to school in Lisa's class? How do you know?

b How many people walk to school?

c How many people come to school by bus or car?

d How many people are there in Lisa's class?

e Draw a pictogram to show this data.

③ A dice is rolled 21 times. A vertical line chart is drawn of the results.

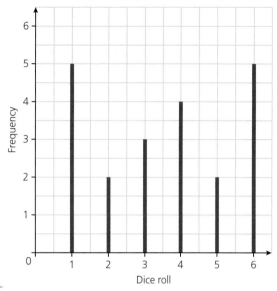

a There are two modes. What are they?

b What is the median score?

④ Mrs Patel sets her classes a test and wishes to group the results. They are percentages.

57	82	73	64	67	41	75
33	88	79	48	66	58	71
60	64	73	52	66	35	22
81	93	52	67	70	45	56
94	51	69	49	55	71	81
56	62	50	73	85	81	47
56	64	67	96	48	70	72

Why would $20 \leqslant m < 30$, $30 \leqslant m < 40$ up to $90 \leqslant m < 100$ be suitable groups for the results?

Displaying grouped data

 Activity

Sanjay and 4 of his friends measure the length of their feet, in cm rounded to the nearest mm:

22.5, 24.2, 23.3, 24.1, 25.8

and record their shoe sizes:

5, 7, 6, 7, 9

a Why are the foot lengths rounded?

b The shoe sizes are not rounded. Why not?

c What is the modal shoe size?

d Why is there not a modal foot length?

The shoe sizes are **discrete data**. The UK sizes include $5\frac{1}{2}$, $6\frac{1}{2}$, ... as well as the whole numbers. They do not include any other values such as $5\frac{1}{3}$ or 6.235 in between.

The foot lengths are **continuous data**. ◄─── Continuous data does not have gaps in the possible values.

They are both examples of **numerical** data. Numerical data consists of numbers.

24.1 cm and 24.2 cm are both size 7. The lengths in between 24.1 and 24.2 such as 24.102674 are also size 7.

Continuous data is usually rounded before it is recorded. ◄─── Rounded data is still continuous even if it looks as if there are gaps!

Categorical data is mentioned in *Key Stage 3 Mastering Mathematics Book 2* section 14.2 on pie charts.

It is data that is not numerical. It describes a property or characteristic. Sometimes digits are included but they are not used in calculations. They are used to identify something. A phone number is an example of a number used to identify something.

Worked example

Which of these are examples of the following types of data?

| Heights of meerkats | Colours of mobile phone cases | Numbers of people at events |

| Car number plates | Marks in an exam | Ages | Makes of car |

a discrete data
b continuous data
c categorical data

Solution

a Numbers of people at events are discrete data. ◄─── You can only have a whole number of people.

   Marks in an exam are discrete data. ◄─── These are usually whole numbers; half marks are never given.

b Heights of meerkats are continuous data. ◄─── Heights take all values within a range although they can only be measured to a certain accuracy.

   Ages are continuous data. ◄─── Age is rounded down but it is still continuous even if it looks as if there are gaps!

c Colours of mobile phone cases are categorical data. ◄─── Colours are not numerical.

   Makes of car are categorical data. ◄─── Makes of car are not numerical.

   Car number plates are categorical data.

   ▲─── They contain numbers but these are used to identify the car. Bus numbers are also identifiers.

A **frequency diagram** is plotted from a grouped frequency table. It consists of bars placed on a linear scale covering the range of values in the groups.

Worked example

Plotting a frequency diagram

Alex and Emily measured the heights, h m, of girls in their athletics club.

1.45	1.57	1.60	1.48	1.60	1.77	1.56	1.55	1.66	1.66
1.70	1.62	1.60	1.42	1.52	1.55	1.59	1.72	1.52	1.62
1.80	1.52	1.75	1.55	1.70	1.63	1.44	1.73	1.50	1.54
1.36	1.62	1.54	1.64	1.55	1.82	1.47	1.68	1.55	1.70
1.60	1.75	1.63	1.75	1.44	1.60	1.60	1.42	1.58	1.80

a Display this information using a grouped frequency table.

b Use your grouped frequency table to plot a frequency diagram.

c Describe the distribution of the data.

> The groups are 0.1 m (10 cm) wide. There are six groups.

Solution

a

Height, h (m)	Frequency
$1.30 \leqslant h < 1.40$	1
$1.40 \leqslant h < 1.50$	7
$1.50 \leqslant h < 1.60$	15
$1.60 \leqslant h < 1.70$	15
$1.70 \leqslant h < 1.80$	9
$1.80 \leqslant h < 1.90$	3

b Frequency diagram showing the heights of girls in an athletics club.

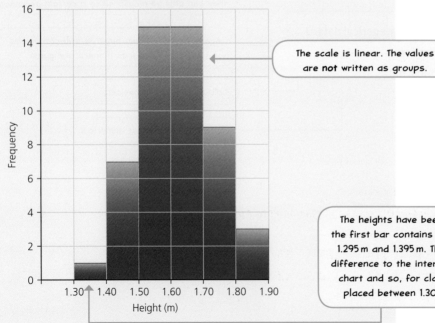

Frequency diagram showing the heights of girls in an athletics club

> The scale is linear. The values are **not** written as groups.

> The heights have been rounded, so the first bar contains heights between 1.295 m and 1.395 m. This makes little difference to the interpretation of the chart and so, for clarity, the bar is placed between 1.30 m and 1.40 m.

c Most of the girls are between 1.5 and 1.7 m tall. A few are shorter than this and some are taller.

14.2 Now try these

Band 1 questions

1 State whether each type of data is categorical or numerical.

   a flavours of crisps   **b** amount of salt in packets of crisps

   c methods of transport   **d** passwords

   e PIN numbers   **f** times taken to walk to school

2 Molly writes a table like this.

Time, t (hours)	Tally	Frequency
$0 \leqslant t < 5$		
$5 \leqslant t < 10$		
$10 \leqslant t < 15$		
$15 \leqslant t < 20$		

   a What does $0 \leqslant t < 5$ mean?

   b Which category does 5 hours belong to?

   c Explain why $0 \leqslant t < 5$ is a better group size than $0 \leqslant t < 6$?

3 State whether each type of data is discrete or continuous.

   a The number of people in cars passing the station

   b The amount of money earned by an investment

   c The wingspans of eagles

   d The score shown when a dice is rolled

   e The maximum heights of balls when bounced

   f The weights of new-born dolphins

4 Zelma draws a frequency diagram of the heights of some broad bean plants.

Heights, h (m)	Frequency
$0.8 \leqslant h < 0.9$	7
$0.9 \leqslant h < 1.0$	9
$1.0 \leqslant h < 1.1$	25
$1.1 \leqslant h < 1.2$	9

The horizontal scale is shown below.

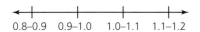

0.8–0.9   0.9–1.0   1.0–1.1   1.1–1.2

Explain why Zelma should not use that scale?

5 Zoe has measured the height in cm of the adult goats on her farm.

Here are her results.

132	121	146	134	114	125	137	129
127	130	124	136	141	118	129	136
123	128	135	132	129	117	140	135
139	131	127					

a Copy and complete this tally chart.

Height, h (cm)	Tally	Frequency
$110 \leqslant h < 115$		
$115 \leqslant h < 120$		
$120 \leqslant h < 125$		
$125 \leqslant h < 130$		
...		

b Which class has the highest frequency?

6 This frequency diagram shows the ages of children at a summer camp.

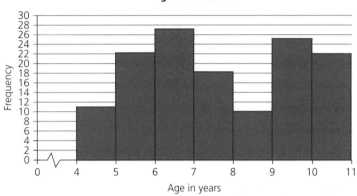

Ages of children

a How many children are between 6 and 7 years old?

b How many children are over 8 years old?

c How many children are between 8 and 9 years old?

d What is the median age of the children?

Band 2 questions

7 Matt works at a swimming pool.

He is doing a survey to find out what age groups use the swimming pool most.

He writes down the ages, y years, of all the people who visit the pool one morning.

Here are his results.

32	55	41	12	13	13	62	45	23
6	4	3	29	27	56	19	17	34
47	8	7	11	15	70	33	26	14
37	13	14	22	30	45	52	15	14
31	53							

a Make a tally chart using groups $0 \leqslant y < 5$, $5 \leqslant y < 10$, $10 \leqslant y < 15$ and so on.

b Draw a frequency diagram.

c How many people visited the pool that morning?

d Which age group used it most?

8 Mr Harris has given his class a test. He has given each student a mark, m, out of 50.

Here are the results for his class.

32	38	43	21	30	46	29	35
37	42	27	25	33	32	16	48
39	37	26	19	40	23	35	24
8	35	39	41	36			

Fluency

Reasoning

Mr Harris is going to give each student a grade.

He wants to make a tally chart to show his results.

a Copy and complete the table to show what grades Mr Harris' students received.

Grade	Mark	Tally	Frequency
E	$0 < m \leqslant 10$		
D	$10 < m \leqslant 20$		
C	$20 < m \leqslant 30$		
B	$30 < m \leqslant 40$		
A	$40 < m \leqslant 50$		

b What is the modal grade awarded?

c Draw a frequency diagram to show the results.

d What grade does a mark of 20.5 get?

9 Sarah keeps a record of her scores when she plays her new computer game.

Here are her scores, s points, for the first few weeks.

17	55	82	134	168	143	182	174
240	113	194	98	257	322	286	301
126	264	228	319	160	200	258	320
247	281	177	346				

The maximum possible score is 500.

a Make a tally chart using groups 0–49, 50–99, 100–149 and so on.

b Draw the frequency diagram.

c What do you think the frequency diagram will look like after a few months?

10 Neila times how long her friends can hold their breath for. The time is t seconds.

She records her data in the table below.

Time t (seconds)	Frequency
$0 \leqslant t < 10$	0
$10 \leqslant t < 20$	1
$20 \leqslant t < 30$	3
$30 \leqslant t < 40$	19
$40 \leqslant t < 50$	12
$50 \leqslant t < 60$	5

a How many people took part?

b Draw a frequency diagram.

c Estimate the median time. Is it in the modal group?

d One of Neila's friends holds his breath for 30.5 seconds.

Which group does this time go in?

11 The maximum temperature, in °C, is recorded in Buenos Aires for each day in June.

16.4	12.8	17.6	19.1	16.6	15.5
11.2	18.7	19.5	16.1	15.3	14.2
15.8	15.7	14.9	14.4	13.4	12.1
13.9	11.9	13.1	12.6	10.9	13.5
14.2	15.4	16.6	15.9	15.6	14.3

a Draw a frequency diagram.

b On how many days was the temperature:

    i at least 16 °C but less than 18 °C   **ii** less than 14 °C   **iii** at least 12 °C?

c Describe the distribution.

⑫ Sophie carried out a survey to find out the ages of people using her local swimming pool during one hour.

She draws a frequency diagram to show her results.

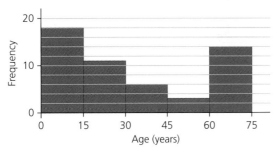

a How many people aged 60 or over used the pool during the survey?

b Do you think Sophie carried out her survey in the morning or the evening?

Explain your answer.

Band 3 questions

⑬ Stephen and his sister Anna share a computer.

Stephen and Anna both keep a record of the length of time, in minutes, that they use the computer each day for one month.

Time, t (minutes)	Stephen frequency	Anna frequency
$0 \leqslant t < 15$	0	8
$15 \leqslant t < 30$	2	4
$30 \leqslant t < 45$	5	2
$45 \leqslant t < 60$	11	3
$60 \leqslant t < 75$	10	2
$75 \leqslant t < 90$	2	7
$90 \leqslant t < 105$	1	4
$105 \leqslant t < 120$	0	1

a Draw frequency diagrams to show

   i Stephen's data   **ii** Anna's data.

b Anna thinks Stephen uses the computer more than she does. Do you think that Anna is right?

Explain your answer.

⑭ A group of people go on a course to maintain a new machine. At the end they are given a test.

These are their marks, as percentages.

Marks, m	Frequency
$10 \leqslant m < 20$	2
$20 \leqslant m < 30$	1
$30 \leqslant m < 40$	2
$40 \leqslant m < 50$	4
$50 \leqslant m < 60$	5
$60 \leqslant m < 70$	7
$70 \leqslant m < 80$	5
$80 \leqslant m < 90$	3
$90 \leqslant m < 100$	1

a   Draw a frequency diagram to display the data.

b   What is the modal group?

c   Estimate the mean using the grouped frequency table.

d   Which is the more useful diagram, the frequency diagram or the grouped frequency table? Explain why.

e   The pass mark is 60. What percentage of the people pass?

15   Zubert is a diver. He holds a competition to find out how far his friends can swim underwater without taking a breath.

He records the results in a frequency table.

Distance (metres)		Frequency
At least	Below	
0	10	2
10	20	11
20	30	4
30	40	2
40	50	1

a   How many people take part in the competition?

b   What is the shortest possible distance swum by any of the participants?

c   Display this information as a frequency diagram.

d   Describe the distribution.

e   Calculate the percentage of people in the modal group.

16   Here is some data about the members of Crowden Football Club.

Name	Age (years)	Height (cm)	Goals, g, this season
Nabil	11	138	16
Lee	13	150	11
Laamia	11	123	2
Younis	12	141	7
Lorraine	13	135	0
Chantel	11	152	3
Heidi	13	129	14
Sabrina	13	137	9
David	12	131	0
Jody	11	148	17
Youssu	14	164	0
Patricia	12	149	2
John	11	128	15
Stuart	12	137	1
Crystal	13	145	22

a   Display the goals scored in a grouped frequency table.
Use groups of $0 \leqslant g < 5$, $5 \leqslant g < 10$ and so on.

b   Display the height data in a grouped frequency table.
Use groups $120 \leqslant h < 130$, $130 \leqslant h < 140$, etc.

c   Display the age data in a frequency table.

d   Find the median of each set of data.

e   Draw the frequency diagrams to illustrate the data.

f   Which player do you think is most representative of the group. Why?

g   Who is most likely to be the goalkeeper? Explain your reasoning.

17 Below are the weights, in kg, of all the babies born in a hospital in one month.

Weights, w (kg)	Boys frequency	Girls frequency
$2.8 \leqslant w < 3.0$	1	3
$3.0 \leqslant w < 3.2$	6	7
$3.2 \leqslant w < 3.4$	8	14
$3.4 \leqslant w < 3.6$	14	14
$3.6 \leqslant w < 3.8$	19	18
$3.8 \leqslant w < 4.0$	20	13
$4.0 \leqslant w < 4.2$	11	10
$4.2 \leqslant w < 4.4$	4	1
$4.4 \leqslant w < 4.6$	1	0

a Draw appropriate diagrams to compare the data.

b Describe the similarities and differences between the weights of the boys and girls.

18 Take your pulse for one minute. This is your pulse rate.

a Find the pulse rate for each person in your class. (You will need at least 20 measurements.)
Record this in a suitable grouped frequency table.

b Use suitable charts and statistical measures to summarise your data.

14.3 Scatter diagrams

✔ Skill checker

① Write down the coordinates of A, B, C and D.

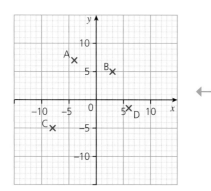

The x coordinate is written first.

② Write down the numbers indicated by the arrows.

③ Two cars are represented on the graph.

Decide whether each of the following statements is true or false.

▸ The older car is cheaper.
▸ The more expensive car is older.

④ Two people are represented on the graph.

Decide whether each of the following statements is true or false.

▶ The taller person is younger.
▶ The older person is shorter.

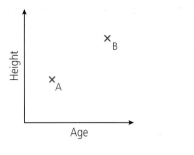

Scatter diagrams

A **scatter diagram** is drawn using pairs of data as coordinates.

 Activity

Ms Calligraphy asks 10 students in her class to write their first names, in a line, as many times as they can in 30 seconds.

She asks them to measure the length of their writing in cm, rounded to the nearest mm.

Student	Number of times name written	Length of writing (cm)
1	10	20.2
2	11	30.3
3	9	20.4
4	12	28.7
5	11	24
6	14	21.9
7	11	31.5
8	6	16.8
9	13	25.1
10	11	31.3

a Jo has a very short name. Where do you think her result is?

b Marc writes slowly. Where do you think his result is?

c Katherine writes slowly. Where do you think her result is?

d Where do you think Katherine's result is compared with Marc's?

e What can you say about the person whose result is at (14, 21.9)?

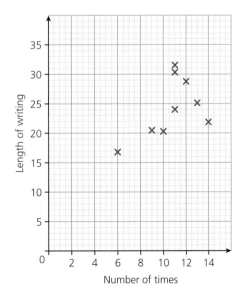

(6, 16.8) represents the data from one of the students.

The results in the activity are mostly grouped in one area of the graph.

The number of repetitions of the names is not related to the length of the writing.

Correlation is when there appears to be a link between how one measure changes when another measure changes.

There is no correlation between the number of repetitions and the length of the writing.

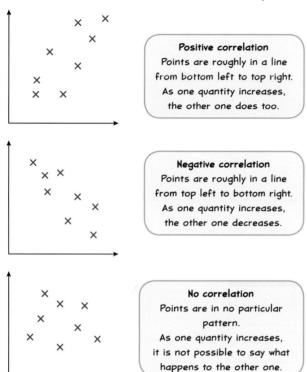

Positive correlation
Points are roughly in a line from bottom left to top right. As one quantity increases, the other one does too.

Negative correlation
Points are roughly in a line from top left to bottom right. As one quantity increases, the other one decreases.

No correlation
Points are in no particular pattern.
As one quantity increases, it is not possible to say what happens to the other one.

A **line of best fit** can be drawn when there is correlation.

It is a straight line that follows the trend of the data.

Worked example

Oliver and Susai are having an argument.

Oliver says, 'I think that people with long legs can jump further than people with short legs.'

Susai says, 'Rubbish! The length of a person's legs does not affect how far they can jump.'

They decide to collect data from their friends to find out who is right.

	Alan	Barry	Claire	Dipak	Ernie	Flora	Gurance	Habib	Ivan
Inside leg measurement (cm)	60	70	50	65	65	70	55	75	60
Standing jump distance (cm)	85	90	65	90	80	100	80	95	70

a Draw a scatter diagram.

b i Describe the correlation in the scatter diagram for Oliver and Susai's data.

　ii Does the scatter diagram support Oliver or Susai?

c i Draw a line of best fit.

　　Jemima has an inside leg measurement of 70 cm.

　ii Use your graph to estimate what distance she is likely to jump.

d Have they got enough data to be certain about their findings?

Solution

a

b i The graph shows positive correlation: as the inside leg measurement increases, so does the distance jumped.

  ii This supports Oliver's claim.

c i A line of best fit is drawn on the graph.

    The line of best fit leaves an even distribution of points on either side of the line.

  ii From the graph we can see that Jemima should jump about 93 cm.

d They do not have enough data to be certain. More points on the graph would help.

14.3 Now try these

Band 1 questions

1 Here are some examples of scatter diagrams.

Copy and complete each sentence using the words in the box.

increases	**decreases**	**positive**	**negative**	**no**

a As the revision time ____ the test mark ____ , so there is ____ correlation between revision time and test mark.

b As the age of the car ____ the price ____ , so there is ____ correlation between age and price of car.

c Hat size does not appear to be related to IQ, so there is ____ correlation between hat size and IQ.

2 A scatter graph is drawn to show how much 5 students enjoy reading and swimming.

Match the points with the students.

Penny quite likes doing both.

Rob enjoys reading very much but is not keen on swimming.

Suzi enjoys both reading and swimming very much.

Tim dislikes both.

Ursula swims a lot but seldom reads.

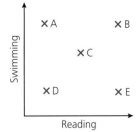

Reasoning

3 The data in the graph show positive correlation. The horizontal axis is the final height of a tomato plant.

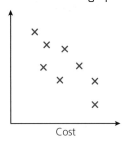

Height

Explain why the amount of fertiliser used could be on the vertical axis.

4 The data in the graph show negative correlation. The horizontal axis is the cost of a car.

Cost

Explain why the vertical axis could be the number of miles on the mileometer at the time it is sold.

5 The results on two papers in a Science exam are plotted on a scatter diagram.

a Describe the correlation.

b **i** What do the zig-zags across each axis mean?

ii Why are they used in this graph?

c Jim scored 54 on Paper 1. What mark did he get on paper 2?

6 Nicky says, 'The scales on a graph have to start at 0.' Explain why Nicky is wrong.

Band 2 questions

7 Describe the correlation you would expect to find between the following data sets.

a Score in history test and score in science test

b Leg length and arm span

c Typing speed and length of grass in garden

d Death rate per 1000 and average salary per capita

8 This scatter diagram shows the relationship between the price of some one-bedroom flats and their distance from the centre of Valletta, the capital city of Malta.

a Copy the scatter diagram and draw a line of best fit.

b Use the scatter diagram to estimate

   i the price of a flat 8 km from the centre of Valletta

   ii the distance from the centre of Valletta of a flat costing €105 000.

9 A group of friends take part in a sponsored swim.

Name	Abdul	Sonia	Lizzy	Geoff	Angey	Carrie	Cherry
Age	20	38	60	51	28	33	26
Number of lengths	30	19	14	11	26	34	42

a Draw a scatter diagram to show this data.

b Describe the correlation between the ages of these swimmers and the number of lengths they swim.

c Terry is 46 and Clara is 31. They also swim.

   i Who do you expect to swim further?

   ii Can you be sure?

10 Claire took ten sets of tests for a coaching certificate.

Each test had a theory section and a practical section. Her results are shown below.

Theory (%)	64	45	56	72	65	78	32	85	76	90
Practical (%)	30	40	50	65	68	70	22	81	73	86

a Draw a scatter diagram showing her results on the theory and practical sections.

b Describe the correlation between Claire's results on the two sections.

c Draw a line of best fit on your scatter diagram.

d Claire took another test.

   She was absent for the practical section but got 60% on the theory.

   Use the line of best fit to suggest a suitable mark for the practical section.

   Can you be certain that Claire would get this mark? Explain your reasoning.

11 Zoe thinks that the more football matches you go to, the less you read.

She collected the data below for the last month.

Name	Amy	Ben	Des	Ella	Mo	Sid
Number of books read	3	7	2	6	3	0
Number of football matches attended	4	5	2	0	3	5

a Plot the data on a scatter diagram.

b What correlation does the graph show?

c Is Zoe correct? Explain your answer by referring to your graph.

12 Skylar says, 'A line of best fit must go through the point (0, 0).' Explain why Skylar is wrong.

13 Trevor measures the floor area of a number of classrooms in his school.

He also counts the number of desks in them.

Area (m²)	25	32	26	38	40	42	48	50	55	65
Number of desks	10	13	16	17	11	15	20	19	17	20

a Draw a scatter diagram and add in a line of best fit if appropriate.

b Another classroom has floor area 46 m².

   Use your scatter diagram to estimate how many desks it can have.

c Comment on the correlation between the area and the number of desks.

⑭ Look at this scatter diagram.

It shows the weight and cost of 4 books taken off a shelf at an antique book shop.

Julie says 'You can see that heavier books cost more.'

a   Why does Julie say this?

Another 7 books are taken off the shelf at random.

Weight (g)	100	250	55	200	205	300	50
Cost (£)	45	15	50	8	10	7	36

b   Copy the scatter diagram and plot the new points.

Robert says, 'There is no correlation between a book's weight and its cost.'

c   Which of the two opinions is the more reliable, Julie's or Robert's? Explain your reasoning.

⑮ Ellie thinks that there is a connection between the number of reported crimes in a town and the number of police officers on the beat.

She collects information for 15 towns in her county for one month.

Town	1	2	3	4	5	6	7	8	9	10	11	12	13	14	15
Number of police officers	6	16	15	28	30	22	12	23	11	20	17	16	19	25	27
Number of reported crimes	180	150	111	70	30	64	80	95	98	36	83	58	121	146	42

a   Draw a scatter diagram for this data set.

b   Describe the correlation.

c   What other factors might affect the number of reported crimes?

⑯ In a fishing competition, the judges measure the length and mass (weight) of each fish caught.

These are the results for the first six fish caught.

Fish	1	2	3	4	5	6
Length (cm)	24	50	29	19	42	45
Mass (kg)	1.5	13.2	5.5	0.9	10.6	7.8

a   Draw a scatter diagram for this data set.

b   Describe the correlation.

c   Another fish is caught which has a mass of 8 kg.

Use the line of best fit to estimate the length of this fish.

Problem solving

17 Shamicka thinks that people who are good at sprinting are also good at long jump.

She collects some data.

Time to run 100 m (s)	Distance jumped (m)	Time to run 100 m (s)	Distance jumped (m)
14.3	1.81	16.0	1.68
12.7	1.94	15.3	1.75
13.9	1.84	13.4	1.88
15.4	1.72	13.6	1.92
14.0	1.88	14.7	1.78
17.3	1.52	12.5	2.08
12.8	2.03	16.4	1.58

a Draw a scatter diagram to show Shamicka's data.

b Is Shamicka right?

c Find the median running time.

d Find the median distance jumped. Is this the same person as in part **c**?

e Shamicka thinks the quickest 25% of people in her sample should be classified as good.

Do the same people feature in the top 25% of jumpers?

18 Choose two body measurements from the table and investigate whether or not they are connected.

Length of arm   Head circumference   Handspan

Wrist circumference   Length of middle finger

a Draw a table to collect your data and think carefully about the number of items of data you will collect and how you will choose them.

b Collect your data and display your results on a scatter graph.

c Describe the correlation between your chosen measurements.

Reasoning

19 Steve says both of these graphs show positive correlation. Explain why Steve is wrong.

a

b

Problem solving

20 Investigate whether some people have quicker reaction times regardless of whether they are using their dominant hand or their other hand.

Key words

Here is a list of the key words you met in this chapter.

Categorical data	Continuous data	Correlation	Discrete data
Frequency diagram	Grouped frequency table	Line of best fit	Modal group
Negative correlation	Numerical	Positive correlation	Scatter diagram

Use the glossary at the back of this book to check any you are unsure about.

Review exercise: working with data

1 A group of 40 people took an aptitude test for a flying school.

The table shows their results.

Score, s	Frequency, f	Midpoint, m	$m \times f$
$40 \leqslant s < 50$	5		
$50 \leqslant s < 60$	10		
$60 \leqslant s < 70$	12		
$70 \leqslant s < 80$	8		
$80 \leqslant s < 90$	5		
Totals			

a Complete a copy of the table and estimate the mean mark.

b The pass mark for entry to the flying school is 65.

Estimate how many people passed.

2 The table summarises the heights of 25 football players in a team.

Height, h (cm)	Number of football players
$140 < h \leqslant 144$	2
$144 < h \leqslant 148$	6
$148 < h \leqslant 152$	10
$152 < h \leqslant 156$	3
$156 < h \leqslant 160$	3
$160 < h \leqslant 164$	1

Calculate an estimate for the mean height.

3 The ages of the people on a package holiday are as follows.

45	38	27	32	30	7	4	28	48	42	15	31
13	10	56	58	37	24	25	69	34	26	44	46
32	35	64	51	60	49	46	17	38	62	57	52
52	53	29	24	27	23	57	45	43	26	37	31

Michael says that groups of width five, $0 \leqslant a < 5$ and so on, are best in this case. Dom says that groups of width 20, $0 \leqslant a < 20$ and so on, are best.

Theresa says that groups of width 10, $0 \leqslant a < 10$ and so on are best.

Explain why Theresa is right.

4 Are the following data sets discrete or continuous?

a The points scored by a group of friends on a computer game.

b The numbers of students in each class at school.

c The weights of moon rock specimens.

d The distances travelled by snails in a day.

e The numbers of letters arriving each day at your house.

5 This table shows the marks (out of 10) given by judges at a local vegetable show.

Name	Marks from Judge 1	Marks from Judge 2
Mrs Giles	1	2
Mr Hands	6	8
Mr Smith	3	3
Mr Taylor	5	5
Mr Thomas	7	8
Ms Barrett	2	3
Mrs Hogg	8	10
Mr Elphick	9	7
Mr Wade	4	6

a Draw a scatter diagram showing the marks of the two judges.

b Is there any correlation between the marks of the two judges? If so, what kind?

c If your graph shows correlation, add in a line of best fit.

6 State the type of correlation, if any, each graph shows.

Fluency

A

B

C

D

7 Are the following data sets numerical or categorical?

a The football teams supported by the students in your class.

b The shoe sizes for the students in your class.

c The favourite TV programmes of the students in your class.

d The lengths of the feet of the students in your class.

e The mobile phone numbers in your contacts list.

Band 2 questions

Problem solving

8 A teacher records the times taken by 25 children to read a story.

Time, t (minutes)	Number of children
$10 \leqslant t < 20$	4
$20 \leqslant t < 30$	8
$30 \leqslant t < 40$	7
$40 \leqslant t < 50$	5
$50 \leqslant t < 60$	1

a Calculate an estimate for the mean time taken to read the story.

b Which time interval contains the median time to read the story?

c A lesson is 45 minutes long. Estimate how many children do not finish the story.

Reasoning

9 Shamicka asks her school friends to record the number of minutes they spend playing computer games during May.

Here are her results.

25	150	262	30	143	0	55	320	260	60
65	140	40	170	74	130	45	125	300	220
96	132	90	185	89	167	68	50	160	82

a   Construct a grouped frequency table using groups of $0 \leqslant t < 50$, $50 \leqslant t < 100$ and so on.

b   Draw a frequency diagram to show this information.

c   Shamicka plans to ask the same question in August.

Predict the shape of the new diagram.

10   The time, in seconds, for 25 fireworks in a display to burn out was recorded.

10	11	12	27	20
16	27	31	14	18
29	15	32	35	33
32	26	34	19	29
35	20	11	28	23

a   Draw and complete a grouped frequency table using the class intervals $10 \leqslant t < 15$, $15 \leqslant t < 20$ and so on.

b   Draw a frequency diagram. What can you say about the organiser's choice of fireworks?

11   Feroza collects data about the wingspans, w cm, of a type of bird.

Wingspan, w (cm)	Number of birds
$125 \leqslant w < 130$	3
$130 \leqslant w < 135$	6
$135 \leqslant w < 140$	10
$140 \leqslant w < 145$	4
$145 \leqslant w < 150$	2

a   The first bird measured had a wingspan of 145 cm. In which class interval is this recorded?

b   Write down the modal class.

c   Estimate the mean wingspan.

Feroza goes to another location.

She measures the wingspans (in cm) of 5 more birds of the same type.

They are 162, 160, 165, 175, 168

d   Calculate the mean of the new birds' wingspans.

Give a possible explanation for the difference from the original group.

12   The table shows the maximum temperature and the number of hours of sunshine in 12 British cities on one day in August.

City	Max temp (°C)	Hours of sunshine	City	Max temp (°C)	Hours of sunshine
London	24	10	Southampton	25	9
Birmingham	22	9	Norwich	23	11
Manchester	20	8	Liverpool	22	8
Edinburgh	17	9	Exeter	25	10
Glasgow	18	6	Newcastle	20	9
Bristol	23	7	Nottingham	21	8

a   Draw a scatter diagram to illustrate this data.

b   Draw a line of best fit on your diagram.

c   York is not included in the data.

It had a maximum temperature of 19 °C on the day the data was recorded.

Estimate the number of hours of sunshine in York that day.

d   Brighton had 12 hours of sunshine on the same day.

Estimate the maximum temperature in Brighton.

⑬ Vicki thinks that older people watch more television.

She carries out a survey.

She chooses 20 people of different ages.

They each keep a record of how much TV they watch during one week.

Here are her results.

Name	Age	Hours of TV	Name	Age	Hours of TV	Name	Age	Hours of TV
Fatima	12	25	Goulu	56	12	Sally	16	23
Evan	82	6	Tara	6	20	George	8	32
Harold	45	18	Comfort	36	14	Ali	6	22
Susan	27	18	Leroy	38	11	Paris	16	18
Gerald	62	12	Malini	45	9	Meena	28	16
Spike	18	26	Robert	72	10	Rick	62	10
Sunil	21	19	Temba	14	21			

a   Draw a scatter diagram of her results.

b   Is there any correlation between age and the amount of time spent watching TV? What does this mean?

c   Draw a line of best fit on your scatter diagram.

d   Jane Smith is 58 years old. Estimate how much television she watches.

e   Scott McKenzie watches 8 hours of television per week. Estimate his age.

Band 3 questions

⑭ A gardener plants 40 seed potatoes and records the mass of potatoes obtained from each plant.

Weight, w (grams)	$750 \leqslant w < 800$	$800 \leqslant w < 850$	$850 \leqslant w < 900$	$900 \leqslant w < 950$
Frequency	8	12	16	4

a   Calculate an estimate for the mean mass of potatoes per plant.

b   Find the range.

The mean mass of a seed potato is 80 g.

c   Estimate the quantity $\dfrac{\text{mass of crop}}{\text{mass of seeds}}$.

⑮ Here are the times a group of students took to run 100 metres.

Time, t (seconds)	Frequency
$14 \leqslant t < 15$	5
$15 \leqslant t < 16$	9
$16 \leqslant t < 17$	10
$17 \leqslant t < 18$	6
$18 \leqslant t < 19$	8
$19 \leqslant t < 20$	4
$20 \leqslant t < 21$	1
$21 \leqslant t < 22$	2

a   Use your table to identify the median time taken by the students.

b   What is the modal group?

c   Draw a frequency diagram to show the data.

d   Calculate an estimate for the mean time.

e   If you were the coach, what would you do to improve the mean time of the group?

16 Joachim collects data about the reaction times of students in his class. He asks each student to catch a dropped ruler and record how far the ruler falls in cm. The students do it once with their dominant hand and once with the other hand.

The results for 10 of the students are displayed on the scatter diagram.

a A student has results in the bottom left-hand corner of the diagram. What can you say about their reactions?

b Describe the correlation.

c What conclusion could Joachim draw from the correlation?

d Draw the line of best fit on a copy of the graph.

e What line represents the same reaction time with both hands?

f Compare your answers to **d** and **e**. What does it suggest about the reaction times of the students?

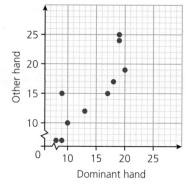

17 190 people take a general knowledge test with 100 questions.

They are hoping to go on a television show.

The table below shows the number of correct answers.

Number of correct answers, q	Frequency
$30 \leqslant q < 40$	80
$40 \leqslant q < 50$	40
$50 \leqslant q < 60$	30
$60 \leqslant q < 70$	20
$70 \leqslant q < 80$	10
$80 \leqslant q < 90$	8
$90 \leqslant q < 100$	2
Total	

a Calculate an estimate for the mean number of correct answers.

b What is the modal group?

c In which group does the median fall?

d Estimate the range.

e People with 75 or more correct answers will appear on the television show.

Estimate how many people this is.

The producer decides that 75 or more is too generous and the qualifying mark should be 82.

f Draw a frequency diagram to show the data.

g Use the frequency diagram to estimate how many people qualify now.

18 Natalie asks her friends to sing a musical note for as long as possible without taking a breath.

The results are shown in the frequency diagram.

a How many people took part in the experiment?

b What is the shortest possible note sung by any of the participants?

c What is the modal group?

d Use the diagram to complete a grouped frequency table of the data.

Don arrives late so his note is not included in the original data.

He sings a note for 35 seconds exactly.

e Explain why Don's result cannot be recorded in the table.

f Rewrite the table using the groups $10 \leqslant t < 20, 20 \leqslant t < 30, 30 \leqslant t < 40$.

Include Don's result.

g What is the modal group now?

Is this what you expected?

⑲ Suja thinks that some people are good at remembering things when they see them. Other people are good at remembering things they have seen written down.

She does a test with 12 of her students. She gives them 2 minutes to remember as many as possible out of 15 pictures of everyday foods. They then write down as many of the objects as they can remember. The test is repeated with a list of everyday sights, not including food.

The table shows the results.

Student	1	2	3	4	5	6	7	8	9	10
First test	8	7	8	10	8	9	7	7	11	10
Second test	7	11	8	13	12	9	9	12	7	11

a Draw a scatter diagram to show the results.

b Describe the correlation. What conclusion can Suja make?

⑳ Investigate whether people estimate the length of a straight line more accurately than they estimate the length of a curved line.

Probability

CHAPTER 15

Coming up...

- ◆ Listing all the outcomes for two or more events
- ◆ Using tables to list all the outcomes for two events
- ◆ Using grids to enumerate all of the outcomes for two events
- ◆ Using probability space diagrams to solve problems involving two events
- ◆ Using Venn diagrams to enumerate all of the outcomes for several events

- ◆ Using Venn diagrams to solve problems involving several events
- ◆ Generating sample spaces for equally likely outcomes for mutually exclusive events
- ◆ Using theoretical sample spaces for several events to solve problems in probability

> Two events are **mutually exclusive** if they both cannot happen at the same time.

→ Heads or Tails?

Anouk and Mustapha play a game.

Each player flips a coin and records the outcome.

Anouk's target is to get TH on two consecutive throws.

Mustapha's target is to get HH on two consecutive throws.

The first player to reach their target wins.

a   Play the game several times. What do you notice?

b   Explain your results.

Change the rules so that the game is fairer.

c   Play the new game several times. Is it fairer? How do you know?

15.1 Probability space diagrams

✔ Skill checker

① What is the probability of:

- a   rolling a six with a single dice
- b   getting a head when flipping a coin
- c   getting a P when picking a letter at random from the word PROBABILITY
- d   getting an I when picking a letter at random from the word PROBABILITY?

② 100 people are asked whether they like strawberry jam and whether they are fans of science fiction films. The table shows the results.

	Likes strawberry jam	Does not like strawberry jam
Likes science fiction films	45	23
Does not like science fiction films	14	18

    a   How many people like both strawberry jam and science fiction films?

    b   How many people like strawberry jam?

    c   How many people do not like science fiction?

    d   What percentage of the people like strawberry jam but do not like science fiction films?

③ Simplify:

    a $\dfrac{12}{24}$ b $\dfrac{12}{18}$ c $\dfrac{3}{18}$ d $\dfrac{15}{20}$

④   a   What is the probability of an impossible event?

    b   What is the probability of a certain event?

Probability space diagrams

Activity

Heather is choosing a meal at a restaurant. She has a choice of mains and dessert.

She chooses from:

Mains	Dessert
Carbonara	Chocolate brownie
Burger	Sticky toffee pudding
Pizza	Apple crumble
Steak	Cheesecake
Fish and chips	
Lasagne	

a   List all of the meals that Heather could choose.

b   Have you listed them in the most efficient way? Comment on your answer.

Worked example

Sam is choosing her breakfast. She can choose one cereal and one drink.

Cereals: Wheatamix, Cornflakes or Sugarloops

Drinks: tea or coffee

a   Draw a diagram to show all the possibilities for Sam's breakfast.

b   How would the list change if Sam had three options for drinks, for example tea, coffee and orange juice?

Solution

a Create a **two-way table** to show the combinations. ◀─── *A two-way table has one set of options as the rows and the second set of options as the columns.*

	Wheatamix	Cornflakes	Sugarloops
Tea	T&W	T&C	T&S
Coffee	C&W	C&C	C&S

◀─── *Listing them this way avoids missing any combinations.*

◀─── *It is clear what the letters stand for, so the choices are abbreviated in the table.*

b There will be an extra row in the table in answer **a** that lists the options involving orange juice.

There are other ways of listing the combinations into tables or grids.

They are referred to as **probability space diagrams**.

They present the combinations as equally likely outcomes.

It is easy to determine the probability of the outcomes using the probability space diagram.

Worked example

Hannah throws two dice, one red and one green.

a Draw and complete a table to show all the possibilities for their total scores.
b Draw and complete a coordinate grid to show all the possibilities for their total scores.
c What is the probability that the total score is exactly 5?
d Would the answers be the same with two red dice?

Solution

a Create a **two-way table** to show the combinations.

The scores on the red dice are the rows and the scores on the green dice are the columns.

The total score has been calculated for each combination.

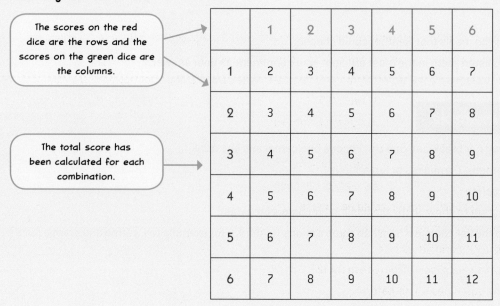

	1	2	3	4	5	6
1	2	3	4	5	6	7
2	3	4	5	6	7	8
3	4	5	6	7	8	9
4	5	6	7	8	9	10
5	6	7	8	9	10	11
6	7	8	9	10	11	12

b A coordinate grid can also be used to show all the outcomes.

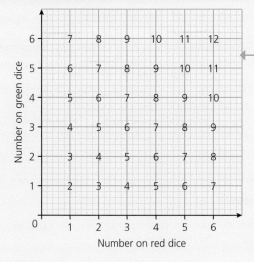

An advantage of using the grid is there is no need to draw out a table.

c $\dfrac{4}{36} = \dfrac{1}{9}$ ← There are 36 outcomes altogether and 4 of them are 5s.

d The answer would be the same. The colour of the dice makes no difference.

15.1 Now try these

Band 1 questions

1 Davina needs to choose one top and one pair of trousers or shorts to pack in her overnight bag.

She can choose from these items.

Tops	Trousers/shorts
Blue sun top	Green shorts
Red t-shirt	Navy shorts
Cropped top	Cream trousers
White shirt	Black trousers
Pink t-shirt	

   a Make a list of all the different combinations of tops and trousers or shorts Davina can choose.

   b How can you work out the number of different possibilities without listing them all?

2 Frankie chooses from a menu with a choice of starters and mains. He does not want a dessert.

Starters	Mains
Soup	Spaghetti bolognese
Crispy chicken wings	Curry
Garlic flatbread	Lemon chicken
	Sausages and chips

   a How many possible meals could he choose?

   b List the outcomes systematically.

3 Hari throws a dice and flips a coin.

   a How many possible outcomes are there?

   b List the outcomes systematically.

Reasoning

Fluency

4 Samira throws two 4-sided dice. Each dice has its faces labelled 1, 2, 3 and 4.

    a How many possible outcomes are there?

    b List the outcomes systematically.

5 In a game, two fair 8-sided dice with faces numbered from 1 to 8 are thrown and the scores shown added together.

    a What is the smallest possible total?

    b What is the largest possible total?

    c Find the probability that the total is 16.

6 Marie is deciding what to have for lunch. She wants two courses.

Lunch Menu

First course

Cod and chips
Lasagne
Cheese salad
Chicken curry

Second course

Apple pie
Cheesecake
Trifle

First course	Second course
Cod and chips	Apple pie

    a Copy and complete the table of all the possible lunches Marie could choose.

    b How do you work out the number of possible lunches?

Band 2 questions

7 The table shows the totals when these spinners are spun.

		\multicolumn{8}{c}{Blue}

		Blue							
		1	2	3	4	5	6	7	8
Red	1	2	3						
	2								
	3								
	4								

    a Copy and complete the table. The first two entries have been done for you.

    b There are 32 numbers in the table. How many of them are 12?

    c What is the probability that the total is 12?

    d Write a list of all the possible totals.

8 Some children are playing a game using two dice labelled 0, 1, 2, 3, 4, 5.

   a Copy and complete this table to show all the possible totals when the two dice are thrown.

	0	1	2	3	4	5
0	0					
1					5	
2						
3						
4						
5						10

   b James has the next turn and needs 10 to win. What is the probability he wins on this turn?

9 A spinner has five equal sections, numbered 0 to 4.

Jessica spins it twice and adds up her two scores.

   a Make a list or table to show all the possible outcomes.

   b What is the probability that Jessica gets 1?

10 In a game, two fair dice are used.

One has four faces, labelled 2, 4, 6 and 8.

The other has eight faces, labelled 1 to 8.

The score is the difference between the numbers on each die.

   a Make a table or list showing all the possible outcomes.

   b Find the probability of scoring 3.

11 Stephanie has two bags.

Each bag contains four balls: one red, one green, one blue and one yellow.

She picks a ball at random from her first bag.

Then, she picks a ball at random from her second bag.

   a Copy and complete this table to show all possible pairs of balls.

		First ball			
		R	G	B	Y
Second ball	R	RR	GR		
	G	RG			
	B				
	Y				

   b How many possible outcomes are there altogether?

   c What is the probability that she chooses two red balls?

12 Baz says, 'I cannot see the point in drawing a probability space table. It's too much like hard work.'
Give two reasons why Baz is wrong.

13 Max has two bags.

One bag contains five red discs numbered 1 to 5.

The other bag contains six blue discs numbered 1 to 6.

Max picks one disc from each bag at random.

Copy and complete the table showing the possible results.

		Blue disc					
		1	2	3	4	5	6
Red disc	1	(1, 1)	(1, 2)			(1, 5)	
	2	(2, 1)			(2, 4)		
	3						
	4		(4, 2)				
	5	(5, 1)			(5, 4)		

b Explain the difference between the outcomes (1, 2) and (2, 1).

c Calculate P(total of 3).

14 In a game, a five-sided spinner and six-sided spinner are spun and their scores are added together. The spinners are fair.

a Copy and complete the table to show all the possible outcomes.

		Spinner 2					
	+	1	2	3	4	5	6
Spinner 1	1	2					
	2				6		
	3						
	4		6				
	5				9		

b Work out the probability of scoring 3.

c Give one advantage of this table compared with the one in question **13**.

d Give one disadvantage of this table compared with the one in question **13**.

15 Loki throws a red dice and a blue dice and multiplies the scores.

a Copy and complete the probability space diagram.

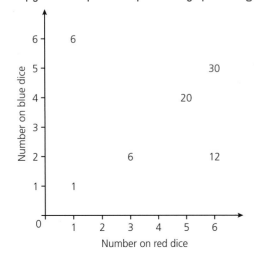

Reasoning

Problem solving

b How many times does 6 appear in the diagram?

c How many times does 7 appear in the diagram?

d What is the modal number in the diagram?

16 Here are nine heart cards numbered 2 to 10 and nine spade cards numbered 2 to 10.

Abdul shuffles the heart cards and places them face down in a row. He does the same with the spade cards.

Abdul chooses one card from each row at random.

a Make a table to show all the possible outcomes.

b How many different possible outcomes are there?

c Work out the probability that he picks two tens.

17 James and Kate decide to play a game with three coins.

James wins if he gets three heads or three tails, otherwise Kate wins.

a Make a list of all the possible outcomes of flipping three coins.

b Explain, by referring to the list in **a**, why this game is not fair.

c Devise a fairer game that still favours one player. Justify your answer.

18 Kamala and Hilary play a game. They throw two dice, each numbered −2, −1, 0, 1, 2, 3.

The total of the two numbers on the dice gives the score for each turn.

a Draw a probability space diagram to show the outcomes.

b Devise a game that you would expect Kamala to win one-sixth of the time and Hilary would win the rest of the time.

c Devise a game that you would expect Kamala to beat Hilary in the ratio 7 : 5.

15.2 Venn diagrams

✔ Skill checker

① Write down all of the factors of 20.

② Write down the first five multiples of 7.

③ Write down a prime number that is a factor of 20 and a factor of 35.

④ Write down a number that is a multiple of 7 and a multiple of 8.

Venn diagrams

We have used Venn diagrams in chapter 1 with prime factorisation.

🖊 Activity

The numbers 1 to 10 are sorted into the regions of this Venn diagram.

Set A is the set of square numbers $\leqslant 10$.

Set B is the set of odd numbers $\leqslant 10$.

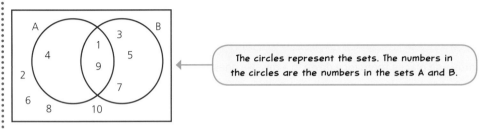

The circles represent the sets. The numbers in the circles are the numbers in the sets A and B.

a Explain why 1 and 9 are in the overlap between the two sets.

b Why are 2, 6, 8, 10 not in either of the circles?

c Why is 4 the only number in its region of the diagram?

d 11 is added to the diagram. Where should it go?

Venn diagrams are a powerful representation of combinations of events.

They can represent two events or three events.

Worked example

Nick has some cards with different shapes printed on them.

This Venn diagram describes the shapes printed on the cards.

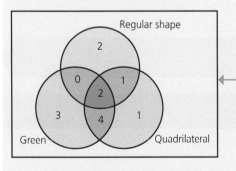

There are 3 'events' represented by the Venn diagram: Regular shape, Green and Quadrilateral.

a How many cards are there in Nick's pack?

b Nick picks a card at random. What is the probability that his card is

    i a quadrilateral

    ii a green quadrilateral

    iii not green?

c Draw the shape in the central crossover.

    Write a sentence about the probability of picking it.

Solution

a There are 13 cards. ←

> Add the number of cards in all of the regions. The outside region is empty.

b i $P(\text{quadrilateral}) = \dfrac{8}{13}$ ←

> Add the number of cards in the regions in the pink circle.

ii $P(\text{green quadrilateral}) = \dfrac{6}{13}$ ←

> Add the number of cards in the regions in the green circle.

iii $P(\text{not green}) = \dfrac{4}{13}$ ←

> Add the number of cards in the regions that are not in the green circle.

c

The probability of picking a card with a green square at random is $\dfrac{2}{13}$

Worked example

a Find the highest common factor of 42 and 54.
b Find the lowest common multiple of 42 and 54.

Solution

First find the prime factorisation of each number.

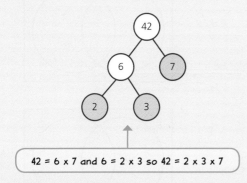

> $42 = 6 \times 7$ and $6 = 2 \times 3$ so $42 = 2 \times 3 \times 7$

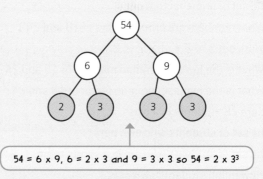

> $54 = 6 \times 9$, $6 = 2 \times 3$ and $9 = 3 \times 3$ so $54 = 2 \times 3^3$

Next draw a Venn diagram.

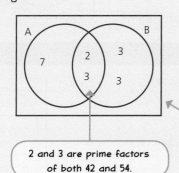

Set A is the set of prime factors of 42.
Set B is the set of prime factors of 54.
54 has a repeated prime factor of 3.

> 2, 3, 3, 3, 7 are multiplied to produce a number that is divisible by both 42 and 54.

> 2 and 3 are prime factors of both 42 and 54.

a   6 is the highest common factor of 42 and 54. ← [6 = 2 x 3]

b   2 × 3 × 3 × 3 × 7 = 378 is the lowest common multiple of 42 and 54.

    None of 2, 3, 3, 3 and 7 can be left out so there is no lower common multiple of 42 and 54.

15.2 Now try these

Band 1 questions

1 There are 10 students in an after-school club.

A is the set of people with names beginning with J.

B is the set of people with four letters in their name.

a   How many people have 4-letter names?

b   How many people do not have 4-letter names?

c   Explain why Mandy is not in set A or set B.

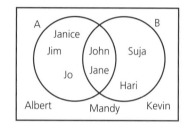

2 What is the highest common factor of 24 and 18?

3 Write 44 as the product of prime factors.

4 What is the lowest common multiple of 12 and 18?

5 A is the set of prime factors of 18.

B is the set of prime factors of 24.

a   What numbers are prime factors of 18 **and** 24?

b   Work out 3 × 2 × 3 × 2 × 2.

c   What is the lowest common multiple of 18 and 24?

d   What is the highest common factor of 18 and 24?

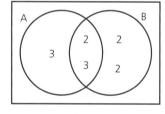

6 There are 28 students in a class.

P is the set of students who own pets.

Q is the set of students who are in a sports team.

a   How many students own pets?

b   How many students are in a sports team?

c   How many students do not have pets **and** are not in a sports team?

Band 2 questions

7 The Venn diagram shows the students studying GCSE PE. Some like watching cricket (C), and some like watching darts (D).

a   How many students like watching both darts and cricket?

b   What is the probability that a student, chosen at random, likes watching both darts and cricket?

c   What is the probability that a student, chosen at random, likes watching cricket?

d   What is the probability that a student, chosen at random, does not like to watch either darts or cricket?

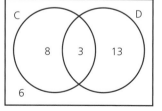

8 The Venn diagram shows the students in Year 9. Some like chocolate (C), and some like toffee (T).

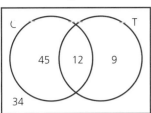

    a How many students like at least one out of toffee and chocolate?

    b What is the probability that a student, chosen at random,

      i likes chocolate   **ii** does not like toffee   **iii** likes toffee but does not like chocolate?

9 The Venn diagram shows the membership of a club.

Some play squash (S), others play tennis (T).

Some play both games and some neither.

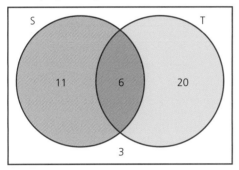

A member is selected at random.

    a Explain why the probability that the member plays squash is $\dfrac{17}{40}$.

    b Find the probability that the member plays both squash and tennis.

    c Find the probability that the member does not play squash.

10 Use the Venn diagram to find:

    a the highest common factor of 60 and 70. Justify your answer.

    b the lowest common multiple of 60 and 70. Justify your answer.

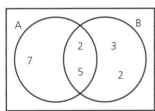

11 **a** Draw a Venn diagram to show the prime factors of 20 and 72.

    b Use the Venn diagram find:

      i the highest common factor of 20 and 72   **ii** the lowest common multiple of 20 and 72.

⑫ There are 30 students in a class. Some are learning French (F) and some are learning German (G).

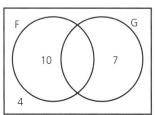

    a   How many students are not learning French or German?

    b   How many students are learning both French and German?

    c   What is the probability that a student, chosen at random, is

       i   learning both French and German   **ii**   learning just French   **iii**   learning French?

Band 3 questions

⑬ Out of 80 members of a cricket club 52 like coffee (C) and 37 like tea (T).

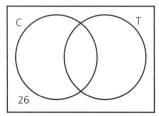

    a   Complete the Venn diagram.

    b   How many do not like either coffee or tea?

    c   How many like both coffee **and** tea?

    d   What is the probability that a club member, chosen at random, does not like tea?

⑭ Set A is the set of factors of 360.

Which of the following could **not** be a description of set B? Justify your answer.

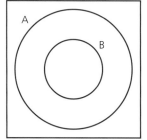

    i   1, 2, 3, 4, 5, 6

    ii   the factors of 72

    iii   the multiples of 60

    iv   the factors of 45

⑮ The diagram shows the percentage of students studying physics, history and geography at GCSE.

What is the probability that a student, chosen at random:

    a   studies geography

    b   does not study physics

    c   studies history and geography but not physics?

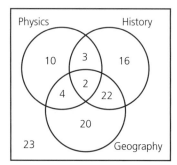

16 The Venn diagram shows the prime factors of 18, 54 and 60.

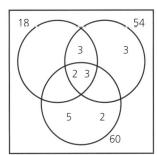

a   What is the highest common factor of 18, 54 and 60? Explain how you can use the Venn diagram to find it.

b   Explain why the top left-hand region is empty.

c   How can you tell from the Venn diagram that 18 is a factor of 54?

d   What is the lowest common multiple of 18, 54 and 60? Explain how you can use the Venn diagram to find it.

17 a   Draw a Venn diagram to show the prime factors of 12, 42 and 105.

b   What is the highest common factor of 12, 42 and 105?

c   What is the lowest common multiple of 12, 42 and 105?

18 Mark is eating biscuits from a box with four different types of biscuit.

8 biscuits have chocolate and fruit and no nuts .

7 biscuits have both chocolate and nuts, but no fruit.

6 biscuits have just nuts.

4 biscuits contain just fruit.

a   Draw a Venn diagram for the biscuits in the box.

Mark chooses a biscuit at random from the box. He likes biscuits with chocolate.

b   Find the probability:

i   that Mark likes the biscuit

ii   that Mark does not like the biscuit.

15.3 Combined events

✔ Skill checker

① Simplify:

a $\dfrac{12}{16}$

b $\dfrac{30}{45}$

② Work out:

a $1 - \dfrac{1}{4}$

b $1 - \dfrac{3}{8}$

③ Two 8-sided dice are thrown. How many outcomes are there?

④ A normal dice is rolled once. What is the probability of rolling a square number?

Activity

Throw two dice and add the numbers to give a score. If that score is on your bingo card you cross it out.

Make up your own 3 by 3 bingo card with 9 numbers on it.

You may repeat numbers on the card but only cross them off one at a time.

Play the game once.

a What is your opinion of the numbers you chose? What were good choices and what were bad choices?

b Make up a new bingo card and play again.

c Were the numbers a better choice this time? What worked well? What can be improved?

This game is best played as a class with the teacher rolling the dice. Each student has their own bingo card. The aim is to cross off all of the numbers on your card.

d Make up a new bingo card and play again.

Worked example

Hannie throws two dice, one red and one green.

	1	2	3	4	5	6
1	2	3	4	5	6	7
2	3	4	5	6	7	8
3	4	5	6	7	8	9
4	5	6	7	8	9	10
5	6	7	8	9	10	11
6	7	8	9	10	11	12

What is the probability the total score is

a exactly 3   **b** 3 or less   **c** greater than 12   **d** a prime number?

Solution

There are 36 possible equally likely outcomes.

There are 2 ways of getting 3, 1 + 2 and 2 + 1, so 2 favourable outcomes.

a Probability of exactly $3 = \dfrac{2}{36} = \dfrac{1}{18}$

There are 3 ways of getting 3 or less.

b Probability of 3 or less $= \dfrac{3}{36} = \dfrac{1}{12}$

It is impossible to get more than 12.

c Probability of greater than $12 = 0$

Prime numbers are 2 (1 way), 3 (2 ways), 5 (4 ways), 7 (6 ways), 11 (2 ways).

d Probability of a prime number $= \dfrac{15}{36} = \dfrac{5}{12}$

Key Stage 3 Mastering Mathematics: Book 3

352

Band 1 questions

1 Diana chooses a t-shirt and shorts.

T shirt	Shorts
white	red
white	green
blue	red
blue	green
yellow	red
yellow	green

a How many different outfits are there?

Diana chooses an outfit at random.

b Find the probability that she chooses:

  i red shorts with a blue T shirt

  ii green shorts with a white T shirt

  iii an outfit with a yellow T shirt.

2 Benny chooses a meal.

	Ice cream	Apple pie
Curry	Curry, Ice cream	Curry, Apple pie
Pizza	Pizza, Ice cream	Pizza, Apple pie
Fish	Fish, Ice cream	Fish, Apple pie
Chicken	Chicken, Ice cream	Chicken, Apple pie

a How many different meals can he choose?

Benny chooses a meal at random.

b Find the probability that he chooses

  i fish and apple pie

  ii a meal that includes pizza

  iii a meal that includes apple pie.

3 Alex throws two coins.

		Second coin	
		Heads	Tails
First coin	Heads	HH	HT
	Tails	TH	TT

a How many equally likely outcomes are there?

b Find the probability that he throws

  i two heads

  ii one of each

  iii no heads.

4 Kris throws a dice and flips a coin.

The table shows the possible outcomes.

	1	2	3	4	5	6
H	H1	H2	H3	H4	H5	H6
T	T1	T2	T3	T4	T5	T6

a Explain how you can work out that there are 12 different outcomes without counting them.

b Find the probability that he gets

  i a tail and an even number

  iii a tail and a square number

  ii a head

  iv a head and an 8.

⑤ Mia throws two 4-sided dice. Each dice has its faces labelled 1, 2, 3 and 4.

		Second dice			
		1	2	3	4
First dice	1	2	3	4	5
	2	3	4	5	6
	3	4	5	6	7
	4	5	6	7	8

a Explain how the numbers in the table have been calculated.

b Find the probability of getting a score of:

  i 8   **ii** 5   **iii** 1.

c Find the probability of getting a score between 1 and 10.

⑥ In a game, two fair 8-sided dice numbered from 1 to 8 are thrown and the scores shown added together. The table shows the different totals possible.

		Dice 2							
	+	1	2	3	4	5	6	7	8
Dice 1	1	2	3	4	5	6	7	8	9
	2	3	4	5	6	7	8	9	10
	3	4	5	6	7	8	9	10	11
	4	5	6	7	8	9	10	11	12
	5	6	7	8	9	10	11	12	13
	6	7	8	9	10	11	12	13	14
	7	8	9	10	11	12	13	14	15
	8	9	10	11	12	13	14	15	16

a How many different equally likely outcomes are there?

b How many different totals are there?

c Find the probability that the total is:

  i an even number   **ii** a prime number

  iii a square number   **iv** a multiple of 5

  v a triangle number.

> **Remember**
>
> A triangle number has a pattern of dots in the shape of a triangle.
>
> 1, 3, 6, 10, …

Band 2 questions

⑦ The table shows the totals when the spinners are spun.

		Blue							
		1	2	3	4	5	6	7	8
Red	1	2	3	4	5	6	7	8	9
	2	3	4	5	6	7	8	9	10
	3	4	5	6	7	8	9	10	11
	4	5	6	7	8	9	10	11	12

a Write a list of all the possible totals.

b Find the probability of:

    i   getting a total of 7

    ii   getting a total of less than 5

    iii getting a total of at least 9.

c An event has a probability of $\dfrac{3}{32}$. Give two examples of what it could be.

8 Some children are playing Snakes and Ladders using two dice labelled 0, 1, 2, 3, 4, 5.

The table shows all the possible totals when the two dice are thrown.

	0	1	2	3	4	5
0	0	1	2	3	4	5
1	1	2	3	4	5	6
2	2	3	4	5	6	7
3	3	4	5	6	7	8
4	4	5	6	7	8	9
5	5	6	7	8	9	10

a James has the next turn and needs 5 to win. What is the probability he wins on this turn?

b Mark will land on a snake if he gets 10.

    What is the probability he lands on a snake?

c Fiona will land on a ladder if she gets 4 or 11.

    What is the probability she lands on a ladder?

9 A spinner has five equal sections, numbered 0 to 4.

Jeremy spins it twice and multiplies the two numbers.

Copy and complete the table to show all the possible outcomes.

	0	1	2	3	4
0	0	0			
1					
2		2			
3					
4					16

a How many different equally likely outcomes are there?

b How many different scores are there?

c Find the probability that Jeremy scores:

    i 16   **ii** an odd number   **iii** a square number   **iv** 0.

10 Sanjit has two bags.

Each bag contains four balls: one white, one green, one black and one yellow.

He picks a ball at random from his first bag.

Then, he picks a ball at random from his second bag.

a Copy and complete this table to show all possible outcomes.

		First ball			
		W	G	B	Y
Second ball	W	WW			
	G				
	B				
	Y				

b What is the probability that he chooses two balls of the same colour?

c What is the probability that he chooses at least one green ball?

d What is the probability that he chooses one yellow ball and one of a different colour?

⑪ Two dice are used in a game.

One has four faces, labelled 1, 3, 5 and 7.

The other has eight faces, labelled 1 to 8.

The score is the difference between the numbers on the two dice.

a Make a table showing all the possible outcomes.

b Find the probability of scoring:

   i 0   **ii** 1   **iii** 2   **iv** 5 or more.

c What score has a probability of $\frac{1}{32}$?

⑫ A class is playing bingo.

Numbers are generated by rolling two 6-sided dice, with faces numbered 1 to 6, and adding the scores.

Each of the children in the class chooses four numbers.

They win when all of their numbers have been generated.

What numbers would you have on your card? (You can have the same number more than once if you wish.)

Explain your choices.

⑬ Bob and Andrea are playing a game with one red dice and one blue dice.

The red dice is numbered 1, 1, 3, 4, 5, 5.

The blue dice is numbered 2, 2, 3, 4, 5, 6.

a Copy and complete the table of the possible outcomes.

		Blue dice					
		2	2	3	4	5	6
Red dice	1	1, 2	1, 2				1, 6
	1	1, 2					
	3						
	4						
	5	5, 2					
	5						5, 6

b Find the probability of:

   i a 1 on the red dice and a 2 on the blue dice   **ii** an even number on both dice

   iii an odd number on both dice   **iv** a 2 on both dice.

Band 3 questions

14 Karl buys two raffle tickets. He draws a probability diagram.

	Win	Lose
Win	WW	WL
Lose	LW	LL

Karl says, 'Three of the outcomes have me winning a prize. That means I have a 75% chance of winning.'

Explain why Karl is wrong.

15 Mary has two bags.

One bag contains five red discs numbered 1 to 5.

The other bag contains six blue discs numbered 1 to 6.

Mary picks one disc from each bag at random.

Calculate:

a P(same score on both discs)

b P(score on the red disc is greater than the score on the blue disc)

c P(score on the red disc is less than the score on the blue disc)

d P(scores add up to 7).

16 Erica has two bags.

One bag contains five black marbles numbered 1 to 5.

The second bag contains five white marbles numbered 1 to 5.

Erica picks one black marble and one white marble at random.

a Draw a probability diagram to show the possible outcomes.

b Find the probability that Erica gets:

    i two even numbers   **ii** two odd numbers.

c What is the probability that Erica gets:

    i identical numbers   **ii** a bigger number on the white

    iii a bigger number on the black?

d Add together your answers from part **c**. Explain the result.

17 Here are nine Heart cards numbered 2 to 10 and nine Spade cards numbered 2 to 10.

Suja shuffles the Heart cards and places them face down in a row. She does the same with the Spade cards.

Suja chooses one card from each row at random.

Work out the probability that:

a the two numbers are the same   **b** the two numbers are different

c the number on the Heart is bigger   **d** the two numbers are both even

e the two numbers are both prime   **f** the two numbers are both square numbers.

18 In a game, a five-sided spinner and six-sided spinner are spun, and their scores are added together.

Work out the probability of scoring:

a   a total of 6   **b**   a total of 7

c   a total of 6 or 7   **d**   any total other than 6 or 7

e   an even total   **f**   an odd total

g   a total that is a square number   **h**   a total that is not a square number.

19 Two identical dice have six faces. They are rolled and the numbers are added.

What numbers are on their faces if:

- P(even number) = 1
- there is at least one odd number on the dice
- $P(2) = P(22) = \dfrac{1}{36}$
- the numbers on the dice form an arithmetic sequence
- 12 is the modal score.

Key words

Here is a list of the key words you met in this chapter

Probability space diagram   Two-way table   Venn diagram

Use the glossary at the back of this book to check any you are unsure about.

Band 1 questions

Fluency

1 Helen takes five tops and three pairs of shorts on holiday. She chooses one top and one pair of shorts at random one day.

a Make a list of all the possible combinations she could choose.

b What is the probability that she chooses a top and a pair of shorts which are the same colour?

Reasoning

2 The prime factors of 30 are 2, 3 and 5 because $30 = 2 \times 3 \times 5$.

The prime factors of 55 are 5 and 11 because $55 = 5 \times 11$.

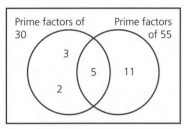

a What number is a prime factor of both 30 and 55?

b Work out the product of all four of the numbers in the circles.

c Explain why the answer to **b** is a multiple of 30.

Problem solving

3 Sadiq chooses a drink and a snack. The drinks available are tea, coffee and orange juice.

The snacks available are pastries, muffins and cheese scones.

a Make a list of the combinations of drink and snack that Sadiq can have.

b Explain the system you used in **a** to make sure you had listed all of the possibilities.

Reasoning

4 The numbers from 1 to 10 are shown in the diagram.

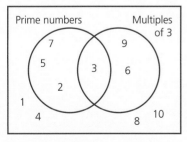

a How many of the numbers are prime numbers?

b How many of the numbers are **not** multiples of 3?

c A number from 1 to 10 is chosen at random. Find the probability that it is not a prime number.

5 A bag contains one red cube, one green cube, one blue cube and one white cube. One cube is removed from the bag, replaced and another cube taken from the bag.

The probability diagram shows the possible outcomes.

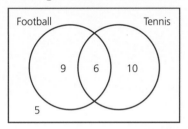

		Second cube			
		R	G	B	W
First cube	R	RR	RG	RB	RW
	G	GR	GG	GB	GW
	B	BR	BG	BB	BW
	W	WR	WG	WB	WW

a How many of the outcomes have at least one green cube?

b Find the probability of picking:

    i two blue cubes

    ii two cubes of the same colour

    iii two cubes with different colours.

c Explain why the answers to **ii** and **iii** add to 1.

6 30 people working in an office are asked if they like to watch football and tennis.

The diagram shows the results.

Football   Tennis

9   6   10

5

a How many people like to watch football?

b How many people like to watch tennis?

c One of the people, who said they liked watching both football and tennis, changes their mind and says they only like watching football. What changes in the diagram?

7 Siân throws two 4-sided dice. Each dice has its faces labelled 1, 1, 2 and 4. The numbers showing on the two dice are added to get her score.

She draws a probability diagram to show the outcomes.

		Second dice			
		1	1	2	4
First dice	1	2	2	3	5
	1	2	2	3	5
	2	3	3	4	6
	4	5	5	6	8

a How many equally likely outcomes are there?

b How many different scores are there?

c Find the probability that:

    i the score is 2   **ii** the score is 5 or more   **iii** the score is **not** 3.

Fluency

8 Sophie has two spinners with sides numbered 1, 2 and 3.

She spins both spinners and adds the results.

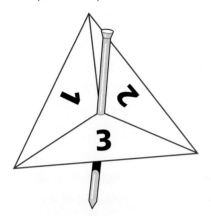

a Copy and complete the table to show all the possible outcomes.

		Second spinner		
		1	2	3
First spinner	1		3	
	2			5
	3			

b What is:

i the most likely total

ii the least likely total?

c Work out the probability that the total is:

i 5

ii less than 4

iii a square number

iv a prime number.

9 In a game, two fair 6-sided dice numbered from 1 to 6 are thrown. The score is the higher number out of the two.

a Draw a probability diagram to show all the possible outcomes.

b What is the least likely outcome?

c Find the probability of:

i scoring 4

ii scoring more than 3

iii scoring at least 3.

10 a Write these as products of their prime factors.

i 28

ii 48

b Copy and complete the Venn diagram to show the prime factors of 28 and 48.

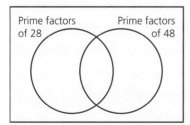

c Use the Venn diagram to find:

i the highest common factor of 28 and 48

ii the lowest common multiple of 28 and 48.

11 At Oak High School 18% of students study GCSE history and not geography and 33% of them study GCSE geography and not history. 30% of the students do not study either history or geography.

    a What percentage of students study both history and geography?

    b Copy and complete the Venn diagram.

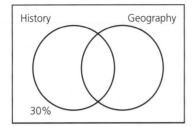

    c Find the probability that a student chosen at random:

       i studies history   **ii** does not study geography   **iii** studies history but not geography.

12 A bag contains two red balls and 2 blue balls. Jan removes one ball at random and then replaces it before choosing another at random.

    a Draw a probability diagram to show the 16 equally likely outcomes.

    b Find the probability of choosing:

       i two balls of the same colour   **ii** at least one red ball   **iii** a red ball as the first ball.

Band 3 questions

13 Jodie collects information on the pets owned by students in Year 9 at her school. She presents the information in a Venn diagram.

There are 120 students in Year 9. 48 students have cats as pets and 62 students have dogs as pets. There are 33 students who do not have a cat or a dog.

Draw a Venn diagram to show this information.

14 Janek runs a tourist information website in his local town.

He wants to put accommodation information on his site in the easiest way for people to understand.

He has information about the hotels they use in a Venn diagram.

However, Janek thinks it would be better to show the information in a two-way table instead.

    a What might the heading of the rows and columns of the two-way table be?

    b Complete a two-way table for Janek.

    c What other information would Janek need to give customers coming to the website who wanted to book accommodation in the local area?

15 Rudi throws two dice, each labelled with the numbers 1 to 6. The score is the highest common factor of the two numbers.

   a Draw a probability diagram to show all the outcomes.

   b What is the most likely score? Explain why that is the case.

   c Find the probability of:

      i   scoring more than 1

      ii scoring a number greater than 6

      iii scoring an even number.

16 Bag A contains 3 white balls and 2 red balls. Bag B contains 2 white balls and 3 red balls. A ball is taken at random from each bag.

   Find the probability that they are different colours.

17 Lorraine has a set of cards with the numbers from 2 to 20 printed on one side.

   a Mark each one in its correct position on a copy of this Venn diagram.

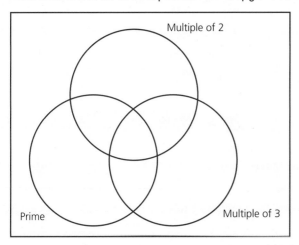

   b A card is picked at random. What is the probability that it is:

      i   a multiple of 2   **ii** a multiple of 3   **iii** a multiple of both 2 and 3

      iv a prime number   **v**   a prime multiple of 3?

   c Why is the centre intersection empty?

18 **a** Draw a Venn diagram to find the lowest common multiple of 18, 21 and 70.

   b What is the highest common factor of 18, 21 and 70?

19 Design two spinners so that:

   ● there are 15 equally likely outcomes

   ● the score is the sum of the numbers on the spinners

   ● the highest score is 11

   ● the lowest score is 3

   ● the numbers on each spinner make an arithmetic sequence

   ● the probability of scoring 7 is 0.2.

20 Two bags contain identical numbers of red and blue balls. There are 5 balls in each bag.

   There are more red balls than blue balls in each bag.

   A ball is removed, at random, from each bag.

   The probability that the balls are different colours is 0.32.

   How many blue balls are in each bag?

Chapters 14–15

Band 1 questions

Fluency

1 Decide whether the following sets of data are categorical, discrete or continuous.

   a   the number of eggs laid by garden birds   **b**   the colours of garden birds

   c   the wingspans of garden birds   **d**   species of garden birds

   e   weights of garden birds

Reasoning

2 A bus company is interested in the distance travelled to work by local residents.

They asked a random sample of 100 workers and recorded the results in this table.

Distance, x miles	$1 \leqslant x < 3$	$3 \leqslant x < 5$	$5 \leqslant x < 7$	$7 \leqslant x < 9$	$9 \leqslant x < 11$
Frequency	10	25	50	5	10

   a   What is the modal class?

   b   Estimate:

        i   the mean   **ii**   the range.

   c   What use is information like this to a bus company?

Fluency

3 Shani throws two 4-sided dice. The dice are labelled with the numbers 1 to 4.

The score is the difference between the numbers.

   a   Copy and complete the probability space diagram.

		Second dice			
		1	2	3	4
First dice	1				
	2				
	3				
	4				

   b   What is the mode of the scores?   **c**   Find the probability of the modal score.

Reasoning

4 20 students in Year 9 are asked whether they like fruit or vegetables.

The Venn diagrams shows their responses.

   a   How many students like both fruit and vegetables?

   b   Find the probability that a student chosen at random does not like vegetables.

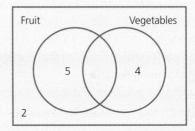

364

Problem solving

5 Peter and Jane wonder whether people with long arms also have long legs.

They collect data from 10 of their friends.

Person	1	2	3	4	5	6	7	8	9	10
Arm length (cm)	42	45	43	42	43	45	36	48	43	44
Leg length (cm)	66	71	65	64	68	68	64	75	66	71

a Plot the data in a scatter diagram.

b Describe the correlation.

c Do people with long arms also have long legs?

d Which point is an outlier? Should it be included in the data?

Reasoning

6 Tomi measured the handspans of 30 students in Year 9.

Handspan, h cm	Frequency
$14 \leq h < 15$	1
$15 \leq h < 16$	4
$16 \leq h < 17$	7
$17 \leq h < 18$	14
$18 \leq h < 19$	4

a Find the probability that a student, chosen at random, has a handspan between 16 and 17 cm.

b Find the probability that a student, chosen at random, has a handspan more than 16 cm.

Band 2 questions

Fluency

7 The grouped frequency table gives information about the distance 100 students travel to school.

Distance travelled, d km	Frequency
$0 \leq d < 8$	40
$8 \leq d < 16$	25
$16 \leq d < 24$	15
$24 \leq d < 32$	8
$32 \leq d < 40$	12

a What percentage of the 100 students travel at least 24 km to school?

b Calculate an estimate for the mean distance travelled to school by the students.

c What is the probability that a student, chosen at random, travels at least 24 km to school?

Reasoning

8 Two 6-sided dice are labelled with the numbers 0 to 5.

The dice are thrown, and the score is calculated by multiplying the numbers.

a Copy and complete the probability space diagram for the outcomes.

		Second dice					
		0	1	2	3	4	5
First dice	0						
	1		1				
	2	0					
	3						15
	4						
	5						

b   Find the probability of:

   i   a score of 0   **ii**   a score greater than 1   **iii**   a score greater than 30.

9   Emily collects the ages of 60 people taking their driving test over one week at the local test centre.

40, 24, 32, 17, 18, 21, 29, 18, 39, 17, 20, 30, 17, 19, 17, 18, 21, 30, 46,

17, 26, 19, 17, 21, 18, 19, 28, 18, 21, 37, 19, 31, 40, 18, 21, 18, 25, 18,

40, 18, 33, 18, 21, 18, 44, 19, 21, 19, 19, 25, 19, 20, 21, 22, 23, 27, 30,

31, 39, 50

a   Construct a grouped frequency table for this data set.

b   Why aren't any of the ages less than 17?

c   What is the modal age group? Why do you think this might be?

d   Find the group with the median age. Do you think this is a useful measure for this data set?

e   Draw a frequency diagram of this data.

f   What do you notice about the shape of frequency diagram? Give a reason for this.

g   What percentage of people who took their test were over 20?

10   Rani planted 15 packets of rare seeds. She recorded the number, n, that germinated from each packet. Her results are given in this table.

Number germinating, n	Frequency
$10 \le n < 15$	3
$15 \le n < 20$	6
$20 \le n < 25$	4
$25 \le n < 30$	2

a   Calculate the mean number of seeds germinating from each packet.

b   A packet of seeds is chosen at random.

   What is the probability that more than 19 of the seeds will germinate?

11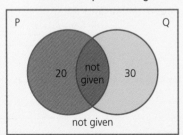

A random sample of 100 people are tested for immunity against two diseases, P and Q.

20 are immune to P only and 30 are immune to Q only.

15 are immune to both P and Q.

The rest are not immune to either disease.

a   Copy the Venn diagram and fill in the missing numbers.

b   A person is chosen at random. Estimate the probability that the person is immune to:

   i   both diseases   **ii**   neither disease   **iii**   disease Q.

12 The table shows the child mortality and income for nine countries.

The child mortality measure is the number of deaths before the age of five, per 1000 live births.

The income is GDP per person in international dollars.

Country	Botswana	Brazil	Columbia	Egypt	Iran	Mexico	NZ	Philippines	Togo
Child mortality	51.3	63	35.2	85.8	53.7	44.8	11.2	56.7	145
Income	8500	10 300	7730	5900	11 600	13 600	24 000	4010	1300

a Plot a scatter diagram to show this information.

b Describe the correlation and interpret it in context.

c Draw a line of best fit.

d Belarus has a child mortality rate of 15.2. Use the line of best fit to estimate its income.

13 Diane uses a Venn diagram to find the highest common factor of 30 and 48.

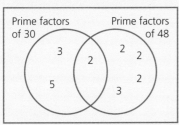

She says that the highest common factor of 30 and 48 is 2.

Explain why Diane is wrong and what mistake she has made.

Band 3 questions

14 Use a Venn diagram to find the highest common factor and lowest common multiple of 108, 140 and 300.

15 An ice-cream seller kept a daily record of the highest temperature and the number of ice-creams sold.

The results are shown below.

Temperature (°C)	32	30	31	27	20	25	23	14	27	21	19	18	21
Number of ice-creams sold	190	180	188	156	36	150	150	100	160	158	136	186	156

a Show this data on a scatter diagram.

b Describe any correlation between the two variables.

c How is this information useful to the ice-cream seller?

d There is an outlier in the data. State which it is and suggest a reason for it.

e What is the maximum number of ice-creams sold in any one day?

Why might this information be useful to the ice-cream seller?

f What is the temperature range over the time the ice-cream seller recorded these data?

g The next day the temperature is forecast to be around 17 °C.

How many ice-creams do you estimate will be sold?

h The bank asks for a business plan.

Calculate the mean number of ice-creams sold per day.

How would this influence the business plan?

16 Two 6-sided dice labelled 1 to 6 are thrown. The score is the lowest common multiple of the two numbers on the dice.

a Draw a probability space diagram to show the outcomes.

b Find the probability of:

i a score that is an even number   **ii** a score of less than 3   **iii** a score of at least 3.

c What do you notice about the answers to **b ii** and **b iii**? Explain why that is so.

17 The table shows the salaries of the 25 people employed by a small firm.

Salary, £s	Number of people
$0 \leq s < 10\,000$	6
$10\,000 \leq s < 20\,000$	11
$20\,000 \leq s < 30\,000$	5
$30\,000 \leq s < 40\,000$	2
$40\,000 \leq s < 50\,000$	1

The managing director is considering offering a wage increase of 5%.

He thinks of three ways to achieve this:

1 Give everyone a 5% increase on their current salary.

2 Find 5% of the mean salary and increase all salaries by this amount.

3 Find 5% of the median salary and increase all salaries by this amount.

    a Which members of staff would benefit most from each scheme?

    b Which scheme do you think he should choose? Give a reason for your answer.

18 David is collecting data on the heights of adult men for a clothing company.

He measures the heights of 50 adult men.

Maya collects similar data from 50 women.

Height, h cm	Women Frequency	Men Frequency
$135 \leq h < 140$	1	0
$140 \leq h < 145$	1	0
$145 \leq h < 150$	1	0
$150 \leq h < 155$	2	1
$155 \leq h < 160$	3	2
$160 \leq h < 165$	11	5
$165 \leq h < 170$	14	8
$170 \leq h < 175$	9	9
$175 \leq h < 180$	5	12
$180 \leq h < 185$	2	7
$185 \leq h < 190$	1	4
$190 \leq h < 195$	0	2

a Draw frequency diagrams for the men's and women's heights.

b Describe what your graphs show.

c What are the modal heights?

d **i** Which gender has the greater range of heights?

    ii What effect will this have on the garments produced by the clothing company?

e What other data might it be useful for the clothing company to collect?

f What is the probability that an adult, chosen at random, is between 165 and 175 cm tall?

19 Use the information below to complete the Venn diagram representing the percentage of students studying Mathematics, English and Biology at an FE College.

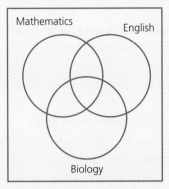

20% of students do not study any of the three subjects.

41% of students study Biology.

40% of students study English.

47% of students study Mathematics.

7% of students study all three subjects.

18% of students study Mathematics and English.

20% of students study Mathematics and Biology.

11% of students study Biology but not Mathematics or English.

20 Two 6-sided dice labelled 1 to 6 are thrown. The score is the mean of the two numbers on the dice.

a Draw a probability space diagram to show the outcomes.

b Find the probability of:

i a score that is not a whole number

ii a score of 3.5

iii a score of at least 6.5.

c What do you notice about the numbers in the diagram? Explain why that is so.

Glossary

Accuracy The accuracy of a measurement tells you how close it is to the actual value.

Acute An acute angle lies between 0° and 90°.

Addition (add) Addition or adding is finding the total of two or more amounts. For example, 3 + 4 = 7.

Adjacent Adjacent means next to. In a right-angled triangle the adjacent is the side which is next to the angle.

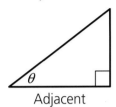
Adjacent

Allied angles A pair of angles on the inside of a pair of parallel lines and on the same side of a transversal. Allied angles are sometimes referred to as C angles because of the shape they make.

Alternate angles A pair of angles on the inside of a pair of parallel lines, but on opposite sides of a transversal.

Angle An angle is a measure of turning. Angles are measured in degrees. For example, a full turn is 360°.

Angle bisector An angle bisector is a line which cuts an angle exactly in half.

Angle of depression When you look down at an object then the angle of depression is the angle between the horizontal and the line of sight.

Angle of elevation When you look up at an object then the angle of elevation is the angle between the horizontal and the line of sight.

Approximate The answer to a calculation which has been found by rounding the numbers in the calculation. An approximate answer is close to the solution but not the exact solution.

Arc An arc is part of the circumference of a circle.

Area The area of a shape is the amount of surface that it covers. Area is measured in square units such as mm^2, cm^2, m^2 and km^2.

Arithmetic sequence An arithmetic sequence is a sequence where the difference between any two terms is a constant. For example, 7, 11, 15, 19, ...

Arrowhead An arrowhead is a kite with a reflex angle.

Average An average is a measure of the typical value in a data set. Common averages are the mean, the mode and the median.

Axes Axes is the plural of axis. An axis is a fixed reference line for the measurement of coordinates. The x-axis is horizontal and the y-axis is vertical.

Bar chart A bar chart is a chart that uses rectangular bars to display data. The height of each bar represents the frequency.

Base The base of a shape is the line or surface on which it appears to be standing.

Bearing An angle measured clockwise from North.

Best buy The cheaper or cheapest option when a decision must be made between two or more similar items for sale. The best buy can often be decided using the unitary method.

Biased Data is biased if some outcomes occur more or less than would be expected. For example, a dice is biased if the number 6 hardly ever comes up.

BIDMAS BIDMAS is a way of remembering the order in which you carry out the different operations in a calculation: Brackets, Indices, Division, Multiplication, Addition and Subtraction.

Bisect Bisect means to cut into two equal parts.

Bisector A bisector is a line which cuts an angle, line or shape in half.

Brackets Brackets are a way of grouping numbers or algebraic terms together. For example, $(3 + 5) \div 2$ means the same as $8 \div 2$.

Cancel To cancel a fraction is to simplify it by dividing the numerator and denominator by a common factor.

Capacity The capacity of a 3-D shape is the volume it can hold. It is measured in cubic units such as mm^3 and cm^3, or for liquids litre (l) and millilitre (ml).

Categorical Categorical data is non-numerical data that can be put into groups such as favourite colour or types of pet.

Categorical Categorical data is non-numerical data that can be put into groups such as favourite colour or types of pet. It describes a property or characteristic. Sometimes digits are included but they are used to identify something, not to calculate.

Centilitre 1 centilitre (1 cl) is one hundredth of a litre.

Centimetre 1 centimetre (1 cm) is one hundredth of a metre.

Centre of rotation The centre of rotation is the 'pivot' point about which an object is rotated.

Certain If an event is certain, its probability is 1. For example, it is certain that the sun will rise tomorrow.

Chance The chance of something happening is how likely it is to happen. Words can be used – it is unlikely that Sam will get up before midday. Or numbers can be used – the probability of Sam getting up before midday is about 0.09.

Circle A circle is a shape made up of all the points that are a specific distance from the centre.

Circumference The circumference is the perimeter of a circle.

Clockwise The direction followed by the hands of a clock.

Coefficient The number written in front of a letter.

Co-interior angles See allied angles.

Column method Digits are written with units in the same column, tens in the same column, hundreds in the same column, etc.

Common denominator The common denominator of two or more fractions is a common multiple of all of the denominators. It is used when adding or subtracting fractions.

Common factor A common factor of two or more numbers is a number that divides exactly into all the numbers. You simplify fractions by cancelling by a common factor.

Compound measure A quantity that is made up from more than one other quantity. Examples include density (which uses mass and volume) and speed (which uses distance and time).

Concave All sides are oriented inwards.

Concentric Concentric circles have the same centre but different radii. (sizes). They look like ripples after a stone is dropped into water.

Cone A cone is a 3D shape that has two faces: a flat circular base and a single curved face forming a single vertex. It could be described as a circular based pyramid.

Congruent Congruent shapes are exactly the same shape and size – they are identical.

Construct Draw accurately using only a compass and a straight edge.

Continuous data Continuous data does not have gaps in the possible values.

Conversion graph A conversion graph is used to change one unit into another. This could be changing between miles and kilometres, pounds to a foreign currency, or the cost of a journey based on the number of miles travelled.

Convex At least one side is oriented outwards.

Coordinates Coordinates are a way of showing position on a pair of axes or graph. For example, the point $(3, -5)$ is 3 to the right and 5 down.

Correlation **Correlation** is when there appears to be a link between how one measure changes when another measure changes.

Corresponding angles A pair of angles in identical positions relative to a transversal.

Corresponding sides **Equivalent** sides on a pair of shapes (the shapes are either **congruent** or one is an **enlargement** of the other).

Cosine The cosine of an angle, cos θ, in a right-angled triangle is the ratio of the side adjacent to the angle and the hypotenuse. $cos\ \theta = \dfrac{adjacent}{hypotenuse}$

Cube (shape) A cube is a 3-D shape with six identical square faces.

Cube (number) To find the cube of a number you multiply the number by itself twice. For example, the cube of 5.6 (5.6^3) is $5.6 \times 5.6 \times 5.6$ or 175.616.

Cube root The cube root of a number is the number that, when multiplied by itself twice, gives the original number. The inverse of cubing is cube rooting. For example, the cube root of 27 is 3 (as $3 \times 3 \times 3 = 27$). The symbol $\sqrt[3]{}$ is used for the cube root of a number, so $\sqrt[3]{27} = 3$.

Cuboid A 3D shape whose six faces are all rectangular or square. A rectangular prism.

Currency The money used in a country, for example the currency of the UK is pounds.

Currency conversion The process of changing one currency to another, for example pounds to euros. A currency conversion can be done using a **conversion graph**.

Curve For example, the circumference of a circle. A curve can also be the shape of a graph described by the relationship between two variables, for example $y = x^2$.

Cylinder A cylinder is 3-dimensional shape with a constant circular cross-section.

Data A group of facts or statistics, it can be numerical (for example heights) or non-numerical (for example favourite crisp flavour).

Decagon A ten-sided polygon.

Decimal A decimal is a number written using a decimal point. For example, 82.17. The digits after the decimal point represent a value less than one.

Decimal place The number of decimal places of a decimal is the number of digits after the decimal point. For example, 3.2 is written to one decimal place and 5.678 is written to three decimal places.

Decimal point The decimal point is the dot in a decimal number. The digits before the decimal point represent whole numbers, the digits after the decimal point represent fractions. For example, the number 4.37 means four units plus three tenths plus seven hundredths.

Denominator The denominator is the bottom integer of a fraction. It tells you how many equal parts the whole is divided into. For example, $\dfrac{3}{8}$ has a denominator of 8, so the 'whole' has been divided into eight equal parts.

Density A type of compound measure measuring the mass per m^3 or per cm^3, etc.

Density = Mass ÷ Volume.

Diameter A diameter is a line that passes through the centre of a circle and joins two points on the circumference.

Difference The difference between two numbers is the result of subtracting the smaller from the larger. For example, the difference between 15 and 6 is $15 - 6$ or 9.

Digit A digit is one of the symbols 0, 1, 2, 3, 4, 5, 6, 7, 8 or 9. Digits are used to write numbers.

Directed A number with a positive or a negative sign in front of it. If a sign is missing, then we assume it is positive.

Direct proportion Two quantities are in direct proportion if, when one increases, the other increases by the same multiple. An example is the number of items bought and their total cost.

Discrete data Discrete data does not include any in between values. It has gaps.

Distance-time graph See **Travel graph**.

Divide To divide two numbers you share the first number into the number of equal parts given by the second number. For example, 24 divided by 3 is 8 $(24 \div 3 = 8)$.

Division Division is the process of dividing two numbers.

Divisor In a division the divisor is the number you divide by. For example, in the division $24 \div 3$ the divisor is 3.

Edge In a 3D shape, an edge forms the boundary between two faces. In a cube, for example, there are 12 edges that form the boundaries between the 6 faces.

Enlargement An enlargement changes the size of an object. When a shape is enlarged the image is mathematically **similar** to the object but a different size. Note: the image may be smaller than the object.

Equal If two quantities or expressions are equal, they have the same value. The symbol = is used to show equality. For example, $14 + 8 = 22$.

Equally likely In probability, if two events are equally likely they have the same probability of happening. For example, when you roll a fair six-sided dice the possible outcomes of 1, 2, 3, 4, 5 or 6 are equally likely. They each have a probability of $\frac{1}{6}$.

Equation An equation is where one expression is equal to another. An equation always contains an equals sign. For example, $6 + 4 = 16 - 6$. When an equation contains an unknown it can be solved. For example, the solution to the equation $x + 4 = 16 - x$ is $x = 6$.

Equilateral An equilateral triangle has three equal angles (all 60°) and three sides of equal length.

Equivalent Equivalent fractions represent the same value. For example, $\frac{3}{5}$ and $\frac{9}{15}$ are equivalent.

Estimate To estimate the answer to a calculation is to use rounding to find an approximate answer.

Evaluate Evaluate means work out the value of.

Evens or even chance Evens or even chance are ways of saying the probability is 0.5.

Event An event is any of the possible outcomes from an experiment. For example, I roll two dice and add the numbers together. What is the probability of the event 'my total is 10'?

Expand To multiply out or remove the brackets from a term.

Experiment An experiment or trial is a procedure in probability that can be repeated over and over again and where we know what the possible outcomes are. For example, rolling two dice and recording the total of the two numbers.

Exponential function An exponential function is in the form $y = a^x$ where a is a positive constant.

Exponential graph A graph showing an exponential function.

Expression An expression is numbers and symbols grouped together. For example, $3x - 8$. An expression does not contain an equals sign.

Exterior The exterior angles of a polygon add up to 360°.

Exterior angle

Face In a 3D shape, a face is a surface that forms a part of the boundary of the shape. For example, a cube has six faces.

Factor A factor of a number divides into that number exactly. For example, the factors of 18 are 1, 2, 3, 6, 9 and 18.

Factorise Opposite of expand.

Fair In probability a dice or coin is fair if all the possible outcomes are equally likely.

Fibonacci sequence The Fibonacci sequence begins 1, 1, 2, 3, 5, 8, ... Each term is the sum of the previous two terms.

Fibonacci-type sequence Any sequence in which each term is the sum of the previous two terms, for example 3, 4, 7, 11, 18, ...

Formula A formula is a rule or relationship that contains a variable (or variables) that is represented by a letter (or letters). For example, the formula for the area of a triangle is $A = \frac{1}{2} bh$.

Fraction A fraction represents a part of a whole.

Frequency The frequency of a data value is the number of times it occurs.

Frequency diagram A frequency diagram is plotted from a grouped frequency table. It consists of bars placed on a linear scale covering the range of values in the groups.

Frequency table A frequency table shows the frequency of each data value in a data set.

Geometric sequence A geometric sequence is a sequence where the ratio between any two consecutive terms is a constant. For example 5, 10, 20, 40, ℰ (in this sequence the ratio is 2).

Gram Gram (g) is a metric unit of mass. 25 g is approximately the mass of an ordinary bag of crisps.

Graph A graph is the depiction of a relationship between (usually) two variables. For example, it is possible to draw a graph of the relationship $y = x^2$.

Gradient The gradient is a measure of how steep a line is. The gradient of the line joining two points can be calculated as the change in the y values divided by the change in the x values.

Greater than The symbol > indicates the value to the left is bigger than the one to the right.

Grid method A method for multiplying numbers which involves dealing with units, tens, hundreds, etc. separately.

Grouped frequency table A grouped frequency table is obtained when the data set is sorted into groups defined so that there is exactly one group for each item of data.

Height The height is the distance from the base to the top.

Heptagon A heptagon is a seven-sided polygon.

Hexagon A hexagon is a six-sided polygon.

Highest common factor (HCF) The highest common factor (HCF) of two numbers is the greatest integer that divides exactly into both numbers. For example, the highest common factor of 6 and 15 is 3.

Horizontal A horizontal line is parallel to the horizon. It runs from left to right.

Hundreds In place value, hundreds is the place value of the first digit in a three-digit number. In the number 714, the 7 represents seven hundreds.

Hundredths In place value, hundredths is the place value of the second digit after the decimal point. In the number 7.14, the 4 represents four hundredths. In the number 7246, the 2 represents two hundreds.

Hypotenuse The hypotenuse is the longest side of a right-angled triangle.

Image When a shape undergoes a transformation, the resulting shape is the image.

Impossible An event with probability 0 is impossible.

Improper fraction In an improper fraction, the numerator is greater than its denominator.

For example, $\frac{8}{3}$ is an improper fraction.

Included angle The angle between two given sides.

Included side The side between two given angles.

Index The singular of **indices**.

Indices The index is the power to which a number is raised. For example, in 4^3 the power (or index) is 3 and so $4^3 = 4 \times 4 \times 4$. The plural of index is indices.

Inequality Compares the size of two values, showing if one is less than , or greater than, the other.

Integer An integer is a positive or negative whole number (including zero).

Interest Interest can be: 1) a payment made to an investor or 2) money charged for borrowing. See also **simple interest**.

Interior Inside a shape.

Internal The sum of the interior or internal angles of an n-sided polygon $= 180° \times (n - 2)$.

Intersect Intersect means to cross or meet. Two lines intersect at the point where they cross.

Inverse proportion Two quantities, x and y, are in inverse proportion when the product of the two quantities xy is constant, i.e. when an increase in one quantity causes a decrease in a second quantity. For example, when the number of men building a wall is doubled then the time to build the wall is halved.

Isosceles An isosceles triangle has two equal angles and two sides of equal length.

Key A key is used on some diagrams such as pictograms to show what a symbol represents. For example, Key: ☐ represents four people.

Kilogram Kilogram (kg) is a metric unit of mass equal to 1000 grams. 1 kg is approximately the mass of a bag of sugar.

Kilometre Kilometre (km) is a metric unit of distance equal to 1000 metres. 1 km is $2\frac{1}{2}$ times round an ordinary athletics track.

Kite A kite is a quadrilateral which has two pairs of adjacent, equal sides. Other properties are one pair of equal angles and diagonals that cross at right angles.

Length The length of an object is a way of measuring its size. For example, the length of this rectangle is 13 cm.

Less than The symbol < indicated the value to the left is smaller than the one to the right.

Likely An event with probability greater than 0.5 but less than 1 is likely.

Line A line is a straight one-dimensional figure with no thickness and extending infinitely in both directions. It is often called a straight line.

Line of best fit A line of best fit can be drawn when there is correlation. It is a straight line that follows the trend of the data.

Line segment A line segment is part of a line. It has a beginning and an end.

Linear Relating to a straight line. An arithmetic sequence can be described as linear, since on a graph of the terms of the sequence, the points would lie on a straight line.

Litre Litre (l) is a metric unit of capacity equal to 1000 millilitres. 1 litre is usually the capacity of a carton of fruit juice.

Long division A method for dividing numbers which clearly shows how each remainder is calculated.

Long multiplication A method for multiplying two numbers.

Loss If an item is sold for less than the buying price, the loss is the difference between these two prices. If the selling price is greater than the buying price, there is a **profit**.

Lower bound Measurement is only approximate, the actual value of a measurement could be $\frac{1}{2}$ the rounded unit below the given value. The lower bound is the least possible value that the true measurement could be.

For example, the length of a pencil is 15.5 cm to the nearest millimetre. So the lower bound is 15.5 cm $- \frac{1}{2}$ mm = 15.45 cm. The actual length, l, of the pencil is greater than or equal to 15.45cm, so $15.45 \leq l$.

Lowest common multiple (LCM) The lowest common multiple of two numbers is the least integer that is a multiple of both numbers. For example, the lowest common multiple of 6 and 15 is 30.

Lowest terms A fraction is in its lowest terms (or simplest form) when it can't be simplified or cancelled any further.

Mass The mass of an object is a measure of how much matter it contains. Mass is measured, for example, in kilograms. In maths at this level, mass and weight are considered to be the same thing.

Mean The mean is found by adding together all of the data values and then dividing this total by the number of data values. The mean is one of the three main ways to measure an average.

Median Median is the middle value when the data set is organised in order of size. The median is one of the three main ways to measure an average.

Metre Metre (m) is a metric unit of length equal to 1000 millimetres. 2 m is roughly the height of a tall man.

Metric unit Examples of metric units are:
- For length: millimetres, centimetres, metres and kilometres
- For mass: grams, kilograms and tonnes
- For volume: millilitres and litres.

Milligram Milligram (mg) is a metric unit of mass equal to one thousandth of a gram. Milligrams are used to measure out doses of drugs. For example, a small aspirin might contain 75 mg.

Millilitre Millilitre (ml) is a metric unit of capacity equal to one thousandth of a litre. For example, a teaspoon holds 5 ml.

Millimetre Millimetre (mm) is a metric unit of length equal to one thousandth of a metre. For example, a small ruler is 150 mm long.

Millions In place value, millions is the place value of the first digit in a seven-digit number. In the number 2 714 806, the 2 represents two millions.

Mirror line The line in which a shape reflected is known as the mirror line.

Mixed number A mixed number is made up of a whole number and a fraction. For example, $2\frac{3}{4}$ is a mixed number.

Modal The mode of a set of data can be called the modal value.

Mode The mode is the value occurring most often in a data set. The mode is one of the three main ways to measure an average.

Multiple The multiple of a number is the result when you multiply that number by a positive integer. For example, the multiples of 6 are 6, 12, 18, 24, 30, …

Multiplication (multiply) Multiplication comes from repeated addition, so 7×3 is the same as $7 + 7 + 7$ or 21.

Multiplier The multiplier is the number you are multiplying by. For example, in 3×7 the multiplier is 7.

Mutually exclusive events Two events are mutually exclusive if they both cannot happen at the same time. For example, when rolling a dice, getting a 3 and getting a 5 are mutually exclusive as you can't get both a 3 and a 5 from rolling one dice.

Negative A value which is less than zero.

Negative correlation Negative correlation occurs when points are roughly in a line from top left to bottom right of a scatter diagram.

As one quantity increases, the other one decreases.

Nonagon A nine-sided shape.

Number line A line with numbers indicating their size relative to each other.

Numerator The numerator is the top number in a fraction. For example, $\frac{3}{8}$ has a numerator of 3.

Numerical data Numerical data consists of numbers only.

Object The object is the shape that a transformation is applied to.

Obtuse An obtuse angle lies between 90° and 180°.

Octagon An octagon is an eight-sided polygon.

Odd An odd number is an integer that is not a multiple of 2. For example, 1, 3, 5, ..., 57, ..., etc.

Operations An operation is a procedure that is carried out to a number, such as dividing or raising to a power. See *BIDMAS* for the order in which to carry out operations.

Outlier In a set of data an outlier is a value that lies outside the range of the rest of the data – it is much larger or much smaller. It also refers to a value that does not fit the same pattern as the rest of the data.

Pair of compasses An instrument for drawing a circle, or an arc of a circle. Usually referred to as a compass.

Parabola The shape of a quadratic graph.

Parallel A pair of parallel lines can be continued to infinity in either direction without meeting.

Parallelogram A parallelogram is a quadrilateral that has two pairs of parallel sides. Other properties are that opposite sides are equal and opposite angles are equal.

Pentagon A pentagon is a five-sided polygon.

Percentage A percentage (%) is a number expressed as a fraction of 100. For example, 38% is equivalent to $\frac{38}{100}$ or 0.38.

Percentage change A change in a quantity expressed as a percentage of the original quantity. For example, if the price of an item falls from £4 to £3, the decrease is £1 and the percentage decrease is 25% (since $\frac{1}{4} = 25\%$).

Percentage decrease The decrease in a quantity expressed as a percentage of the original quantity. For example, if the price of an item falls from £4 to £3, the decrease is £1 and the percentage decrease is 25% (since $\frac{1}{4} = 25\%$).

Percentage error The error in the measurement of a quantity expressed as a percentage of the true quantity. For example, if the length of an object is 50 cm and is measured as 49 cm, the error is 1 cm and the percentage error is 2% (since $\frac{1}{50} = 2\%$).

Percentage increase The increase in a quantity expressed as a percentage of the original quantity. For example, if the price of an item rises from £4 to £5, the increase is £1 and the percentage increase is 25% (since $\frac{1}{4} = 25\%$).

Percentage loss If an item is sold for less than it was bought, the percentage loss is the difference in the buying and selling price expressed as a percentage of the cost price. For example, if the cost price of an item is £5 and the selling price is £4, the loss is £1 and the percentage loss is 20% (since $\frac{1}{5} = 20\%$).

Percentage profit If an item is sold for more than it was bought, the percentage profit is the difference in the buying and selling price expressed as a percentage of the cost price. For example, if the cost price of an item is £4 and the selling price is £5, the profit is £1 and the percentage profit is 25% (since $\frac{1}{4} = 25\%$).

Perimeter The perimeter of a shape is the distance around the outside edge of the shape. Perimeter is measured in mm, cm, m or km.

Perpendicular Two lines are perpendicular if they meet at right angles.

Perpendicular bisector The perpendicular bisector is a line which cuts another line in half. It is at right angles to the original line.

Pi, π The Greek letter pi is the number 3.14159..., it is equal to the circumference of a circle divided by its diameter.

Piece-wise linear A function comprising more than one straight line segment.

Pictogram A pictogram is a chart that uses pictures or symbols to display data.

Place value The place value of a digit is the number that a particular digit in a number represents. For example, in the number 4137.59, the 4 represents four thousands and the 9 represents nine hundredths.

Polygon A polygon is a closed 2-D shape made up of straight lines.

Position-to-term rule The position-to-term rule (or nth term) is a way of describing the terms of a sequence using their position in the sequence. For example, the position-to-term rule for the sequence 7, 13, 19, 25, 31, ... is $6n + 1$.

Positive A value which is greater than zero.

Positive correlation Positive correlation is when points are roughly in a line from bottom left to top right of a scatter diagram. As one quantity increases, the other one does too.

Powers For example, in 4^3 the power is 3 and so $4^3 = 4 \times 4 \times 4$.

Power of 10 10 raised to an integer power. For example, $10^3 = 1000$.

Prime A prime number is a number with exactly two factors: one and itself. The prime numbers are 2, 3, 5, 7, 11, ... Note: 1 is not a prime number as it has only one factor.

Prism A 3D shape that has a constant cross-section and that does not have any curved faces.

Probability Probability is the study of chance. The probability of an event happening is a measure of how likely that event is to happen.

$$\text{Probability} = \frac{\text{number of favourable outcomes}}{\text{total number of equally likely outcomes}}$$

Probability scale The probability scale goes from 0 (an impossible event) to 1 (a certain event).

Product The product of two numbers is the result of multiplying them together. For example, the product of 8 and 3 is 24 ($8 \times 3 = 24$).

Profit The profit is the difference between the selling price and buying price of an item. If the selling price is lower than the buying price there is a loss.

Proportion A proportion is a part of a whole. Proportions can be given as fractions, decimals or ratios.

Protractor A protractor is an instrument used for measuring angles.

Pythagoras' theorem A theorem that says that the square of the hypotenuse (longest side) of a right-angled triangle is equal to the sum of the squares of the two shorter sides. It is written as $a^2 + b^2 = c^2$.

Quadrant A quadrant is a quarter of a circle.

Quadratic In a quadratic expression the highest power of any of the terms is 2. A quadratic expression can be written in the form $ax^2 + bx + c$ where a, b and c are constants.

Quadrilateral A quadrilateral is a four-sided polygon (a four-sided plane shape).

Radius A radius is a line that joins the centre of a circle to a point on the circumference. The plural is radii.

Random An event is random if it is done without method or conscious decision.

Range Range is a measure of the spread of a data set. The range is the difference between the highest and lowest data values.

Ratio A ratio compares two quantities.

Real-life graph Any graph that arises from a real-life situation rather than just an equation. Real-life graphs include travel graphs and scatter graphs.

Reciprocal The reciprocal of a number is 1 divided by that number. So the reciprocal of 4 is $1 \div 4 = \frac{1}{4} = 0.25$ and the reciprocal of $\frac{1}{5}$ is $1 \div \frac{1}{5} = 5$.

Reciprocal function A function of the form $y = \frac{k}{x}$ where k is a constant. If x and y are inversely proportional then $y = \frac{k}{x}$.

Reciprocal graph A graph of a reciprocal function.

Rectangle A rectangle is a quadrilateral with the following properties: two pairs of parallel sides; four equal angles ($90°$). It also has opposite sides of equal length.

Reflection A reflection is a 'flip' movement about a mirror line. The mirror line is the line of symmetry between the object and its image.

Reflex A reflex angle is an angle between $180°$ and $360°$.

Regular shape A shape where all angles are equal sizes and all sides are an equal length.

Reverse percentage A calculation that allows you to work out the original cost, size, etc, after an increase or decrease.

Rhombus A rhombus is a quadrilateral with four equal sides. It also has two pairs of parallel sides, equal opposite angles and diagonals that cross at right angles.

Right angle A right angle is $90°$.

Right-angled triangle A triangle where one of the internal angles is $90°$.

Rotation A rotation is a 'turning' movement about a specific point known as the centre of rotation.

Rounding (round) Rounding is a way of rewriting a number so it is simpler than the original number. A rounded number should be approximately equal to the unrounded (exact) number. For example 86 rounded to the nearest 10 is 90.

Scale In a scale drawing, the scale is the ratio or multiplier that tells you how much bigger (or smaller) the original is than the drawing.

Scalene A scalene triangle has three sides of different lengths and three different angles.

Scatter diagram A scatter diagram is drawn using pairs of data as coordinates.

Sector A sector is part of a circle that looks like a piece of pie, it is enclosed by two radii and part of the circumference.

Semi-circle A semi-circle is half a circle.

Sequence A sequence is a collection of terms arranged in a specific order.

Short division An abbreviated version of long division where the remainders are evaluated without writing down the calculation.

Sign A symbol written in front of a number to indicate whether it is positive or negative.

Significant figure The first significant figure of a number is the first non-zero digit in the number. The second significant figure is the next digit in the number and so on. For example, in the numbers 78046 and 0.0078046 the 1st significant figure is 7, the 2nd significant figure is 8 and the 3rd significant figure is 0.

Similar Two shapes are similar if corresponding sides are in proportion and corresponding angles are equal; the shapes are enlargements of each other.

Simplify To simplify an expression you write it in an equivalent way but using smaller numbers or fewer terms. You can simplify a fraction, ratio or an algebraic expression. For example, you can simplify $\frac{9}{15}$ to $\frac{3}{5}$ or $x + x + y + y + y$ to $2x + 3y$ or 21:35 to 3:5.

Sine The sine of an angle, sin θ, in a right-angled triangle is the ratio of the side opposite the angle and the hypotenuse. $sin\,\theta = \frac{opposite}{hypotenuse}$

Solid Another word for a 3D shape.

Solve To solve an equation you find the value of the unknown that satisfies the equation. For example, the solution of $7x = 35$ is $x = 5$.

Speed A type of compound measure measuring the distance travelled per second or per hour, etc.

Average speed = Distance travelled ÷ Time taken

Square (shape) A square is a quadrilateral with four equal sides and four equal angles (90°). It also has two pairs of parallel sides and diagonals that cross at right angles.

Square number A square number is the result when an integer is multiplied by itself. The square numbers are 1, 4, 9, 16, 25, ...

Square metre A square metre (m^2) is a unit of area. 1 m^2 is equivalent to the area of a square of side 1 m.

Square root The square root of a number is the number that, when multiplied by itself, gives the original number. The reverse of squaring is square rooting. Every number has two square roots. For example, the square root of 9 is 3 (as $3 \times 3 = 9$) or -3 (as $-3 \times -3 = 9$). The symbol $\sqrt{}$ is used for the positive square root of a number, so $\sqrt{9} = 3$.

Square-based pyramid A 3D shape whose base is a square. It has four other faces, all of which are isosceles triangles, meeting at a single point.

Standard form Standard form is a way of writing very large or very small numbers. A number in standard form is written as $A \times 10^n$ where $1 \le A < 10$ and n is a positive or negative integer. For example, $0.000\,034 = 3.4 \times 10^{-5}$ and $590\,000\,000 = 5.9 \times 10^8$

Straight-line graph A straight-line graph, or linear graph, is a graph in which the points are arranged in a straight line.

Subject The subject of a formula is the variable (letter) which appears on its own.

Substitute To substitute is to replace the variables (letter symbols) in an expression or formula with numbers.

Sum The sum of two numbers is the result of adding them together. For example, the sum of 8 and 3 is 11 $(8 + 3 = 11)$.

Surface area The total area of all the **faces** of a 3D shape. For example, the surface area of a cube is 6 × the area of one face.

Symmetry A shape has symmetry if it does not change under a transformation such as reflection or rotation.

Tally chart A tally chart is a way of collecting or representing data using tally marks. For example,

Score	Tally	Frequency
0		
1		
2					
3								
4									
5					
Total:		

Tangent The ratio of the opposite side to the adjacent side in a right-angled triangle. $tan\,\theta = \frac{opposite}{adjacent}$

Tens In place value, tens is the place value of the first digit in a two-digit number. In the number 57, the 5 represents five tens. In the number 7246, the 4 represents four tens.

Tenths In place value, tenths is the place value of the first digit after the decimal point. In the number 0.83, the 8 represents eight tenths.

Term Each number in a sequence is a called a term.

Term number The term number gives the position of a term in a sequence. For example, in the sequence 3, 13, 23, 33, 43, ..., the term number of 13 is 2 as it is second in the sequence. The term number is often referred to as n.

Term-to-term rule A term-to-term rule describes how to use one term in a sequence to find the next term.

Terminating decimal A terminating decimal has digits that do not continue forever. For example, 0.123 and 0.987654321.

Thousands In place value, thousands is the place value of the first digit in a four-digit number. In the number 7246, the 7 represents seven thousands.

Thousandths In place value, thousandths is the place value of the third digit after the decimal point. In the number 0.691, the 1 represents one thousandth.

Tonne Tonne (t) is a metric unit of mass equal to 1000 kilograms. 1 t is approximately the mass of a small car.

Total The total is the result of adding numbers together.

Transformation A transformation changes either the size, shape, position or orientation of an object. Examples of transformations are reflection, rotation, enlargement and translation.

Translation A translation is a sliding movement.

Trapezium A trapezium is a quadrilateral with one pair of parallel sides.

Travel graph A travel graph (or **distance-time graph**) is a diagram showing the journey of one or more objects on the same pair of axes. The vertical axis is distance, and the horizontal axes is time.

Triangle A triangle is a three-sided polygon.

Triangle numbers The sequence of numbers 1, 3, 6, 10, 15, ...

Trigonometry An area of maths that involves calculating unknown angles and lengths in triangles.

Turn A full turn is a rotation of 360°.

Two-way table A two-way table has one set of options as the rows and the second set of options as the columns.

Unitary method A method used to determine a best buy. The unitary method finds the cost of 1 item, when two or more purchase options are available. For example, if 6 eggs cost £1.20 the unit price is 20p; if 10 eggs cost £1.50 the unit price is 15p and the pack of 10 eggs is the best buy.

Units (number) In place value, units is the place value of the digit in a single-digit number. In the number 8, the 8 represents eight units. In the number 7246, the 6 represents six units.

Units (shape) The standard units used for measurement, such as kilogram, metre and second.

Unknown The unknown is the letter you are trying to find a value for in an equation. The unknown is most commonly given the symbol x.

Unlikely An event with probability greater than 0 but less than 0.5 is unlikely.

Upper bound Measurement is only approximate; the actual value of a measurement could be $\frac{1}{2}$ the rounded unit above the given value. The upper bound is the greatest possible value that the true measurement could be. For example, the length of a pencil is 15.5 cm to the nearest millimetre. So the upper bound is 15.5 cm $+ \frac{1}{2}$ mm = 15.55 cm. The actual length, l, of the pencil is less than 15.55 cm, so $l <$ 15.55.

Variable A variable is a quantity that may change in maths problems, such as the area of a triangle. A variable is usually represented by a letter.

VAT VAT stands for value added tax. This is a tax that is added to most goods that we buy. The Government sets the percentage VAT that is charged.

Vector A vector is a quantity with both magnitude (size) and direction. A vector can be written using two components: the first denoting movement in the x-direction and the second the movement in the y-direction. In this form a vector is often used to describe a translation.

Venn diagram A venn diagram is a diagram made from overlapping circles, which is used to display sets.

Vertex A vertex of a shape is a point where two sides meet.

Vertical A vertical line is perpendicular to the horizon. It runs up and down.

Vertical line chart A vertical line chart is a chart that uses vertical lines to display data. The height of each line represents the frequency.

Vertically opposite Vertically opposite angles are formed when two lines cross. Vertically opposite angles are equal.

Volume Volume is the amount of space that a 3-D shape takes up.

Weight Weight is an everyday term that means the same as mass. When science and maths get more precise, a different definition in used.

Width The width of an object is a way of measuring its size. For example, the width of this rectangle is 11 cm.

11 cm

13 cm

x-coordinate The x-coordinate is the horizontal value in a pair of coordinates. It is how far along the point is. In the coordinate (7, 2) the x-coordinate is 7.

y-coordinate The y-coordinate is the vertical value in a pair of coordinates. It is how far up the point is. In the coordinate (7, 2) the y-coordinate is 2.

y-intercept The point at which a straight line meets the y-axis.